AND THEN CAME
MAN

And Then Came Man

By
HARTMUT BASTIAN

Translated from the German by
DESMOND I. VESEY

Edited and with a Foreword by
D. H. DALBY
B.Sc., Ph.D., F.L.S.

New York · THE VIKING PRESS

Foreword

By D. H. DALBY, B.Sc., Ph.D., F.L.S.

GEOLOGY is a basic science, taking its place with meteorology in rousing interest among students of the natural sciences, especially as it is not included in the average school syllabus. Its basic nature is shown by Man and animals being ultimately dependent on plants, and plants in their turn on soils, for their nourishment and growth. Soils are the product of interaction between the rocks and weathering processes—both of which are so important in physical geography and geology.

A book such as this cannot fail to fascinate and provoke and fill any student with the determination to go further into the past to find the answers to so many of the questions posed by Life in general and by Man in particular. The present book traces the history of the Earth from its start as a ball of fire through the gradual appearance and subsequent elaborations of life, up to the present period of Man's domination (which, incidentally, could well lead to the Earth's return to a ball of fire once more).

The scientific study of geology started late, surprisingly late, and soon came into conflict with earlier theories of creation and evolution. As the flood of evidence revealed by the study of the rocks has increased in force, so it has become necessary to re-orientate our views and to abandon such devices as were resorted to by medieval cartographers, who could only fill up with clusters of monsters splashing round the edge of the Unknown, to hide the deficiencies in their knowledge.

Nevertheless, there is still much disagreement (often vehemently stated) over matters such as continental drift, and the precise course of Man's evolution.

Efforts have been made in this book to present the most up-to-date theories and discoveries, but even as I write new discoveries are being made, and the story of the Earth is continually having to be amended. The Mohole project will reveal fundamental information about the structure of the Earth's crust, whilst artificial satellites and rocket probes yield startling facts about the constitution of the upper atmosphere and even the depths of space.

In editing this book I have tried to apply the latest, and most reliable, time scale—that of Professor Holmes (1959)—so some of the geological periods may appear to be of unfamiliar length. It is impossible to achieve absolute finality in Latin names, so the reader must remember that in the eyes of one palaeontologist two organisms may appear to be the same, yet another may equally "correctly" regard them as being distinct. Much of the book is concerned with theories to explain geological phenomena, and here too one can never expect any one theory to meet with unanimous approval.

Contents

List of Plates

11

Illustrations, Diagrams and Maps in Text

Tables

Acknowledgements

THE illustrations in the text were drawn by Gerhard Boden and F. P. von Zglinicki. The illustration of the oldest blue-green alga is drawn, by permission of Verlag Sebastian Lux (Murnau), from a photograph published in *Oryx* of May, 1954. Table No. 4, The Pleistocene Ice Age, is reproduced by kind permission of A. V. Gibson, from his book *Instructions in Archaeology*.

For the photographic illustrations acknowledgements are due as follows: Robert Schmitt (Darmstadt), Nos. 10, 11, 12, 13, 15, 17, 18, 21, 22; Ullstein Bilderdienst (Darmstadt), Nos. 5, 33, 40, 41, 45; F. & E. Heimhuber (Sonthofen/Allgäu), No. 1; Conzett & Huber (Zürich), Nos. 2 and 34; H. Bastian (Darmstadt), Nos. 3, 4, 6; Arizona Highways, Phoenix, Arizona (photo Josef Muench), No. 7; Chicago Natural History Museum, Nos. 8, 9, 14, 19, 20, 27, 28, 29, 30, 37, 38, 39; Dr. J. L. B. Smith, Dept. of Ichthyology, Rhodes University, Grahamstown, C.P., South Africa, No. 16; Natur-Museum Senckenberg, Frankfurt a. M., Nos. 23, 24, 31, 32; The American Museum of Natural History, No. 25; the Museum of Comparative Zoology, Cambridge, Mass., No. 26; Geologisch-Paläontologisches Institut, University of Halle a. S., Nos. 35, 36; Verlag Kohlhammer GmbH. (from *Die Felsbilder von Europa*, by Herbert Kühn), Nos. 42, 43, 44, 46.

CHAPTER ONE

The Discovery of Earth's History

I T is not usual to describe the subject matter of one of the natural sciences as being like a fairy tale or romance; but in the case of the science of prehistory, with which this book is concerned, there is a perpetual temptation to do so. To start with, there is something extraordinary in the abyss of pre- history which has to be plumbed, in the mystery of past worlds which have never been seen, worlds with their exuber- ant varieties of plant and animal life, with their weird, unfamiliar appearance and endless topographical changes. The emergence and growth of life, culminating in present- day Man, is a romance, fascinating and dramatic, packed with excitement and surprises.

The roots of practically every branch of the natural sciences can be traced back to the ancient Greeks. But, astonishingly enough, that is not so in this case. Here, neither Aristotle, Plato nor Socrates can be cited; at most, Heraclitus's rather overworked remark "Everything flows" can, in this science too, be taken as the ultimate, basic beginning of wisdom.

This is not intended as any disrespect for sages such as Democritus of Abdera, Aristarchus of Samos, Euclid and Archimedes, who are all deeply to be revered. The almost perfect theory of Democritus—the idea of the atom—unerr- ingly directed the forward march of the science of atomic physics up to the end of the last century. Aristarchus's con- ception of the heliocentric solar system was a premature work of genius markedly resembling our present views. Euclid's basic plane geometry is, as ever, of inestimable value to all mathematicians; and the beginnings of experimental physics were laid down by Archimedes. But today certain concepts and systems of thought exist which are typically ours, occi- dental and without historical forerunners, having sprung from our own highly developed scientific mentality. To these belongs the conception of prehistory with which this book deals, the prehistory of the world as a frame for the dynamic evolution of nature throughout all its physical and biological past, with the appearance of Man as its final climax, but not with mankind as its focus.

Of course, among the thinkers of classical civilisations there was an inkling of prehistory, of prehistory as the early history of man. Local, primitive Creation myths are in evidence everywhere as part of an imaginary, never clearly defined prehistory. In the beginning were the gods, and they created the Earth together with all creeping and flying this and that, including humanity. The "how" and the temporal duration of this prehistory remained, nevertheless, unexplored.

Here and there, however, remarkable prehistoric monsters put in an appearance, notably when a dynasty of rulers desired to make credible their descent from the gods and thus extravagantly—though more than obscurely—cloaked themselves with hundreds of thousands of years of ancestry. But we cannot regard such fantasies as the origins of our present-day science of prehistory. For prehistory was not then even a conception. Just as today we are beginning, with amazement, to perceive the bold outlines of certain recent scientific discoveries, so the realisation of the growth and disappearance of a primitive world before mankind existed is a special and definitely late discovery of the last two centuries.

Also, the fact that richly varied forms of life existed inconceivably long ago never occurred to, never was even remotely considered as a subject for inquiry by, thinkers of old. Yet it is impossible that the travel-loving Greeks, whose lengthy journeys were made either on foot or on slow-moving animals. never came across the fossilised remains of mussels, snails and other sea creatures by the wayside or in rock fragments. Xenophon certainly did, and Thales of Miletus, one of the Seven Sages of Greece, was so interested in the coveted and precious amber that he must on occasion have handled pieces in which plants or insects were embedded. The contemporary explanation of the presence of these and other fossils on land and in the mountains far from the sea was not exactly wrong —it was a purely superficial guess. It was said that gigantic tidal waves and floods had, at some time or other, swept these things up and deposited them inland.

The fact that catastrophic storms occurred sporadically was known from experience, and the legends of all oriental peoples are rich in descriptions of particularly violent convulsions of the ocean. So there was no reason to speculate about the possibility of a prehistoric era in which mankind did *not* play the dominant part; in which, perhaps, Man had not even existed. To the classical way of thinking, mankind on earth was the centre of the universe. There could not be or have been any reality without man and his consciousness —not even the worlds of the gods. Yet the gods were indeed regarded as the origin of everything before mankind was created, in spite of the fact that only after that event, with the advent of human brains, did the gods themselves first come into existence. How senseless, to Greek thought of that time, to conceive of an Olympic hierarchy ruling for thousands of years over nothing but plants, animals, and inanimate rocks. So prehistory remained for about two thousand years a dark, necessarily simple-minded affair, unilluminated by the slightest intellectual light from the limpid sky of sunny Hellas.

Man's intellectual development has been sufficiently explored to make this astonishing fact perfectly understandable. The Greek genius burned itself out in a few centuries. The sober greatness of Rome exhausted itself in organising humans politically with every conceivable combination of whips and carrots. Speculative suggestions about profitless possibilities were outside the scope of such a civilisation. The world of unworldly Christianity that followed on took the Bible for its source of information. And the venerable contents of that book were accepted as the exposition of a series of dogmas which at the time were simply and literally accepted as comprising the whole of natural science. The creation of the world in six days satisfied even enquiring minds as being an adequate explanation and the truth. Also, on the basis of primitive Jewish myths, the age of the earth was determined at about 5,500 years.

All fossil discoveries were explained as "freaks of nature" or as a combination of "seminal air" with rocks—or even,

humorous though it may now seem, as prototypes which the
Creator tried out before deciding on his final designs. In this
confusion of naïve ideas, it was the Bible that was also responsible for the sensible suggestion that these discoveries were
animals that had succumbed to the Flood. The ancient Greeks
had indeed already thought along the same lines. That this
legendary flood really happened seems today more certain
than ever. Only its geographical extent has been overestim-
ated. Probably there was a locally confined catastrophic
inundation involving Mesopotamia and various other mainland areas in the neighbourhood. But it is quite certain that
half Europe never lay under water, at least not during the
period covered by the Biblical narrative.

For a long time such explanations and inventions satisfied
the intelligent man, so far as he ever bothered his brains
about these things; and up to about two hundred years ago
the subject matter of this book was totally unknown. Before
then there were no such concepts as geology (the science of
the formation of the earth), palaeontology (the science of life
in prehistoric times), or palaeoethnology (the study of prehistoric man). So all this complex of knowledge is overwhelm-
ingly new, indeed the newest of all, for even physics, chemistry, astronomy, biology, and other similar sciences are in
their latest forms merely flowerings, modern outgrowths
rooted far back in the thinking and discoveries of the past.

What was the climate of the intellectual world two hundred
years ago, about 1760?

For one thing, it was very liberal and modern in the
present-day sense. The bitterest intellectual battles for the
emancipation of scientific inquiry had long ago been fought
and won. The apparently impregnable cosmology of the
ancients and of the Christian Middle Ages had been over-
thrown by Copernicus, Bruno, Kepler and Galileo. The
secret of the heavens—misinterpreted for millenniums—was
wholly solved, the mechanics of the heavenly bodies established by Newton. The real shape and surface of the Earth
emerged from the plethora of voyages, exploratory or exploita-
tory. Physics was in the ascendant in the realms of mechanics,
optics and the intensely investigated phenomenon known as
electricity. Chemistry had long ago cast off its childish apparel

of alchemy and revealed itself as a miraculous body of knowledge in its own right. Anatomy and physiology were being built up, stone upon stone, towards their present-day great structures. In 1756 an unknown man from Koenigsberg named Kant was thinking epoch-making thoughts about the nature of the world. Intellectuals such as Descartes, Leibnitz, Huygens had long before contributed an abundance of brilliant ideas to science. A world of science, in fact, was growing up alongside the everyday, practical world, helping it on with technical accomplishments and intellectually dazzling discoveries. Only dear old Mother Earth, unobtrusively underfoot, still stayed 5,500 years old, and prehistory remained merely the history of mankind as far back as it was known.

This is really rather astonishing, since mining, for example, was practised as far back as the early Stone Age—first for flints, and later for copper and tin for the preparation of bronze. Salt, too, and subsequently iron, were necessities as much in demand then as today.

Amongst all those involved in the various processes of mining was there not one intelligent person who saw more and thought further than was merely required of him by his work? Was there not one whose attention was caught by the impression of a fern in the coal seam and thus reminded of a living fern outside? Did not a single quarry worker discover fantastic remnants of bones of mysterious animals among the broken stone? Did no adventurous explorer ever rack his brains about the bizarre forms of the rock formations on the sheer side of a mountain?

Apparently not. Or, if so, we know nothing of it. Perhaps we expect too much in posing such questions. After all, the majority of those who might have observed such things were illiterate, over-worked semi-slaves, who would have dumbly ignored any discovery or, perforce, kept it within the circle of their closest acquaintances.

But, to be accurate, it must be admitted here that there were, now and again, people of intellectual acumen who thought more boldly. Leonardo da Vinci (1452-1519), we know, had very individual and most probably accurate ideas about the origin of fossilised remains. In a visionary way he at least anticipated the later scientific investigators of an unknown past world.

Even more perspicaciously than Leonardo, the Danish doctor Niels Stensen (1638-1686), who lived for a long time in Italy, delved into these unexplored secrets of nature. With brilliant insight he propounded theories which, in their accuracy, even then could have laid a sure foundation for the whole science of geology—if any attention had been paid to them and they had not been immediately forgotten!

Occurrences such as these are not rare in the intellectual history of Man. A classic example from not so long ago is that of Gregor Mendel (1822-1884) who discovered the rules of heredity. This brilliant Augustinian father from Brünn first studied physics, then did a little dilettante work in the field of botany and quietly established a basis for the whole of the science of heredity. His concepts, today regarded as fundamental, were named, long after his death, the "Mendelian Laws" in his honour. Yet in his day this amateur outsider was almost wholly ignored, so that for decades his vital discoveries went unheeded. This was at a time—it was 1865—when an almost unprecedented battle of opinions over Darwinism was raging, and Darwin himself stated regretfully and resignedly that the laws governing heredity were unfortunately completely unknown. And so they remained, until about 1900 when they were rediscovered almost simultaneously by de Vries, Chermak and Correns, each independently of the other.

In the previous century a very similar fate threatened to befall the revolutionary ideas of the French naturalist Jean Lamarck (1744-1829). Although his theories of the natural evolution of all forms of life at first aroused great excitement and were also much discussed, he was finally defeated by the grossly misused authority of his opponents—particularly the great anatomist, Cuvier—and he died in poverty and was forgotten and with him expired his "finally defunct" hypothesis of evolution. It required the subsequent storm over Darwin's theories to resurrect him from undeserved oblivion and make him the subject of intense posthumous discussion.

The accumulated science and knowledge of the Ancients

suffered a complete eclipse in the early Middle Ages, to such
an extent that no one knew even the names of the Greek
sages, let alone what they had taught. It was the Arabs who
rediscovered them, translated their assiduously collected
manuscripts and thus re-introduced them to the intellectual
world of the Christian West where, after almost eight hundred
years of oblivion, Aristotle, Euclid and Plato suddenly began
to enjoy a startling and considerably exaggerated renaissance.

Such is the way things happen, and the aforementioned
Niels Stensen was not alone in his frustrating experience. But
about a hundred years after him the time was ripe. The
supremacy of the thousand-year-old classical philosophy, consisting mainly of highly theoretical problems which had long
ago been discussed almost to death, was roughly ousted to
make way for the direct questioning of nature, the answers
to which revealed a new vision of the world—the world of
natural sciences. And it only needed increasing boldness and
a few lucky inspirations to bring to light the existence of the
riddle of prehistory and to set people asking for its solution.
Once again it was physicians who were the "midwives",
because geologists did not as yet exist.

The men in question were J. G. Lehmann and Christian
Füchsel, the former of whom was also director of a mining
company. Both lived in the Thuringia-Saxony region, and
they published their geological observations and speculations
in the second half of the eighteenth century. At first nothing
of great interest emerged, partly because Dr. Lehmann persisted in believing implicitly in the Biblical account of the
Flood, and his sole ambition was to prove it. But apart from
a false premise and correspondingly faulty deductions, this
was the first occasion on which stratified rocks and their content of fossilised life were studied reasonably methodically.
Only the immense time-span of this unknown world remained
unguessed at, even in the complementary works of Füchsel,
who actually dared to suggest that the vast rock and limestone
deposits they had discovered could not possibly have been
laid down over such a short period, even if the Flood had been
a solid one! With these two men, it may be said, geology was
born. To begin with, its only real importance was considered
to be in its application to mining; but, above and beyond this

practical aspect, there hovered a multitude of questions about the "how" of Creation, and these questions rapidly became more and more insistent.

There now occurred a name of great importance—that of Gottlob Abraham Werner (1750-1817), a mineralogist from the famous mining town of Freiberg in the Erzgebirge. The line of research that he took up was: how did rocks come to be shaped as they were? There were many known instances of deposits of sedimentary remains of weathered and worn rock in the sea. Clearly, in many cases they were the result of the action of water. Therefore water, and only water, must be the shaping factor in the world of rocks. Mountains and their features had been simply eroded by the seas, after frequent inundation by vast floods.

It is difficult to assess here how far inherent belief in a Biblical Flood dominated Werner's thinking and prevented him from taking up a line which would have revealed to him the one-sidedness of his partially correct assumptions. At any rate, he had no thought that possible effects might have been caused by internal forces below the Earth's surface. Although he was extremely parochial—for he spent virtually the whole of his life in Freiberg—it is impossible that he could have been totally ignorant of volcanic activity and have heard nothing of earthquakes—indeed the Lisbon catastrophe in 1755 was a world-wide topic of discussion. Anyhow, Werner's particular view of geology, which found many adherents, was known as Neptunism, after the Greek sea-god.

In contrast to this, there very soon appeared Plutonism (from Pluto, god of the underworld). Its protagonist was the Scotsman James Hutton (1726-1797). In this first, genuinely fruitful battle of opinions, the pendulum now swung to the other extreme. The Flood at last lost its predominant role. In its place, volcanic forces in the Earth's interior advanced to a position of daemonic power. Now an attempt was made to explain everything "plutonically". That the earth became warmer the deeper one descended into a mine, was a well-known fact. The astronomers alleged that the earth was a product of the sun—a once-glowing ball of gas that had somehow broken loose. All obvious indications suggested that the earth had only cooled on the surface and was, at no very great depth, a seething mixture of white-hot molten substances, barely contained by the thin hardened crust. The volcanoes, indeed, were irrefutable proof of this, their craters being direct passages to the primitive cauldron within. So down with the gentle influence of the waters and up with the high-pressure, rock-shaping elemental forces of the plutonic underworld!

This concept, too, is both one-sided and exaggerated; but the truth would be very nearly arrived at by a reasonable synthesis of both theories. All this, however, was not the important point. The great thing was that geological thinking had emerged in the course of a few decades. The ground "underfoot" had once and for all been discovered and had become a subject for exploration, and to an extent that assumed astonishing proportions; for now an ally joined in, an ally which was to play a vital part in unveiling the picture of prehistory—biology.

During the preceding century biology, too, had developed only precariously in the various guises of anatomy and physiology, botany and zoology. The predominance of the intellectual sciences up to and beyond the end of the Middle Ages had proved a serious hindrance to the growth of the natural sciences, including of course biology. But now the treasury of knowledge could be expended in any direction where it could prove useful.

Of particular importance was the superb attempt of the Swedish naturalist, Carl von Linné (Linnaeus) (1707-1778) to classify the virtually endless varieties of types and species and families of plants and animals into a system which would comprise every living thing—according to sexual characteristics, habits, identity or similarity of form, etc.; and Linnaeus devised the basic, still generally accepted classification into species, genus, family, order and class. This systematisation has, of course, changed considerably over the years and even now is not yet regarded as final.

Linnaeus, in his work, bequeathed to posterity a very valuable legacy. But his universe remained narrow. The possibility of prehistory in the geological sense never occurred to him. The scientific wealth of dead worlds was not even a conceivable possibility to him, let alone the idea, even then being mooted elsewhere, that all living things evolved. He firmly believed that all plants and animals had been *created* —5,500 years ago, during the Biblical Creation—in the very same form as they now appeared in his classifications.

Incomparably further advanced were the ideas of Georg Kufer, who was educated in Germany with Schiller and achieved world fame as Georges Cuvier (1769-1832). He opened up two new fields of science: comparative anatomy and palaeontology. Through his efforts Linnaeus's classifications were considerably improved and expanded. But, above all, he no longer shut his eyes to the increasingly obvious traces of a possible period of prehistory. If the rock-strata of the Paris Basin or the Maastricht chalk yielded the bones of animals hitherto unknown to the present world, then those bones must have belonged to animals who died out "sometime earlier". So the idea of a prehistoric world—as yet not precisely placed in time—was suddenly there as a matter of course. Cuvier was also so bold as to make immediate provision for it in his system. In the case of mussels, snails, etc., it was comparatively simple, and with vertebrates he was helped by his immense anatomical knowledge. He actually succeeded in sketching, on the basis of a few bone fragments, a horse-like ungulate (*Palaeotherium*) which—as we know today—lived millions of years ago, and his sketch was so accurate that later, when a complete skeleton of the animal was discovered, it corresponded almost exactly with the drawing. This masterpiece can be seen today in the Jardin des Plantes in Paris.

Cuvier, then, was a scientific inquirer of quite exceptional genius and his brilliance was in no way dimmed by the fact that his theoretical evaluation of his discoveries, particularly in regard to geological prehistory, led him to the most unfortunate results. During his lifetime it had already become known that there must have been a whole series of prehistoric epochs, in each of which a very different animal world flourished. How had it come about that all these extremely numerous animal species had died out? Very simply, according to him. At the end of every fairly well defined geological age there had been a colossal catastrophe, with brilliant fireworks from the volcanoes (here the Plutonists came into their own), classical floods (thus including the Neptunists), and other devastations. The whole of the living world ended each time in a gigantic holocaust, and that was the end of everything that had hitherto flourished. After the catastrophe was over, life on earth renewed itself until the next debacle.

A Cuvier was not to be contradicted. Fortified by his success and his very real authority, he became totally intolerant of all ideas other than his own. Lamarck was the chief sufferer, for his brilliant conception of a continuous development of all living creatures was simply argued away. And this was bad, for the parallel conception of a continuous transformation of the earth's surface was—to say the least—delayed. But it must have occurred to Cuvier, as he arranged prehistoric animals in his system, that the deeper-lying ones, those therefore from earlier geological strata, must also be more primitive animals. There was a perfectly clear "upwards" direction in the strata lying one upon another. How, then, was one to explain that ascending scale of living creatures which arose from epoch to epoch?

A truly revolutionary idea, which suddenly proved the immense importance of palaeontology to the progress of geology, and one which Cuvier too had made successful use of, occurred to the English engineer, William Smith (1769-1839). Smith constructed roads and canals, and in addition to this very useful occupation still found time to examine the broken stratified rocks with their contents of fossilised remains of living things. He proved, with amazing insight, that, for the purpose of determining the age of identical geological strata which may crop up in entirely different localities, it is not the similarity of the mineral content that counts, but the presence of certain forms of life which were specifically present, were "predominant" during precisely that era. Certain species of fossil existed only in such and such a period and in no other. And where these predominant (or "zone") fossils are found— no matter whereabouts on earth—it can be assumed that the formations containing them were all formed at the same geological time, however different the rocks comprising them may now appear.

This hunt after zone fossils has ever since been one of the most urgent tasks of geology. In practically every case, their discovery permits a sure identification of contemporary mineral formations. But they provide even more information than this. Until recently it had been assumed that of, say, ten layers of sediment under water, the lowest was the oldest and the topmost the latest. Today we know for certain that this is true in most cases. But nowhere on earth is there a complete series of all rock formations formed on the ocean bed as sediment; it has been estimated that the total depth of such a sediment would be from 35,000 to 50,000 feet. Also, the mineral deposits which "amalgamate" into rocks are seldom left undisturbed. Mighty folding processes (which will be more precisely described later) have not only often completely displaced the original horizontal layers through bending and breaking, but have also at times pushed older layers over younger ones so that their time-sequence would be completely confused and indecipherable were it not for the zone fossils, whose presence works so to speak like a label. So when today a geologically minded climber finds the remains of a certain species of ammonite 25,000 feet up in the rock of the Himalayas, he can say with certainty that this towering rock was formed at the same time as an undisturbed horizontal layer, containing the same ammonite species, deep down in a European mine.

This was the key to the solving of the mystery of prehistory. After triumphant investigations over an almost incredibly short space of time, the geological history of the Earth was "established" in a few decades. In every civilised country of the world men went out to study prehistory, its problems and possible laws. Every quarry now became an El Dorado. Man had learnt to see and had found, practically wherever a systematic search was made, fossil treasures. Unbelievably rich lodes of unknown forms of life were revealed. Stones began to speak, and men learned to understand their language. Primeval swamp forests in strange forms emerged to the inward eye from the coal in the mines. Ocean floors came alive with an unfamiliar world of animals. Salt pans revealed former vanished seas. Rust-red rocks spoke of vast deserts. Weird giant animals were reconstituted from schist and limestone, their complete forms being realised by astonishing scientific deductions. Scratches on polished rock surfaces told of extensive glaciation in regions that nowadays are tropical. A faraway, dream-like world, a world beyond the imagination of the human mind only a century before, arose in a vision of gigantic proportions, vivid, glittering, exciting, fascinating in its wonder and strangeness.

CHAPTER TWO

The Earth and the Forces at Work on It

WE have seen how the idea of prehistory spread throughout the Western world of science, particularly after 1800. But the dissipation of the old, set ideas about the origins and age of the world was only a very gradual process. In an exhaustive work on the animal kingdom, the great French naturalist the Comte de Buffon (1707-1788) had suggested that the real age of the Earth must be at least 75,000 years. His was a brilliant if premature revolt against accepted thought. Shortly after this, there were further estimates putting the Earth's age back to hundreds of thousands, and even millions, of years.

These could not be anything but vague, ill-founded guesses: but they were genuine attempts to probe into a hitherto unknown no-man's-land—a fact which was realised. There were no illusions that absolute and accurate dating would be produced by this first attempt. Even today this problem is not fully solved. The geologists of that early period contented themselves with determining the sequence of the layers of sedimentary rocks, according to their age, and from this data producing a time-table. Systematic classification—on the lines of Linnaeus—was realised to be an indispensable basis for scientific research. Because of the intermixture of geological strata already mentioned, this was no easy task. It followed that the evidence of fossilised life became enormously important. A possible sequence of rock formations was deduced from observation of the varying degrees of development of these fossils. Where certain layers produced remains of mammals belonging to the highest class of vertebrates, it followed in general that such a sediment was newer than layers containing no mammals but only traces of, say, reptiles or amphibians, whilst a rock containing only simple non-osseous animals or primitive seaweeds would probably be infinitely older than both. In most cases a well-established sequence of strata was confirmed. And below all these fossiliferous strata were the sedimentary rocks, containing no form of life; from which it could logically be deduced that these rocks were the oldest of all, having been formed at an extremely remote period in time when—bold thought!—life had not yet appeared. This deduction revealed one of the most important discoveries in the whole course of the investigation of prehistory: namely that the appearance of more highly differentiated and developed forms of life seemed to be an essential part of Earth's maturing.

Proper classification naturally requires clear nomenclature. But in this respect early scientists were rather haphazard. Whether a man is called Smith, Brown or Robinson is of slight importance. His personality is what counts. Astronomy is equally happy-go-lucky. The vast majority of the constellations were named in antiquity. Half Greek mythology is enthroned in the skies. Why change the names? The planets and stars are well established, easily distinguishable—and that is sufficient. The scientific value of astronomy is unaffected by names.

Though superficially similar, the case of geological terminology is in fact very different. What more logical than to ascribe the origin of strata in which coal was formed to a Carboniferous Period, even though other deposits are also present? There is equal justification for the names of the Cretaceous Period, although not only chalk was produced during that age. Other descriptions are derived from areas where the formations in question were first properly investigated: the Permian Period owes its name to the Russian district of Perm in the Urals; the Algonquin is called after the discoveries made in the former hunting grounds of the Algonquin Indians in North America; Cambria is the ancient name of Wales; the Silurian Period immortalises the Celtic tribe of that name; and the Devonian is, of course, named after Devon.

As in biology, there are certain main groups, which are then further subdivided in order to distinguish the finer variations. The main groups are the formations. Originally these were quite simply divided into Primary (the oldest), followed by Secondary, Tertiary and Quaternary. But nowadays the Secondary and subsequent formations are called the Palaeozoic (first era), Mesozoic (middle era), and Cainozoic (latest era). The Palaeozoic is regarded as having been preceded by an earlier era—the Eozoic or pre-Cambrian era—while before that there was the Archaean, and, earliest of all, that remote epoch before the Earth solidified. The rocks formed during a particular period are said to belong to a system—thus the rocks of the Jurassic system were deposited during the Jurassic period. Rock systems are further divided into series and formations—most of which are named after the localities where they were recognised. Reference to the tables on the Earth's history (pp. 84 and 85) will make the whole scheme clear. These show the international system generally accepted, though in some cases scientists in different countries prefer to use their own terminology. For example, the Americans do not invariably differentiate the Carboniferous Period from the ensuing Permian. They speak of the Permocarboniferous as a single formation. Similarly, they use the term "Algonquin" (mentioned above) for rocks of the upper part of the Pre-Cambrian; whereas in Britain the name Torridonian is used for certain Pre-Cambrian sedimentary strata. Such variations are always matters for international discussion and agreement, and it is likely that in the future the present classifications will undergo modifications—which, in fact, will make little or no difference to the time sequence. This time sequence is firmly established; was established, indeed, in the last century, so effectively did men labour in the first great era of geology.

Since 1890 nothing of revolutionary importance in this respect has emerged. The basic picture of prehistory was outlined almost a hundred years ago, and has remained essentially unchanged. Important contributors to the science were Sir Charles Lyell of England (1797-1875) and Karl Ernst von Hoff of Germany (1771-1837). These men put an end to Neptunism, Plutonism and Cuvier's Catastrophic Theory; and they conceived the theory of Actualism which, despite critical "ifs" and "buts", still dominates geological thought and research.

What is Actualism? Primarily it states that the formative forces at present at work under and upon the Earth's surface and crust are identical with those of every other geological epoch. These forces include weather, the erosive effect of rivers and seas, and certain subterranean influences.

On the face of it, this theory may not carry entire conviction. Admittedly, it is a known fact that violent rainfall, especially in mountain country, can cause landslides. It is also known

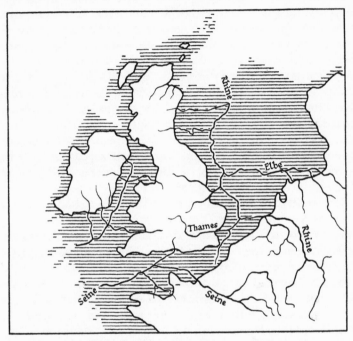

1. The Shelf-region of the North Sea (including the British Isles) which at the beginning of the Pleistocene Ice Age was dry land

that rock becomes weathered as a result of fluctuating temperature, wind, rain, and chemical effects; that microscopic organisms have power to disintegrate rock; that soil can then be swept away by rivers and deposited as sediment. The erosive, undermining, destructive power of the ocean's waves is a familiar phenomenon; minor changes in landscape can be effected by volcanic eruption and earthquake. It is evident that certain coastal regions of the Mediterranean have, since classical times, suffered from land subsidence; floods due to storms in the North Sea have turned a large part of the low-lying Netherlands into a lake (the Zuider-Zee), which has had recently to be re-drained by man.

All this is known; and the continuous effects of these "lesser" natural forces are accepted. But are they great enough to account for the titanic physical changes which have taken place during the course of the Earth's history? There was a time when our present-day mountain giants—the Alps, the Himalayas, the Andes, the Caucasus—had not yet arisen; a time indeed when they were no more than the bottoms of shallow seas. And there were other eons when North America and Europe were joined together by massive land bridges which now lie submerged below the oceans, or even perhaps when the two continents were actually vastly closer together than they are now. All this implies upheavals on a major scale. So must there not have been catastrophic occurrences in the interior of the Earth causing, among other things, floods of inconceivable extent?

Admittedly, there is no need to be over-orthodox. A synthesis of several outdated theories could account for the vast upheavals which took place in the forming of the Earth's surface, and still the Actualist theory would hold good. Periods of especially pronounced vulcanism, no rare phenomena, are definitely proved. Cracks, displacements and distortions within the Earth's crust could have caused sudden collapses leading to catastrophic results over a wide area. The immense East African Rift—a cleft averaging 1,200 feet in depth and up to 30 miles in width, stretching from the Zambezi to the Jordan Valley—certainly did not come about by gradual erosion. Similar "distortions" are today by far the most frequent origins of earthquakes. Even meteors from outer space—which must indeed have been of immense size and correspondingly extremely rare—have been invoked by theorists as being partly responsible for changes in the Earth's surface. But apart from the genuinely violent origins of the Earth—a purely natural development at a time when the crust and water first appeared—there has never really been any *necessity* for such catastrophes. Revolutionary occurrences of this sort must always be regarded as exceptional.

In all past epochs, as today, the rule is that of gradual change, brought about by forces working inside and outside the Earth. In this context the geologists speak of "exogenic" (external) and "endogenic" (internal) dynamics. To the external processes belong the weathering of rocks, the erosion of stone and, above all, the widespread process of deposition of sediments on the ocean floor.

The obvious weathering process has already been mentioned. It happens as a result of the incessant mechanical and chemical action of the atmosphere, which gradually loosens and splits even the mightiest mountains into separate boulders, and then reduces these to sand, most of the more soluble material being dissolved away in the process. Changes in temperature, cracking as a result of water freezing in clefts of rock, downpours of rain, wind blasting, the disruptive penetration of plant roots—all make their contributions to the sum total of atmospheric weathering.

Erosion is caused by running water (fluvial), wind (aeolian), ice (glacial) or the sea (marine). River erosion has two main consequences: firstly, the carrying away of sand and other fine particles, together with substances invisibly in solution; secondly, the carving out of entirely new landscapes as a result of the erosive effects of the river's own currents. In many parts of the world whole mountain chains which long ago had already been reduced to a level plain have become fashioned into new mountains by a combination of river action and land uplift. Sometimes this river-erosion produces such staggering natural wonders as the Grand Canyon in Arizona, where the river's course has sliced through layers of variegated rocks to a depth of over 5,000 feet.

It is fairly easy to estimate the amount of material a river carries down to the sea. The Amazon holds the record, sweeping away, year after year, 1,300 million tons of solid matter from the mainland into the Atlantic. The Mississippi moves 300 million tons, and the Danube 40 million. Because all rivers act in this way, the amount of material shifted by erosion adds up to a formidable total. Nevertheless, figures are deceptive; for over many generations the loss of land to the sea is barely perceptible. Aeolian erosion, too, whereby dust is carried away by the wind over the oceans, plays a

substantial role, the precise extent of which is still difficult
to assess.

At all events, the final destination of the erosion cycle is
the bed of the sea, where the important process of sedimentation begins. The chief source of these sedimentary layers in
the past has already been mentioned: the disintegration of
sand, gravel, lime and other components of the mainland,
which by one means or another were precipitated into the
sea. Generally speaking, the coarser particles were deposited
nearest the river which carried the material from the land,
and only the finer particles travelled out into the deep ocean
waters. Subsequent physical changes (consolidation and lithi-
fication) then transformed these loose sediments into hard
rocks—such as conglomerate, sandstone and mudstone. The
general term for such physical changes is diagenesis.

Later, the plant and animal worlds also added a substantial
accretion to these sedimentary deposits. The skeletons and
shells of numerous animals such as molluscs, echinoderms,
brachiopods, corals, foraminifera, etc., consisting largely of
calcium carbonate, were absorbed after death into the sediments on the sea floor, and this was the origin of such rocks
as limestone (including chalk) and dolomite (though it is
more usual for lime to be precipitated from solution than to
be deposited in the form of actual shells). Lime deposits of
this kind have formed the basis of such great rock formations
as the limestone Alps, the Dolomites, and numerous formations on the periphery of the Mediterranean. The Egyptian
Pyramids are built of stone hewn from the Moccatam Mountains—material composed of the innumerable shells of dead
nummulites.

It has also been found that extensive areas of the ocean
floors are covered by thick layers of calcareous sediments composed of Globigerina and Radiolaria, which as a result of
chemical and mechanical activity are in process of being transformed into rocks. The reef-building activities of the corals
are well known, and in parts of the Pacific the familiar atolls
are largely a result of their growth.

At this point a logical and reasonable question arises.
Would not all these processes of weathering, erosion and sedimentation have eventually led to the total levelling down of

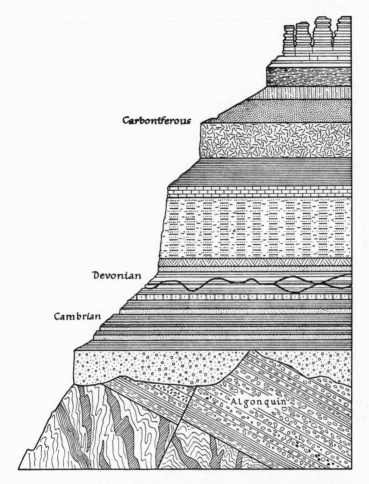

2. Schematic cross-section of a cliff in the Grand Canyon
eroded by the Colorado River

all the continental land surfaces? Indeed, if all land masses
were levelled and distributed evenly over the bed of the sea,
the result would be that the whole Earth would be covered
with water to a depth of about 6,000 feet. But in actual fact,
of course, the land surface rises above the level of the sea for
about a quarter of the globe's total area. Why, in the course

of eons, has it not been swept level and submerged by the sea? The answer is that the inner forces of the Earth. the endogenous forces, are strong enough to offset the various processes of erosion.

Exogenous forces—those working on the Earth's surface from outside—are easy to observe. Extensive investigation of them is being carried out. But the internal forces of the Earth are much more difficult to assess and confront us with many unanswered problems, despite our modern techniques. The process of mountain-building alone has produced a number of hypotheses, the acceptability of any one of which depends merely upon probability.

Astonishingly little is known about the interior of the Earth—certainly nothing precise. This is very perturbing to scientists, but there is little they can do for the present. We cannot conceivably reach the core of the Earth. It will be easier to fly to the Moon or Mars than to make Jules Verne's Journey to the Centre of the Earth. Information obtained from mines and boreholes even 18,000 feet deep is insignificant. 18,000 feet is approximately 3 miles, and with the centre of the Earth lying some 4,000 miles beneath the surface those 3 miles are no more than a pin-prick. Though astronomers with justification speak of Earth as a minute, insignificant body, a grain of dust in the Universe, the inhabitants of Earth understandably regard this "grain" as a mighty planet. Imagine the Earth shrunk to a ball with a diameter of 60 feet (the height of a small block of apartments). One then finds that the highest point on Earth, Mount Everest, will rise only $\frac{3}{4}$ inch above the surface!

Our field of physical knowledge about the Earth extends from the top of the highest mountain to the bottom of the deepest sea, which amounts in all to a difference of 2 inches on a 60-foot globe. Our knowledge of conditions at greater depths remains wholly in the realms of conjecture.

However, modern scientific investigation does not give up easily, and in fact, a whole series of projects have been formulated which, although so far of limited scope, are nevertheless beginning to approach the truth.

We know, to begin with, that the Earth is a planet—and is thus a heavenly body among other, similar bodies. But are the implications of this truism fully understood? Firstly, the Earth, as an object of scientific study, cannot be regarded as an isolated phenomenon; from which it follows that astronomical and geological researches, instead of being separate and distinct, are simply concerned with different aspects of one vast subject—a composite conception which, particularly in recent times, has impinged more and more on geological theory.

As a planet our Earth is one of nine major, non-luminous (dark) bodies travelling in fixed elliptical paths round the ball of glowing gas which we call the Sun. It is generally

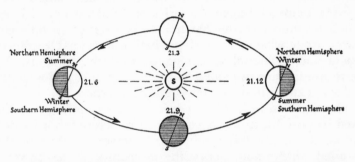

3. Earth's orbit round the Sun in 365 days. The constant inclination of the Earth's axis accounts for the changing seasons

agreed that the planets owe their origin, in some way or other, to the Sun, though the exact process is still highly uncertain. (The volume of the Sun exceeds by 700 times the total volume of the planets, their satellites, the asteroids, and all other bodies in the solar system, such as comets and meteor swarms.) The physical attributes of the planets, such as density, chemical composition, atmosphere, temperature, etc., vary enormously. Only in the case of a few planets (possibly Venus and Mars) can one speak of a similarity to Earth; certainly there is no approach to identity. Thus the Earth—in our solar system at least—is unique, its physical characteristics being determined by its distance from the sun, its density, size, relationship to the Moon, and the radiated warmth received from the sun.

The yearly rhythm of the Earth's "journey round the Sun in 365 days", always at a fixed distance, its rotation about its own axis every 24 hours, the inclination of its axis towards the ecliptic, all govern the climatic zones and the weather, while the gravitational effects of the Sun and the Moon influence the tides and a tide-like movement of the Earth's crust. The Earth's gravity holds its atmosphere in position, and its period of rotation determines the Earth's shape (which is not indeed a perfect sphere). Variations in any of these factors would change the whole "picture" of our planet. Were the Earth to move into the same orbit as Venus, its year would be shorter, the heat from the Sun fiercer, the atmosphere very possibly more turbulent—a series of fundamental changes which would make the Earth in every respect a different planet from what it is, and produce unimaginable physiological and biological variations. In the orbit of Mars, the Earth would have two and a half times less light and warmth, and again an entirely different biological scene.

The Earth is, in fact, what it is because cosmic forces dictated its position in space, consequently determining its prevailing stable physical conditions. However, in spite of the so-called "inexorable" laws, the mechanics of the universe are not immune from minor variations. The eccentricity of the Earth's elliptical path round the Sun, for instance, is not invariably the same, for during the course of 91,800 years it alternates between two extremes, and even the Earth's closest approach to the Sun, the perihelion, varies over a period of 20,700 years. The inclination of the Earth's axis also wobbles slightly in a period of 40,000 years; and the direction of the axis moves in a circle every 26,000 years (precession). There is, in fact, a continual play of forces, pulling back and forth, which in varying degrees affects all bodies in the solar system; and, by and large, this must have a braking effect on the "clockwork" of the planetary system. For instance, it has been suggested—though without proof—that the Earth at birth had a rotation period of 3 hours and subsequently, as a result of the attraction of the Sun and Moon, slowed down to its present 24 hours. In spite of the immense period of time over which this retardation would have taken place, the process would inevitably have caused an important change in the shape of the Earth, since a very rapidly rotating body must be flatter at the poles than one rotating more slowly.

Because of its atmosphere the Earth happens to be comparatively immune from the direct effects of lethal rays from outer space. Space itself is flooded with radiations of every known wavelength and strength, emanating not only from the Sun, but also from the stars and other aggregates of matter in outer space. The well-known cosmic ultra-high-frequency rays are particularly fierce, and the source of their immense energy was for a long time one of the great mysteries of cosmic physics. It is now known that these rays consist chiefly of the nuclei of hydrogen and helium atoms which travel almost at the speed of light—hence their extraordinary energy. How this energy is built up, and how such fantastic speed is achieved, can only be inferred from recent experiments with particle accelerators. In these complicated apparatuses, protons (hydrogen nuclei), alpha particles (helium nuclei) and electrons are accelerated to immense speeds by means of electro-magnetic fields. It is probable that the same process occurs in nature. There may well be electrical fields of tremendous force on every sun; they are certainly known to exist on ours. Furthermore, the immeasurable distances of outer space may also contain magnetic clouds of similar potency. It is obvious that this ultra-radiation throughout the vacuum of space must be of annihilating strength and a menace to every form of life.

As has been indicated, the perfect defence against these deadly radiations is the atmosphere which envelops our world like padded armour. (The great majority of meteors, too, on entering our atmosphere, burn up at a great height and turn into harmless dust, as any "shooting star" shows. Only the extremely rare giant meteors penetrate the atmosphere and survive to make an appreciable dent in the Earth's surface.) Over the vast range of electro-magnetic radiations, our atmospheric envelope cuts out all but the narrow band of "visible" light, infra-red radiation, and a section of ultra-short radio waves between 1.5 centimetres and 10 metres in length. Not until the present century did we first become aware of this second "window into space", and then the foundations were laid for modern radio astronomy.

It is only in recent times that the composition of our atmosphere has been fairly accurately determined. How far it
extends upwards is still a matter for dispute. The top of the
exosphere—where the atmosphere evaporates into absolute
space—lies perhaps 1,000 miles up, though of course it has no
clearly defined upper limit. The region in which we live and
breathe, the region of weather phenomena, is the troposphere;
it is about 5 miles high at the poles, and 10 miles high over
the equatorial regions. Above it, there is a narrow intermediate layer, the tropopause, itself surrounded by the strato-
sphere which, though not sharply demarcated, extends upwards for about another 45 miles. Above this again lies the
immense ionosphere, so important in long-wave radio
transmission.

The constituents of this vitally important mixture which
we call "air" are, at ground level, 78·1 per cent nitrogen,
20·93 per cent oxygen, 0·932 per cent argon, 0·03 per cent
carbon dioxide, with traces of the rare gases neon, helium,
xenon and krypton. (Its content of water vapour varies enormously.) Up to a height of 12 miles, the relative proportions
of the elements remain much the same; but higher up they
begin to change, though nitrogen and oxygen still predomin-
ate. Air pressure and density steadily decrease. At a height of
30 miles, the ground pressure of 1,000 millibars ($=750$ milli-
metres of a mercury column) has already dwindled to one-
thousandth of that figure, and at 150 miles up it is a mere
1,000,000,000th. Atmospheric density diminishes similarly.
Whereas at ground level a cubic centimetre of air contains
the fantastic number of 10^{19} (10 with 18 noughts after it)
molecules, in the ionosphere at a height of 160 miles the
number of molecules is a mere 10^9.

As regards temperatures, the situation is somewhat unexpected. It is a well-known rule that the higher the colder—
the decrease in temperature being 0·6° C. for every 100 metres
(328 feet) upwards—and it could be reasonably deduced that
this decrease would continue steadily into the upper atmosphere. Yet measuring instruments sent up in high-altitude
rockets have revealed an entirely different state of affairs. In
accordance with the rule deduced from measurements made
in the more accessible region of the troposphere, at first the

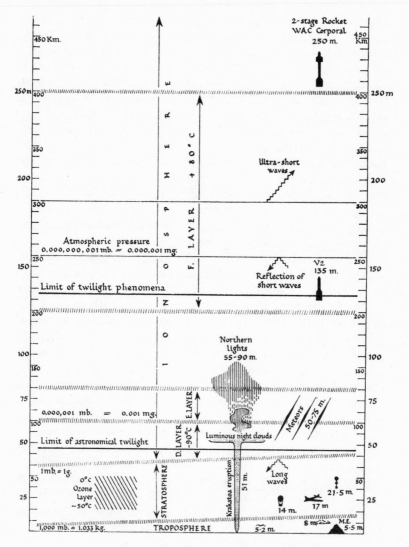

4. Structure of the Earth's atmosphere

temperature does in fact continue to fall steadily to −50° C.; from that point, up to a height of 12 miles, it remains constant; then from 12-30 miles up it *increases* to 0° C. From 30 miles to a height of about 60 miles it drops again to −90° C. This is followed by a fantastic increase to +800° C. at heights of over 125 miles. Modern measurement goes no further; so for the present it must be assumed theoretically that similar high temperatures prevail in the very outermost regions of the atmosphere. Though the "temperature" of these layers is so high, the actual "heat" is inappreciable—an extraordinarily interesting and apparently paradoxical phenomenon. Astronomy has discovered similar conditions on the Sun, for there too the outermost tenuous atmospheric layers extend deep into space at a temperature of 1,000,000° C., incomparably higher than that of the actual surface of the Sun, which is only 6,000° C. How is this possible in the case of Earth, and how is it that we notice no effects?

The answer is that we have been following a fallacious line of reasoning. If it were possible for a man to ascend to the "high temperature" atmosphere in a balloon, he would not burn to death—he would freeze. And freeze to death at 800° C.! What we call "heat" is the effect of molecules in a state of motion. The faster molecules collide with one another the higher the temperature of a gas or any other form of matter. Therefore the varying speeds with which molecules strike against the human body produce the different sensations of heat and cold. But these sensations are valid only for conditions in the world inhabited by us, where there are vast numbers of molecules to impact on one's body and produce this sensation. In the uppermost atmosphere the air is so thin that even the increased speed of the molecules "heated" by the Sun's rays to an apparent temperature of 800° C. is no longer sufficient to make up for the vast decrease in the *number* of molecules in producing heat. Similar considerations apply to the high temperature of the Sun's corona, where the atmosphere is equally attenuated.

Our atmosphere is full of mysteries and peculiarities. A very important phenomenon is that of ionisation, which occurs at various heights in the atmosphere as the result of penetration by ultra-violet radiations from the Sun. Ionisation is a process quite easily understood, even by the least scientifically minded, as the following brief description will show.

Every atom consists of a nucleus and one or more electrons surrounding that nucleus. The nucleus is positively charged, and the electrons negatively. In normal conditions there are just sufficient electrons present to balance the positive charge of the nucleus, thus making the atom as a whole electrically neutral. For instance, in the case of nitrogen there are 7 electrons present in order to balance the 7 positive units in the nucleus. In oxygen there are 8. These electron "envelopes" are easily damaged by outside influences.

5. Model of an oxygen atom

Ultra-violet radiation can knock out one or more of the negative electrons, resulting in the positive charge in the atom becoming predominant. Thus the atom is ionised; it has become an ion. This process takes place on a huge scale in the outer region of the atmosphere, which is consequently called the ionosphere. The whole process can be regarded as a perpetual battle between the invading ultra-violet rays and the protective atoms and molecules of the air, in which the atoms, despite heavy losses, destroy the biologically deadly radiations. The impact of the rays gives the atoms that increased velocity which manifests itself as an increase in temperature.

Fortunately, the atoms and molecules are continually regenerating themselves. The released electron very soon finds an ion which attracts and combines with it. This usually happens at night, when there are no ultra-violet radiations from the Sun. Also, the splitting-up (dissociation) of the molecules into individual atoms of which they are made up is generally short-lived.

These processes vary in duration and do not always take place at precisely the same height, but there are certain regions where the liberation of the electrons (electron concentrations) reaches a maximum, and where extensive electrically conductive (ionised) layers persist for varying periods of time. Formerly these layers were called after their discoverers —Heaviside or Appleton—but now they are generally known as D, E, and F layers (with further subdivisions). These are the layers which are responsible for blocking the penetration of most wavelengths from outer space, and also for preventing similar waves from escaping from Earth into space. In radio technology it is well known that waves of certain lengths are intercepted by atmospheric layers at different heights, and deflected back to Earth again. Without these ionospheric layers there would be no long-distance radio.

Such, roughly, is the composition of our atmosphere as we believe it to be today. In the very earliest times of Earth's existence it was quite different.

Mention has already been made of the hydrosphere: the realm of water, of rivers and oceans and lakes. Its importance, as the antithesis of dry land, is obvious enough. But very little is known about the structure of the ocean bed. Up to a hundred years ago only the very vaguest ideas prevailed. Ineffective methods of sounding the sea-depths left the abysses of the ocean world a mystery and their configuration a sealed book. But things have changed since then. The invention of the echo-sounder has permitted continuous precision depth-measuring, which has been undertaken over extensive areas by a number of international expeditions. The echo-sounding system, such as that developed by Alexander Behm in particular, is quite simple to understand. On one side of the ship is a sound emitter which sends impulses (mostly ultrasonic) down to the sea floor. These waves, moving always at a constant, known speed, reach the bottom and are then reflected back and registered by a receiver on the other side of the ship. The time taken by the sound waves to penetrate down to the ocean floor and bounce back to the ship reveals, by means of a simple calculation, the exact depth at that point. As a result of this invention, the mapping of the under-water world has progressed with amazing rapidity, even though sea-bed contours may not be quite as detailed as those on a land map.

We may therefore speak without exaggeration of the discovery of a new world which could not have been conceivable to science in previous centuries. In actual fact, this world often represents a direct extension of familiar dry land features. Here, as there, are mountain ranges of varying heights, with gentle slopes and abrupt precipices, gorges, valleys, deep canyons, flat basins, table mountains, volcanic craters and towering peaks hardly inferior to the Himalayas. One must remember, for example, that an island with mountain-tops rising perhaps 10,000 feet out of the sea, may have its base at a depth of 15,000 feet below the surface. The sea level is indeed no more than a biological frontier separating different forms of life. The shape of the underwater world is, of course, smoother and rounder than that of the dry land because it is not subject to the effects of atmospheric weathering. The absence of light (below a depth of about 300 feet) is strange and oppressive, but in general the seascapes resemble mainland formations. One striking characteristic is that really deep sea beds are seldom contiguous to a continent, which is almost always perched on a pedestal which projects for a considerable distance all round; this pedestal is the so-called shelf-region and is covered by, at most, 600 feet of water. At the edge of this shelf the ground plunges suddenly and relatively steeply to great depths. Thus the shallow North Sea is no more than a shelf which was dry land until, from the geological point of view, quite recently. The Elbe at that time was immensely broad, like a lake, and encircled the heights of the present Dogger Bank before debouching into the North Sea. Towering above its right bank there rose a varicoloured, forest-clad table-mountain which today is known as Heligoland. The Rhine ran northwards over plains towards the Dogger Bank and received the Thames as a tributary before it reached the sea. The ancient courses of both these rivers have been clearly mapped. (See diagram on p. 33.)

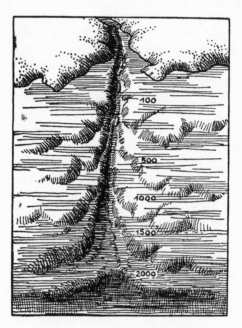

6. The Congo channel. An example of a subterranean canyon

Similar examples of submarine channels are to be found at the mouths of such great rivers as the Hudson, the Congo, the Mississippi, the Ganges, and many others. Deep river beds can be traced on the sea floor over the whole of the shelf-regions, and most of these submarine canyons slope gradually downwards at first, flanked by steep walls, and then descend more and more precipitously in a series of steps until, more than 60 miles out from the coast (in the case of the Hudson and the Congo, 90 miles), they plunge into the deep ocean through a mouth several miles wide. The origin of these channels is difficult to decide with any certainty. The most plausible explanation might seem to be the assumption that in earlier times the sea level lay considerably lower, and that its elevation (or possibly the sinking of the continental shelves) submerged the gorges eroded by the rivers. Certainly one contributory factor is the continuous sedimentation of the ocean floor, which would gradually have raised the general water level. It has been suggested that, in every 1,000 years, 1 millimetre of sediment may be deposited on the sea floor, resulting in a corresponding rise in the level of water. Simple arithmetic on this basis suggests that the Hudson Channel, for example, was already in existence round about a thousand million years ago. But this is totally impossible, since in a far shorter space of time the river systems in all the continents have been frequently demolished and completely renewed in totally different forms. All European river systems, for example, are the product of the Tertiary age, one of the most recent formations. A more likely theory is that these steep-sided chasms have been formed by the eroding effects of fast-moving and extremely localised submarine currents of unknown origin.

Nevertheless, the hasty arithmetical calculation referred to above, in spite of its error, did suggest for the first time the possibility of hitherto inconceivably vast epochs in the Earth's past. And, of course, the formation of the oceans must have occurred appreciably later than the formation of the Earth's solid crust. As far back as 1700 the noted English astronomer Halley (who calculated the orbit and the 76-year period of the comet named after him) put forward an ingenious suggestion for determining the age of the oceans. He assumed that the virgin waters of the world were at first salt-free and that their present salt content was gradually brought down to them by the rivers. Therefore, he said, one simply had to establish the volumetric saline content of the oceans, discover how much salt a year was carried down to them, and thence calculate their age. In Halley's day it was not yet possible to produce the necessary data for such calculations. Indeed, it was only towards the end of the last century that his suggestions were acted upon. The result gave the oceans an age of 90,000,000 years. As we know today, this estimate is far too small—inevitably so because of the inadequate and inapplicable data from which it was deduced. The Earth's hydrosphere is much older than that; far older than all life for which it was the cradle. For, strange and weird as the lightless depths of the great expanses of the oceans may appear to us, they were the womb in which life first appeared and grew, the fount from which sprang the whole biological kingdom.

After the atmosphere (air) and the hydrosphere (water), next in logical sequence comes the lithosphere—the rocky covering of the Earth. But first some description must be given of the composition of the Earth, so far as we know it. This is a tremendous question which unfortunately can only be answered to a very limited extent, and with very considerable uncertainty. The secrets of the atmosphere are yielding themselves up gradually to the recording instruments carried by increasingly efficient rockets and satellites. The aqueous world is being mapped by means of echo-sounding in shallow waters; the mysteries of life are being studied by numerous scientific and amateur divers; while the depths are beginning to be plumbed by bathyscaphes. But the interior of the Earth remains, to all practical purposes, inaccessible.

Yet mankind is nothing if not inventive. So much has already been successfully discovered, in the most diverse fields, by the use of "waves" of all sorts, that it would be surprising if some such means could not be employed to "illuminate" the interior of the Earth. One source of a particular sort of waves originates within the Earth itself—in the form of earthquakes. These natural disasters affecting the rocky skin of the Earth produce waves which travel over the whole world and are detected by seismographs (instruments which record vibrations on moving charts) in earthquake stations dotted all across the world. Thus it is possible to establish precisely the magnitude of earthquakes and the velocities of the waves which they produce, as well as other data. Since the wave movements obey the physical laws governing reflexion, refraction, changes in velocity, etc., they are utilised to form the basis of a very complicated but precise and specialised branch of geology which may very likely be able to provide us with considerable information about the structure of the Earth's interior. In particular, changes in the velocity of the waves indicate varying densities of substances, and the occurrence of sudden violent changes at certain depths could be the result of correspondingly sudden changes in the formations through which the waves are travelling, which in turn suggests that the Earth may be made up of a series of concentric shells.

The simplest picture of the Earth's interior was formerly deduced from the fact that the temperature inside the Earth increases by $1°$ C. for every 100 feet that one descends. According to this an absolute inferno must reign at a depth of 60 miles, and for a long time this by no means illogical assumption was believed to be supported by the evidence of volcanic activity. But such a conclusion is certainly false; for the idea of a gigantic incandescent ball enclosed in an eggshell-thin crust of rock is physically untenable.

Now, astronomical calculations have shown that the Earth as a whole has an average density of 5·52—that is, it weighs 5·52 times as much as a sphere of water of equal size (the density of water being taken as 1). Since the rocks on the Earth's surface and in the "accessible depths" have an average density of 2·7, the density of whatever composes the centre of the Earth must be substantially higher in order to produce the overall average of 5·52. Hence it has been deduced that the Earth has a core of nickel-iron, density 8·2.

This concept of a Nife core (Ni = nickel, Fe = iron) is the one accepted today.

In measuring the size of the actual core of the Earth, calculations were based on variations in the duration of earthquake waves coupled with the assumption of the Nife core, and some approximate figures were arrived at. From the centre of the Earth the core must extend outwards for something over 2,000 miles, being possibly surrounded by a relatively narrow shell composed predominantly of sulphides and oxides. While the inner part of the core is likely to be solid, its outer part is probably in a more plastic or fluid state. The pressure at the outer surface of the central core is about 1·5 million atmospheres.

The material composition of the deep interior of the Earth is still very much in doubt, however. Thus, in 1940, the scientists Kuhn and Rittmann created a sensation with their theory that at the very centre of the Earth was imprisoned genuine, original solar matter: that is, mainly hydrogen and helium in a gaseous state. Even though the whole theory has been strongly challenged, the incredible pressures prevailing at those depths—between 3 and 5 million atmospheres— makes it possible that gaseous matter may in fact behave like rigid bodies and thus conduct earthquake waves. So far it has proved impossible to produce in laboratories the vast pressures necessary to test gases in such a state.

An interesting question is whether in the beginning the Earth contained the so-called trans-uranic elements. These are elements (eleven so far discovered) which are heavier than uranium, element 92, and which are not found on Earth but have been artificially manufactured in the course of extremely brilliant experiments by atomic physicists. Their absence from the universe today—and spectral analysis does not reveal them on the stars—can be explained by their strong radio-activity and, mostly, very short periods of decay. If they once existed in Nature, they have long since radiated them-selves away and been transformed into other, stable elements. This whole question is one of extreme interest, because not only does the present-day manufacture of trans-uranic ele-ments show that man's ingenuity has achieved astonishing advances in penetrating the secrets of matter, but it may also provide an answer to the presence of so many heavy and medium-heavy elements on Earth which, partly at any rate, may have appeared as the product of radioactive decay of the ultra-heavy elements. Apparently this question has not yet been investigated by science. However, many problems about Earth and its origins still face us and at the present time can-not be solved.

Another hypothesis, proposed by a German, Professor Carl von Weizsäcker, suggests that the planets of our system were born in a "cold" state, having been "baked" solid from already cooled matter. The great heat of the Earth's interior (as the centre it is believed to be as high as 3,850° C.) may have developed later as a result of internal pressure and radio-active processes.

Then, again, there is yet another theory that the centre of the Earth is composed of olivine (magnesium and iron silicates). But all this is no more than theory. The Earth's

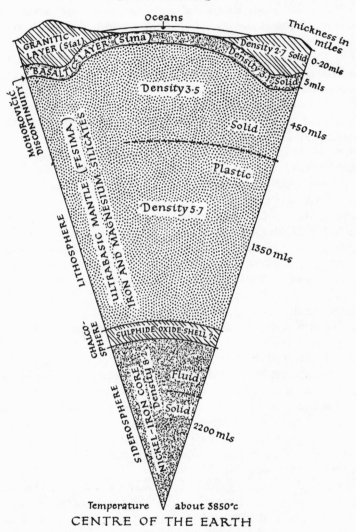

7. Probable structure of the Earth's interior
(*Diagram not drawn to scale*)

interior hides its own secret, and is likely to do so for a long time to come.

We believe we can be slightly more certain about the nature of the rocky covering of the world, especially about the outermost surface on which we live. Broadly speaking, this shell is divided—from the top downwards—into two layers: sial and sima. These names are instructive. *Sial* is composed of the first syllables of the two elements silicon and aluminium, because these two in combination form the predominant rocks. Similarly, *sima* is derived from silicon and magnesium. The sial layer is commonly known as the granitic layer, since it transmits earthquake waves in much the same way as does granite. For similar reasons, the denser sima layer is called the basaltic layer, since it resembles basalt in this particular respect.

The sial crust has an average density of about 2·7, and includes all the main continental blocks but does not extend beneath the great ocean basins. It is thus not a complete shell covering the whole Earth's surface. It varies considerably in thickness—commonly attaining a depth of as much as 20 miles, though beneath the great mountain ranges it may penetrate downwards as much as 35 miles.

The sima layer directly underlies the ocean-floor sediments and may possibly also extend beneath the continental sial blocks. Material of somewhat similar composition may extend towards the centre of the Earth for a very considerable distance, but at a depth of about 3 to 5 miles below the sima layer's upper surface a very sudden change of some kind occurs. It may be a change in chemical composition, or it may be a change in physical state, but whatever it is it makes its presence known by its effects on transmitted earthquake waves. It is called the Mohorovičić discontinuity, after its Yugoslav discoverer. Below this level, we come to the vast thickness of material constituting the mantle. This probably consists largely of iron and magnesium silicates, and is sometimes known as the fesima layer because of the high proportion of iron (Fe) present. In chemical composition this layer somewhat resembles the rocks known as eclogite, peridotite and dunite. The outer part of the mantle is probably in a rigid state, but the evidence from earthquake waves suggests a change from this to a non-rigid plastic state at a depth of about 450 miles.

In order to discover what actually happens at the Mohorovičić discontinuity, an ambitious plan has been made to bore a hole that will reach down as far as this disputed zone. Known for convenience as the "Mohole", it will be bored from a floating boat first through the unconsolidated sediments on the ocean floor, then through a narrow layer of consolidated sediments and volcanic rocks, and then through the full depth of the sima until it reaches the discontinuity. The technical problems to be mastered are considerable, and are very different in nature from those involved in deep-boring on dry land. Quite apart from the extra depth (the deepest oil-well goes a little over 25,000 feet, or less than 5 miles), there is the problem of locating the hole at the bottom of several miles of water in the ocean when a length of core has been removed, and worn equipment is being replaced by new.

Even if the Mohole does actually reach the Mohorovičić discontinuity, the evidence that it will give us about the physical conditions at vastly greater depths will be only indirect. Nevertheless even accurate figures for the actual increase of temperature in the sima crust will be very valuable, as many published values are little more than guesses. At the exceedingly high pressures and temperatures existing below the Earth's outer crust, we can expect matter to behave in a very different way from that at the surface. Much of this rock material is in the form of *magma*, a name given to a particular state where the rock mass is permeated through and through by bases and liquids under enormous pressure. The mass as a whole is sufficiently plastic to be able to undergo slow movement, but, when the restraining pressure is released (as for example during a volcanic eruption), the magma becomes an incandescent mass and, "lubricated" by the enclosed gases, becomes extraordinarily mobile and easily dispersed. It used to be thought that below the rigid crust all the rock was in this mobile and eruptive state, but now it is clear that this state is assumed only in the neighbourhood of cracks and breaches in the rigid crust.

Igneous rocks, formed by the cooling of magmatic material

from the Earth's depths at or near the surface, are put into two main classes. Firstly there are the extrusive rocks, those which actually reached the surface where they flowed out as lava either on land or on the sea-bed. Secondly there are the intrusive rocks, which never actually reached the surface whilst fluid, but solidified embedded in the surface strata. These intrusive rocks have been revealed only by subsequent erosion which has removed the overlying sedimentary beds. In each class of rock, the actual type formed depends on many different factors, such as the constitution of the original magma, the rate of solidification (which is governed by temperature and pressure), presence or absence of fluids saturated with dissolved substances which can enrich the molten rock as it cools, the degree to which the magma has engulfed portions of the surrounding (so-called "country") rock as it bursts through to the surface, and so on. The permutations and combinations of these various factors can lead to a bewildering variety of possible results. It must be appreciated that the full description of the petrology (mineral composition) of these rocks lies far beyond the scope of this book. We can do little more than mention the main types of igneous rock usually encountered.

The basic lavas, derived from the lower sima and fesima layers, emerge at the highest temperature, and so stay fluid longer and thus flow farther. Basalt is the typical extrusive lava of this kind. Rocks of similar composition chemically, but of medium grain size, are called dolerite, whilst intrusive basaltic rock containing very large crystals (due to very slow cooling deep underground) may be called by the general name gabbro. The much less common rocks peridotite and dunite belong to this general group, but have fewer minerals present, and may well originate from even greater depths. These basic and ultra-basic rocks are very rich in minerals such as olivine, hornblende and augite, which are dark green or black in colour and contain much magnesium and iron.

Rock types exist which are somewhat intermediate between the basic and the acidic. An example is syenite, which the ancient Egyptians dug up at Syene (modern Aswan). These rocks often contain combinations of minerals not normally found together.

The more acidic lavas conform to the average composition of the sial layer. Very fine-grained lavas of this type, which must have cooled very fast, are exemplified by such extrusive rocks as rhyolite and dacite, whilst the familiar granite and granodiorite cooled more slowly and so have larger crystals. These rocks are usually light-coloured, because of the abundance of quartz (white or glassy and without colour) and feldspars—usually white or pink. Sometimes a single mineral will form very large crystals in the midst of a ground-mass of minute crystals of the other minerals present. Rocks of this kind are said to be porphyritic.

When the hot, mineral-saturated fluids have cooled slowly within cracks in the country-rock, we have the most favourable circumstances of all for crystal growth, and it is from these mineral-rich veins and lodes that we extract vast quantities of valuable metal ores and gemstones on a commercial scale. Mineral deposits of this kind are often known as gangue.

The third main group, after the igneous rocks which we have just discussed, and the sedimentary ones formed by their decomposition and ultimate re-deposition, are the metamorphic rocks. These have undergone multifarious changes as a result of such influences as heat and pressure, and are now seen as something quite different from their appearance when first formed. Probably most metamorphic rocks were originally sedimentary, but owing to the enormous temperatures and pressures created during phases of mountain building and the upward movement of magma, they have been converted into such rocks as phyllite, gneiss and schist. The intense heating of limestone at some depth has produced marble (if the limestone were very pure) or hornfels (if impure, with much clay present). Extreme lateral pressures have converted many clay-rich sedimentary rocks into slates, rocks which split easily into thin sheets. Some of the very old metamorphic rocks of the pre-Cambrian may well have been formed in conditions no longer present on the Earth, for example as deposits in the ancient salt-rich oceans at a high temperature. Some may even be the first products of the solidification process of the primal molten mass.

At this stage, we can now consider the problem of the formation of mountains, an extremely difficult question, and one which has never been indisputably solved. Obviously, it is easy to imagine that cataclysmic upheavals in the lowest layer of rocks would lead to very considerable uplifting of the over-laying rock masses, the original shape of which would be changed by tensions, fractures and faults. Similarly, very active vulcanism would lead not only to the appearance of volcanoes but also, as a result of the outflow of eruptive rock, to a considerable alteration in the appearance of the landscape. But what was the cause of that violent uplifting of the origin-ally horizontal sediments which produced a large part of the mightiest mountain ranges on Earth?

The physical forces necessary for such movements must be

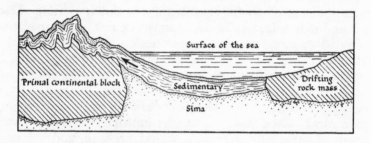

8. Mountain folding as a result of compression of
sedimentary rocks

of enormous magnitude, and we must clearly seek their origin at some depth in the Earth's crust, because there are no surface phenomena which could possibly be responsible.

Because this process of mountain-building has never been witnessed in historical times, we are compelled to fall back on hypotheses. The choice of these is limited severely by the small amount of knowledge we have about the formation of the Earth. The gravitational arrangement of the rock strata is definitely known to us. The light sial layer floats on top, going down to varying depths into the sima below. It behaves rather like a block of ice floating on water. We also assume a certain plasticity in the deeper rock strata, so that a drift, a gradual shifting of the sial continents, must at least be regarded as possible. Thus we are almost forced to the idea that one continental body may move across a deeply sedimented sea-bed towards another continental body which is perhaps more deeply and firmly embedded in the sima, and in the process the intervening sediment is compressed and folded and finally forced up on to the other continent. An excellent experiment illustrating this can be carried out by laying a handkerchief flat on a table and pushing it against the side of a broad box until it finally covers the box in multiple folds. This experiment is rather too simple, but the final effect certainly corresponds quite well with what has been observed in nature. A handkerchief, however, remains in one piece, whereas the brittle, sedimentary rock will frequently break at lines of most violent folding. In this event, the following masses will push themselves like blankets over the previously folded parts, with the result that older sedimentary rock will often be found to lie above younger. These are known as overfold mountains (or Nappes), of which the Swiss Alps are a classic example. The possible combinations of rock strata in the event of such folding are almost incalculable, for every conceivable direction of movement, as well as over-laying, capsizing and re-capsizing, is involved.

That this folding process was caused by the above-mentioned drift of continents is no more than a probability. We do not know for certain. But how else can it be explained? Three geological facts must be emphasised in this connection. Firstly, mountain building of this type was no localised, confined phenomenon. The greatest present-day folded mountain ranges—the Himalayas, the Caucasus, the Alps, the Pyrenees, the Atlas, the combined Cordilleras of North and South America—were all piled up during approximately the same periods: from the Jurassic to the Tertiary, chiefly during the Tertiary. Secondly, these gigantic foldings also took place on previous occasions, in repeated cycles throughout Earth's history, the cycles being interrupted by long periods of tectonic inactivity. At least five such great epochs of folding are known. But probably there were even more. Thirdly, these folds almost always occurred in roughly the same areas, always along the fringes of continental blocks, from which can be concluded that these blocks were comparatively strong and rigid and firmly anchored, and so remained more resistant to pressures which buckled their margins.

This confirms one of the assumptions about the way in which the folding process took place, for here we have continental blocks withstanding a lateral pressure. The evidence of cyclical repetition provides further confirmation, for it is known that even while the folding was in process, external forces came into action to wash down the towering masses into the awaiting geosynclines (the huge down-folded troughs in what were at that time probably only shallow seas in which the sediments accumulated). Then, after a given period, a further folding took place.

The vast area affected is less easily explained. It seems as if half the Earth's crust were suddenly set in motion. What was the cause?

This is an immense question to which the answer is still far from certain. For a long time the view put forward by the geologist Eduard Suess (1831-1914), the so-called Theory of Contractions, held the field. This was based on the once-accepted idea that the Earth was an offspring of the Sun, and had cooled rapidly. This cooling would have proceeded from the outside inwards and, as a result of further loss of heat, the rock crust originally formed would have become too large for the centre of the Earth, which had shrunk even more. And since a freely floating crust could not remain poised around the space which was inevitably forming inside it, it would have followed that the solid surface of the Earth would give way to the gravitational pull towards the centre, and press itself into folds against the shrunken kernel of the Earth. The shrinking of a dried-up apple provides a perfect illustration. Undoubtedly, the simplicity of this hypothesis is attractive, particularly because, in regard to the tectonic processes which may have been released by a shrinking of the Earth's core, it allows the widest possible field for analysis and speculative reconstruction. In actual fact it has never been confuted, though it has been displaced by other and more modern hypotheses which seek explanations in accordance with the laws of mechanics.

The present-day view of the structure of the Earth and its history as a planet suggests that folded mountains were far more probably the result of lateral pressure than of fractures caused by shrinkage of the crust. Some further conclusions are almost self-evident. Inevitably, a continent must become lighter as its surface is eroded. Equally inevitably, the accumulation of sediment will impose immense pressure on the ocean bed. But if the Earth's core were absolutely rigid, the only logical consequence of erosion would be a levelling down of the continental surface and a raising of the ocean surface, which would long ago have led to a world completely covered by water. Since this has not happened, we are forced to consider other processes which may help to provide an explanation. For instance, a lighter continental block may float up from the sima. An example of this, from our own era, is Scandinavia, which was for a long period buried under a tremendous covering of ice, the weight of which submerged it. After the melting of the glaciers it surfaced again, at the rate of about three feet in every hundred years. In the same way that a decrease in weight can lead to a rising of the land surface, so the bed of the ocean can sink under additional weight. Both processes can cause tremendous upheavals—in the former case a release of pressure, and in the latter an increase of pressure. To a varying extent, probably in proportion to the magnitude of the forces operating, the lower depths are brought into motion and react with upsurgings of magmatic masses, not only where the continental blocks have risen but also in other directions, laterally from the sinking geosynclines. Because equilibrium of pressure cannot be achieved at appropriate depths towards the centre of the Earth, sideways movements of the magma are usually the result. A consequence of this is a rising and sinking of the Earth's surface in the most widely differing and distant regions. A state of equilibrium is achieved via the plasticity of the sub-surface, but this is preserved at the cost of every imaginable disturbance on the surface, such as mountain-building, oceanic inundation (transgression), shrinking of the ocean (regression), and vulcanism. This state of embattled equilibrium beneath the Earth's crust has been given the technical name of isostasy.

An even more extreme hypothesis is that which postulates a *subcurrent* in the layer of magma, which is assumed to "conduct" atmospheric conditions—the moving masses of cold and warm air—to a "fluid zone" in the Earth's interior.

Here there are supposed to be radioactive processes which keep the malleable rocks heated to a fluid state, while the cold ocean floors work as counteracting coolants and thus serve to control the flow of rocks.

Such a process is within the realms of possibility. It could easily have led to such movements as have moulded the surface of the Earth.

The actual transformation of the Earth's shape from a very rapidly spinning ellipsoid to a geoid—a " near sphere "—as a result of the slowing down of its alleged original period of rotation from 3 hours to the present-day 24 hours, could have led to considerable changes in the magmatic layer.

So we are, in fact, faced with a number of conceivable possibilities which may all have some sort of relationship to the truth—even the contraction hypothesis. One thing is sure: that it is not possible to account for all the tectonic phenomena by any one hypothesis. We do know also for certain that, throughout its history, repeated and often fundamental upheavals kept altering the face of the Earth. Mountains came and went. Land became water, and water land. And—in actual fact—all this occurred so gradually that the changes would have been almost imperceptible during a brief human lifetime.

But, minute though the effects of the forces at work may seem to be when considered against the background of almost infinite time, it is time which provides the solution to everything.

So now it remains to determine the value of time, the great unknown in the equation which confronts us.

CHAPTER THREE

The Riddle of Time

TIME as an experienced fact is a contemporary concept; and probably everyone thinks he knows what it is. But difficulties soon arise when one is asked to define it; for then one starts to stutter mentally as well as verbally. In the past, philosophers were always responsible for the definition of such fundamentals, and in this respect the dictionary can supply their answer: "As distinct from space, time is the arrangement of things and events in an irreversible order. Time can be regarded as an absolute, one-dimensional continuum which from the standpoint of the present is infinite whether looking backwards (the past) or forwards (the future)." That is a clear and certainly helpful definition. But it is only valid for philosophical modes of thought. It is of no use to modern geophysics, which pursues its own especial and particular way. The very expressions "absolute" and "infinite" which are the basis of the definition have been transformed by Einstein into their opposites, into "relative" and "finite". As a physical reality, absolute time is meaningless, for it cannot be measured by any conceivable means. The only thing that is measurable is the lapse of time between events happening in space. And this lapse of time is related to the speed of light in a vacuum (186,283 miles a second). The time-unit of a second, as experienced by an observer in any given astronomical system, lengthens according to the speed of that system, and if the system should approach the speed of light (which is physically impossible) time would come close to a standstill. At first sight, this stretching of time is an absurd, incomprehensible phenomenon; but within the framework of the universe as conceived by relativity it is not only logically irrefutable but has been recently proved by practical experiment. The proof was found in the conditions prevailing in the Earth's upper atmosphere, mentioned earlier, where the

radiations from outer space bombard the atoms of the ionosphere and, with the loss of some of their own energy, release
inter alia so-called mu-mesons as secondary radiations which
stream onwards towards the Earth's surface and even into it.
Since these particles have a very short life (experiments in
atomic physics have determined that the half-life of a mu-
meson is of the order of a millionth or less of a second), their
passage through the atmosphere would come to an end after
about 500 yards. But the fact that they nevertheless travel a
distance of hundreds of miles is an effect of their own " time "
which is enormously "stretched" by their extremely high
velocity.

The infinity (endlessness) of time, too, at least backwards
into the past, has been strongly doubted. Time must have
begun somewhere, just like space and mass. And before this
beginning there can have been no earlier time!

There is no point in talking here of logical impossibility.
One must try to follow the thought processes of modern
cosmology (science of the universe) and to understand how it
has arrived at these daring and apparently absurd assertions.
This is particularly important for our purpose, since, with a
possible backward limit to Time, we would immediately
have a perfect means of calculating the age of the Earth, a
definite value for that unknown x in the equation which
must establish its age; for in no circumstances can the Earth
be older than the universe to which it belongs. Probably it
is younger than the Sun to which we seem to stand in a sort
of child-mother relationship.

A mere three decades ago there were only hypothetical and
very unclear ideas about the age of all suns. Even the most
eminent scientists had no hesitation in estimating their age
at billions and billions of years, which was tantamount to
recognising infinity in the past. But all this was rather suddenly and radically altered. The theoretical works of Einstein
and others, together with instrumental investigations into
the nature of the universe, led to extremely interesting
conclusions.

It is very well known—but we may as well repeat it—that
our solar system is part of a vaster cosmic unity—the Milky
Way (Galaxy). This immense system includes, beside our

Sun, about 100,000,000,000 other suns, as well as immense clouds of dark and luminous masses of matter in the form of dust or gas, and also minutely divided inter-stellar material (single atoms and molecules in the vast spaces between the individual stars). The shape of this community of stars (the fixed stars in the sky are without exception suns like ours, even though their physical attributes such as diameter, density, temperature, etc., may vary vastly) must, seen as a whole, resemble a flat lens. It is composed of a massive centre, a core around which, rooted in that core, a number of spiral "tentacles" stretch out into space. The diameter of this lens is about 100,000 light years (1 light year = 5·8 × 1,000,000,000,000 miles). This whole gigantic formation swims rather like an island in the ocean of space, clearly defined at its extremities, indeed framed by over 100 spherical clumps of stars, each composed of approximately 100,000 comparatively crowded suns.

Everything in the galaxy is in motion: both the system as a whole and its individual parts and member stars. And here too the principle of revolution about a centre prevails. Our Sun, for example, which is in one of the spiral arms of the system, about 32,000 light years distant from the centre, takes about 240 million years to revolve round the core. This "cosmic" year has recently come to play an important role in geology, as will be mentioned later.

It is impossible to explain briefly how astronomy has reached such precise conclusions. Actual optical observation proved to be the least useful of the means at the astronomers' disposal, for we are situated at the middle of this island-universe and for many reasons are unable to perceive its structure from the inside looking out. To arrive at an understanding of this structure required generations of continuous observations of movements and distances, inspired deductions, the data provided by radio-astronomy and, not least, the drawing of analogies with similar systems lying out in infinite space, for our Milky Way system is very far from being a unique exception in the cosmos—it is more nearly the rule.

Over past centuries astronomers identified a huge number of shimmering spots, mostly spiral in shape, which were once called "spiral nebulae" and are now more correctly termed "spiral galaxies". At first it was believed that these were really cosmic cloud formations. But Kant in his youth was one of the first to suggest that these were not clouds at all; rather they were clusters of stars resembling our own Milky Way only so immeasurably far off that in their aggregate they appeared to us as clouds of light. This view achieved wide acceptance without, for a long time, being provable. The final, indisputable proof only came in the present century when American astronomers, with their ultra-sensitive instruments, were able to detect some remarkably useful stars,

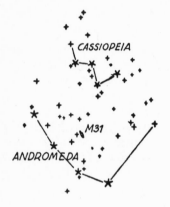

9. Position of the Andromeda Galaxy

known as Cepheid variables, in the spiral galaxy of Andromeda.

This very Andromeda galaxy (M.31) provides an obvious comparison to the spiral galaxy we call the Milky Way, for it resembles it remarkably in form and structure, although it is considerably larger. At any rate we can assume that our own galaxy would look something the same if we could observe it from a distance of 2 million light years; for the Andromeda galaxy is at least that far away from us. It is, as a matter of fact, the furthest object in the whole sky that we can see with the naked eye. On a clear night it shines like a pale spot, just visible to normal eyes, gleaming across that immense distance. It can be found a little below the right side of the W shape of Cassiopeia.

1. Rock foldings on Widemer Kopf in the Allgau Alps.

2. View into the Grand Canyon of the Colorado River. An example of a
landscape created by erosion.

3. The extra-Galactic system known as M. 31 (the spiral galaxy in Andromeda, about 1½–2 million light years away. In many respects it seems to resemble our own Milky Way.

4. Part of the Milky Way in the constellation of Sagittarius. The apparently star-less regions are immense dark clouds.

5. Rock formations, near Cuzco in Peru, 'planed down' by the action of ice. Evidence of former glaciation.

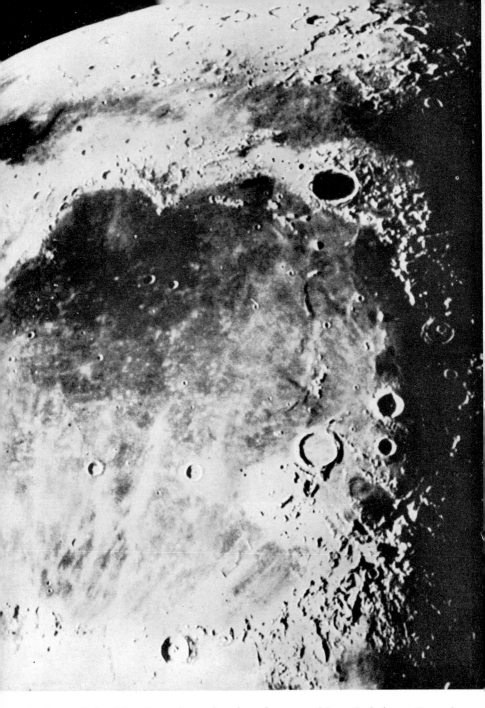

6. Part of the Moon's surface, showing the great Mare Imbrium (Sea of Rain, the Lunar Alps (*top right*), the Lunar Apennines (*lower right*) and the huge craters of Plato (*top, dark*) and Archimedes (*centre*).

7. The Raccoon meteor crater in Arizona.

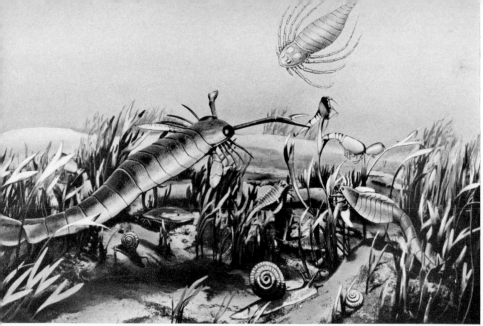

8. Pictorial reconstructions of (*above*) the Silurian sea and (*below*) the Ordovician sea; with seaweeds, corals, trilobites, cephalopods and eurypterids (at bottom).

Murals by Charles R. Knight. Chicago Natural History Museum.

In order to avoid a possible misunderstanding, it must be clearly stressed that none of these external galaxies are "in" any given constellation, because all the stars forming those imaginary "pictures" (stars which are only coincidentally associated together when seen from the viewpoint of the Earth), belong to our galaxy, whereas all the spiral galaxies form their own systems far outside our own. Their verbal connection with the names of Milky Way stars merely indicates the direction in which these extra-galactic (outside the Milky Way) objects are to be located.

Throughout the whole realm of space these galaxies swarm. Their forms and appearance vary, though within fairly narrow limits. Some appear to us as narrow strips, concentrated at the centre (core); others we can see clearly and fully as magnificent spirals. Others, again, appear as tightly rolled spirals, or as almost spherical in shape or even without any visible structure. The further they lie out in space, the fainter and less perceptible they are, naturally. Finally, the capacity of the searching eye at the telescope reaches its limit. Here photography comes to our aid, for photographic film has the great advantage over the human eye of being able to accumulate light impressions. By exposure for long periods—in extreme cases for as much as 100 hours or more—the photographic films or plates conjure out of invisibility minute specks whose light is too faint to be perceived by the human eye, and thus the frontiers of the explorable universe are pushed farther and farther out.

Telescopes almost entirely devoted to this photographic exploration are the gigantic instruments of the American observatories, particularly the 200-inch reflector on Palomar Mountain in California. Direct personal visual observation of the heavens has now retreated well to the background.

But in photography too there are optical limits which as yet cannot be exceeded. The farthest spiral galaxy which the 200-inch reflector can reach by means of photography lies 2,000 million light years out in space. To date, the total number of perceivable universes has been estimated at about 1,000 million, each with an average of perhaps 100,000,000,000 suns.

Is this the limit of the cosmos, the universe? One's every

inclination is to say "yes". But only the power of our lens has failed us, which can be no reason for proclaiming an end to space and further universes. The correctness of this viewpoint has been proved recently by the latest development in the astronomical field—radio-astronomy. While optical instruments such as the conventional telescope operate only with "visible" light, the radio-telescope works in the realm of electromagnetic waves which enable it to detect even more remote objects which emit, as a result of complicated processes, short radio waves, in the centimetre and metre bands, which can penetrate our atmosphere. These radiations are considerably longer than light waves and therefore have the important advantage of being able to pierce, without loss of intensity, even the densest concentrations of dark matter in space which would powerfully diminish or even totally extinguish ordinary light waves. So we can now look forward to receiving these radiations across distances so great that light is no longer powerful enough to bridge them. And indeed we have already received on radio-telescopes (not telescopes in the conventional sense, but gigantic aerials) signals from invisible spiral galaxies that must be at least 6,000,000,000 light years away, and possibly much more.

Up to this point we have not touched upon the problem of "boundlessness", the endlessness of space as the counterpart to the infinity of time; and there is nothing to prevent our assuming that space, beyond the limits of terrestrial perception, continues indefinitely. Nevertheless we can manage to put a question mark after both possibilities of infinity and thus to a slight extent subdue these monstrous conceptions which our minds simply cannot grasp. Einstein's theories culminated in a series of assertions and almost dogmatic demands. *It must be like this for that and that to be so.* And this involved a denial of that infinity of space which Giordano Bruno had prophetically proclaimed and which had subsequently found acceptance in Western thinking. According to Einstein, on the other hand, space must be finite. The proof of the possible correctness of this bold assertion was provided by the American astronomer Edwin Hubble (1889-1953).

Obviously, one of the tasks of astronomy is to ascertain facts about movements in space. For discovering radial movements—that is, those directly towards or away from our point of observation—there is an astonishingly ingenious and sure means which makes it possible to calculate, for example, radial movements of the stars with unexpected accuracy. This method is based on the line shift in the spectrum of the stars.

That may sound a little obscure. Although in this book it is not possible to enlarge upon the marvels of spectrum analysis, at least one may explain the principle on which these measurements are based. Spectrum analysis is the analytical investigation of light. By means of an arrangement of prisms or else by diffraction gratings, the light is drawn out into a broad band (the continuous spectrum) in which—like the rainbow—there is a gradual change of colour from red through orange, yellow, green, blue, indigo to violet. As is known from experiments on Earth, every element in an incandescent state emits its own characteristic spectrum. Because of certain atomic peculiarities, there occur in the atmospheres of the stars reversals of the bright lines of many elements, making them appear as dark lines. (In the Sun these are named "Fraunhofer Lines" after their discoverer.) These lines are the key to "cosmic chemistry", to our knowledge of the chemical composition of the heavenly bodies, of the physical conditions in which they exist, and of much other information about them. For our purpose it is important to stress that each line must appear at an absolutely definite place in the spectrum band, because Nature has assigned to every monochromatic light ray emitted its own particular location in the spectrum. The colours in the spectrum are arranged according to wavelength, red having the longest and violet the shortest.

Now it frequently happens that the dark lines (which, remember, are clearly identifiable) are found not to be obeying this inflexible place-arrangement, but to have shifted sideways, either towards the red or the violet end of the spectrum. This phenomenon, called the Doppler effect, has been interpreted as follows: if a star is moving away from us, the lines shift towards the red; if it is approaching, they shift towards the violet. From the extent of the shift compared to a standard spectrum, it is possible to calculate precisely, by reference to the constant velocity of light, the actual velocity of a star.

In the same way as these measurements are made for individual stars, the procedure can also be applied to extra-galactic systems. Only in these cases it is not possible to isolate the light of an individual sun; it is the "super-spectrum" which has to be studied, the light which emanates from all the stars in an external galaxy. And now comes Hubble's great discovery. He (and others after him) established that the spectra of almost all the extra-galactic systems show a shift towards the red, which means that they are all moving away from us. This astonishing fact becomes still more amazing when calculations showed that this "flight" of the external galaxies becomes faster the farther off they get. It even appears that the increase follows a definite law according to which, for every additional 3·2 million light years that a system moves farther away, its velocity increases by 106 miles per second (the Hubble constant). Very soon, galaxies were discovered speeding away from us at 15,000 and 25,000 and even more miles per second. To date, the acknowledged record is held by a very remote system moving at almost half the velocity of light.

These figures are nothing less than fantastic, for within our own Milky Way we encounter velocities of, at the most, a few hundred miles per second. (The real speed of our Sun round the centre of the galaxy is roughly 75 miles per second.) So the fact that the speed of flight of that record galaxy is already approaching half the velocity of light gives food for thought.

The latest revision of the Hubble constant enables us to calculate the ultimate distance at which universes will reach the speed of light—at least 9,000,000,000 light years. This means that stellar systems moving away at such super-speeds would disappear from our ken, for we know of no means of communication that travels faster than light or, for that matter, any other electromagnetic waves.

It now seems, from more recent investigations, as if the Hubble constant is no longer valid in those unknown regions of maximum velocities, and that the speed of these fleeing galaxies increases at a decreasing rate. In which case the limiting distance of 9,000,000,000 light years can be increased appropriately. Even if (as is frequently done) these fantastic velocities of the distant systems are regarded not as their own actual rate of motion but as an effect, as the expansion of the total universe, the fact still remains that in those "regions" the extension of space comes to an end, for distance and velocity are very closely connected with the age of the cosmos, which can be calculated from them.

A divine command saying "About turn and back at the same speed!" would mean that all bits of matter in the cosmos would have to converge on a central point from which they are at present flying away like the fragments of an exploding bomb. Then—to take a mean figure—in 6,000,000,000 years the concentration would be completed, if the known laws of motion still prevailed, and all the suns, planets, moons, nebulae, etc., would be disintegrated and compressed into a hypothetical "primeval atom" from the explosion of which, on one theory, the universe was created.

Admittedly, there remains still the possibility that this primeval atom may have existed for an unimaginably long time in its original state, so that the period of 6,000,000,000 years may be increased by any figure you like. But modern physicists do not care to indulge in such speculations: for good reasons, of course, since they prefer to assume the origin of the cosmos as being at that particular point in time.

One of the most striking consequences of the theory of relativity is the statement of the equivalence of mass and energy: that is, these two fundamental concepts of physics are not entirely independent of each other, as had been taken for granted up to 1905, but are identical and interchangeable. Mass is only a manifestation of energy, energy in a "frozen" state. Experimental physics in this century has proved this brilliant concept completely. Almost before our eyes, looking at photographic plates, there takes place the transformation of invisible, mass-less radiations into elementary particles of mass: and, vice versa, radiations from elementary particles assume the form of pure energy. On these very processes is based the principle of the atom bomb and virtually all attempts at the utilisation of atomic energy. And the equivalent values precisely conform to the famous Einstein formula: $E = mc^2$ (energy equals mass times the square of the velocity of light).

What, then, do the geologists have to say to this astronomical contribution towards the solution of their toughest problem? To begin with, the immensity of the time element does not stagger them, for they have long accepted that the vast variety of geological changes, including the evolution of life, must have required almost inconceivable eons of time. Also, geological experts themselves have not been inactive. They too have found possible ways of determining the age of the Earth.

The attempt to calculate the age of the oceans from their salt content has already been mentioned. The resulting answer of 90,000,000 years is far too low, as it is based on the present rate of deposit of salt, which is known to be exceptionally high.

Another possible idea was to take the rate of sedimentation as a basis for calculating the age of all the various stratified rocks. But here the uncertainty factors are daunting, for this very irregular process can scarcely be granted even the modest accuracy of a sand-clock. Moreover, the figures of the total depth of all sedimentations are pure estimates and vary enormously. The highest figure suggested is around 500,000 feet. Assuming that a layer of 3 feet takes 20,000 years to deposit (a very dubious guess), then one arrives at an answer of more than 3,000,000,000 years for the Earth's age. From what we know from other sources, this result *sounds* a fairly likely one. But it cannot possibly be used as a basis for scientific calculations.

However, we live in the age of atomic physics which now plays a part in practically all the realms of natural science. And it was from this quarter that help came to the geologists, through the phenomenon of natural radioactivity.

Since the discovery of radium it has been realised that the atom is not the ultimate, indivisible unit of matter, as the ancients believed (*atomos* = indivisible). The atomic nuclei (which alone determine the chemical properties of an element) are, with the exception of the common hydrogen atom, composite formations of an often extremely complicated structure.

In the nucleus, electrically positively charged protons are associated with electrically neutral neutrons. But only the protons determine the characteristics of an element and its place in the periodic system. In the case of the lighter elements, the number of neutrons usually corresponds to the number of protons; but in the heavier elements the neutrons are always far more numerous than the protons. Variations of the number of neutrons in the same element produce isotopes, which are merely different "kinds" of the same element.

Certain elements in which the nuclei contain a smaller number of protons than of neutrons are unstable and expel a number of nucleons (a general name for neutrons and protons) to achieve stability. This takes place chiefly through the discharge of helium nuclei (composed of 2 protons and 2 neutrons), which is the well-known process of alpha-radiation. An element in this state is radioactive, and remains so until, by discharging sufficient helium, it finally reaches a condition of stability which enables the hitherto "overfull" nucleus to continue to exist in peace. But in the meantime a minor miracle has occurred, for the original element—take radium for an example—is now no longer radium, but by the loss of successive pairs of protons essential to its chemical nature has turned into lead. This process of decay (which develops through various intermediate stages) is extremely complicated, but is precisely known. The important thing for our subject is the rate of decay of these elements. In this connection the term "half-life" was introduced, indicating the time taken by any radioactive substance to lose 50 per cent of its original radioactivity, i.e. the time it takes for half of the atoms to disintegrate. In the case of radium its half-life is 1,690 years, by which time half of the radium atoms have decayed into radon; while the half-life of uranium—the real starting-point of the subsequent radium-lead disintegration —is 4.5 thousand million years.

Now here a lucky circumstance helps us. The element lead has also a number of isotopes (i.e. different variations of lead according to the number of neutrons in the atom). Among these the isotope with the atomic weight of 206 (a number indicating the number of neutrons plus protons in the

nucleus) never occurs in nature except as a result of radioactive decay; indeed, it might be called uranium-lead, since
its origins started with the disintegration of uranium.

One can take a piece of uranium ore and determine how
much lead 206 is in it. From the lead content it is simple to
calculate exactly, from the known period of decay, how long
the uranium has been decaying, that is to say when it actually
crystallised out of a molten rock mixture, or when it was
embedded in a certain rock, and this gives the age of the rock
which would have been formed at about the same time. Such
calculations can, moreover, be checked, for not only lead is
produced, but helium as well, and the quantity of helium in
the rock should lead to identical time calculations.

In theory this method of "timing" is ideal because of its
precision and its wide application. Indeed it provides a perfect
clock over thousands of millions of years in Earth's history;
for the spontaneous disintegration of radioactive matter takes
place with absolute regularity, subject to no outside influences and, so far as we know, it is completely immutable.

In actual practice matters are slightly different. First,
uranium is not always to be found where we need it for our
particular purpose. Ideally, in every tiniest fragment of every
formation a uranium clock should be dormant. But this is
not so. In the tertiary strata none at all has been found. Also,
it never occurs in metallic form, only as an oxide or salt, which
complicates investigations. Analysis of lead to determine
whether we are dealing with lead 206 or merely "ordinary"
lead can only be undertaken by a rather limited number of
specialists. Nothing can be done about the volatility of
helium—a very light gas—so that hitherto this means of
"checking" has almost always shown deviations (not very
great in time) from the results given by the lead. Furthermore,
from the geological point of view, it is frequently not possible
to state with absolute certainty that a layer in which the
material under investigation has been found belongs to a
definite epoch.

So there are a whole series of complications which will
undoubtedly be overcome in time by working on a broader
basis; for, hitherto, really only the principle has been tried
out and proved. For instance, uranium alone doubles the

Atomic Number	Half-Life	Atomic Weight
88	Radium 1690 years ↓α	226
86	Radon (Emanation) 3·825 days ↓α	222
84	Polonium (Radium A) 3·05 minutes ↙α ⟍βγ	218

82 Lead 214   85 Astatin 218
(Radium B)   a few seconds
26·8 minutes

⟍βγ   ↙α

| 83 | Bismuth
(Radium C)
19·7 minutes
↙βγ ↘α | 214 |
| 84 | 214   81 | 210 |

Polonium   Thallium
(Radium C′)   (Radium C″)
0·000145 secs.   1·32 mins.

α ↘   ↙βγ

82	Lead (Radium D) 22 years ↓βγ	210
83	Bismuth (Radium E) 5 days ↙βγ α↘	210
84	210 81	206

Polonium   Thallium
(Radium F)   4·23 mins.
140 days

α ↘   ↙β

| 82 | Lead
(Radium G)
Stable | 206 |

RADIUM DECAY TABLE

possible uses of this method, because it allows analysis of the two isotopes, uranium 238 and 235, which have two entirely different disintegration periods and end up as two different isotopes of lead. Hitherto we have been speaking of uranium 238 which ends up as lead 206. U^{235}, notorious as one of the components of the atom bomb, decays into lead 207. In addition, it is not only the lead residue and the helium content that are informative, but also the chemical effect of radio-activity on the surrounding rock masses, This brings us to the so-called halo method of dating, which uses similar calculations based on the ring-like zones of bleaching in the surrounding rock, which are caused by radiation; and for this method not only uranium but also thorium (which decays into lead 208) and several isotopes of other elements are effective.

Investigations of this sort have been made into meteorites—fragments of matter arriving from outer space—which now and again reveal traces of thorium or uranium. Calculations based on their helium content give an age of up to 7,000,000,000 years, a period that agrees quite well with present-day conceptions of the universe. But since the fantastically powerful ultra-radiations of outer space can produce additional helium, the above figure is extremely dubious, and has recently been considerably reduced, which in fact has merely increased confidence in the reliability of the method.

This type of analysis has been carried out in all parts of the world for several decades now. After many checks and counter-checks the time-table of Earth's history has been established as set out on pages 84 and 85. The figures from the palaeozoic onwards, in particular, can be regarded as satisfactory, and are unlikely to undergo any further major readjustment. The total age of the Earth can be estimated at about 4,000,000,000 years, a time span which fits in well with the general picture of the universe. Some scientists have arrived at even higher figures; while others again regard this estimate as far too high. These latter are very critical and mistrustful of calculations based on physics. They say, pessimistically: what can one really know about primal Earth and its state? Who can prove for certain that radioactive decay has continued through all time unchanged and with the regularity of clockwork?

Such doubts are not unreasonable. We have only arrived at a certain stage of knowledge and this is bound to be further adjusted and expanded. All we are trying to show here is how widely separated branches of science, working on entirely different lines, are attempting, with brilliant ingenuity and immense labour, to solve problems that only fifty years ago were considered insoluble.

CHAPTER FOUR

The Origins of the Earth

WHEN the Earth was formed can be determined fairly accurately between acceptable limits. In any case its age must be more than 3,000,000,000 years; and it is unlikely to be older than 4 or 5,000,000,000 years. *How* it was formed, on the other hand, is still almost completely unknown. Astronomy has no comparable example of a cosmic act of this kind. It cannot even be stated with certainty (although it is reasonably probable) that the planetary system of our Sun is a normal phenomenon and not a solitary exception. Our nearest stellar neighbour in space, the star Alpha Centauri which is "only" $4\frac{1}{2}$ light years away,* is too far off for our telescopes to be able to distinguish any dark bodies that may be illuminated by their own suns. Mathematical calculations, however, have been able to establish certain irregularities of movement in the case of a few near stars, which might indicate the presence of planet-sized dark bodies.

The formation of our Earth is bound up with that of all the other solar planets even though it may not have occurred simultaneously. Fundamentally the process—whatever it was —must have been the same in the case of all the planets. Consequently, attempts have continually been made to establish hypotheses for the formation of the whole planetary system. Three possibilities are assumed. First: the planets (including their satellites) were formed independently of, and simultaneously with, the Sun. Second: the planets and the satellites all emerged later but simultaneously from the Sun. Third: the planets were born out of the Sun successively, and the satellites were formed subsequently, in a similar manner, from the planets.

---

* More accurately Alpha Centauri is the nearest bright star; pride of place must go to a faint member of the Alpha Centauri system, known, appropriately, as Proxima.

The first possibility is supported by Kant's old hypothesis and von Weizsäcker's new one. Kant was the originator of the primal nebula theory, which has never since entirely lost its place in the world of scientific thought. According to Kant's view the only possible condition which could follow upon nothingness was a state of chaotic, discrete matter. The transition to the state of order which now exists was then brought about by gravitational forces which gradually swept the area of space containing the primal galaxy, gathering together the individual particles of matter into suns, planets and satellites. It was the forces of gravity, too, that caused the smaller bodies to revolve around the larger ones.

In spite of numerous objections, the fundamental idea behind this hypothesis has remained startlingly modern. Quite recently von Weizsäcker took it up again and investigated mathematically the possible states of motion (currents and turbulence) in such a primal galaxy. Making use of his own ideas and discoveries, he formulated a hypothesis which removed from the Kantian conception several weaknesses, which explained satisfactorily the various peculiarities of the orbits and rotation of the planets and satellites, and which was capable of further extension. As has already been mentioned, it seems probable to von Weizsäcker that the planets and satellites mostly were in a cold state when they were formed and that their internal warmth subsequently derived from radioactive processes.

The second possibility of the origin of the planets, that of a comparatively sudden simultaneous emergence from the body of the Sun, has been supported by a number of scientists —particularly the English astrophysicist Sir James Jeans (1877-1946)—who have offered their own views and explanations. According to them, our Sun at the time in question had a very close encounter with another star. The increasingly powerful gravitational pull which developed as the two suns approached drew great masses of matter up from their surfaces; this matter, at the climax of the encounter, tore loose and—widely scattered—streamed out into the space between the two suns. As the distance between the suns now increased and the gravitational forces consequently decreased, the pull on the detached matter was sufficiently reduced to ensure its continued independent existence in space. It quickly formed into spheres which thenceforward rotated round the Sun, whose own force of attraction proved ultimately decisive.

This hypothesis, too, seems a satisfactory and acceptable one in certain respects, and in many ways it is temptingly convincing. Its weakness, in fact, does not lie in its mechanistic side, but in quite a different direction. When the hypothesis was first formulated, Jeans also believed in an extremely high age for the Earth. But since Earth's estimated age has now been reduced to between the limits of 3 and 5,000,000,000 years it has become apparent that within this "short" time there is no likelihood of such a stupendous encounter between two suns. Indeed, a meeting of this sort in the infinite distances of space must be so rare that the event can be dismissed as wholly improbable. And the hypothesis will be ruled out completely if it is established, even more certainly than it is now, that practically all suns have planets.

For the third possibility the French scientist Pierre Simon de Laplace (1749-1827) provided the basic conception. He considered that the primal Sun was a rapidly rotating sphere of very rarefied, thin gas. The enormous centrifugal force acting on it caused a corresponding deformation of its shape, a flattening at the "poles" and a huge bulge round its equator. This finally resulted in a ring of matter tearing itself loose and hurtling off into space, where it formed into a planet. This happened as many times as there are planets. In the same way, satellites were formed from their parent planets. For a long time the rings of Saturn were regarded as an actual example of this process in action. They were assumed to be a satellite that had never completely developed. Today, however, there is some support for a different theory, namely that the rings are the remains of a satellite which, as a result of approaching too close to Saturn, was disintegrated by the planet's force of attraction. (A satellite's distance from its planet has a critical limit which cannot be transgressed without danger.) Nevertheless, this hypothesis, too, established itself and was profoundly discussed for generations. In the past people frequently spoke of a combined Kant-Laplace theory. But this is quite misleading, as will have been shown from the foregoing descriptions of the two hypotheses. Moreover, the two men never collaborated and, in this particular connection, are hardly likely to have been even aware of each other's work.

What really happened when the Earth was born must be left as an unsolved problem. The only thing certain is that the formation of our Earth took place. And so real geology begins at the time when the Earth started on its orbit round the Sun—which would have been about 4,000,000,000 years ago. In order to gain even a faint idea of the closely connected spatial abysses of the universe and the immense lapse of time between the creation of the Earth and the present day, consider a radio wave emitted, at the time of Earth's creation, from a spiral galaxy 4,000,000,000 light years away and travelling in the direction of Earth—a radio wave moving steadily through space at 186,283 miles per second, never changing its speed, neither obstructed nor delayed by anything. Throughout the whole of Earth's history it will be drawing closer and closer to us.

What, at the time of its birth, was the Earth like? According to one theory, its original diameter was considerably greater than now, an estimated 13,000 miles as compared with 7,912 miles today, and its general temperature was about 6,000° C.

The subsequent development of the young Earth can be deduced to a certain extent by the aid of mathematical calculations and our present chemico-physical knowledge, especially since—knowing the state of the Earth as it is today—we are necessarily concerned only with the changes that would be brought about by a cooling-off process.

To begin with, let us imagine that the Earth was originally in a "solar" condition—an idea by no means proved, and strongly challenged by some authorities—and see what might have happened.

According to the Stefan-Boltzmann Law of Radiation (i.e. the total radiation of a body is proportional to the 4th power of its absolute temperature) the truly remarkable fact is established that a solar-like body the size of the Earth at its inception, could only continue in that state for 120 years, an amazingly short time which really plays no part at all in a total time-framework of 4,000,000,000 years' duration. Earth's initial radiation of heat into space must have been so fantastically wasteful that within that brief period its temperature would have sunk from 6,000° C. to 2,750° C. Indeed, at the end of this stage of rapid cooling the heat would have come down to approximately the boiling point of silicic acid, a substance which much later played an important part in the creation of rocks. (Granite consists of up to 70 per cent SiO₂ —silicic anhydride).

Quickly as the glowing-gas stage passed, there would have been an equally rapid *deceleration* of further cooling during the glowing liquid stage. This would have been the main period of gravitative separation, that is the gradual organisation of the elements and their chemical compounds according to weight, while the Earth was consolidating itself into its present-day composition. It would then have taken another 60,000,000 years before the red-hot stage of under 1,300° C. was reached and the first molten rocks (orthoclase, quartz, leucite) began to suggest a solid surface in the form of drifting silicate blocks. This "surface" in turn was enshrouded by an extremely hot mixture of light gases, a form of primal atmosphere, consisting of hydrogen, carbon monoxide, superheated water vapour, nitrogen, methane, sodium chloride and other admixtures. This atmosphere extended much higher than that of today and was also considerably heavier, so that many solidification processes took place under temperatures and pressures very different from those under which present-day experiments are conducted. One must bear in mind that, according to this theory, practically the whole weight of the oceans, lakes and rivers was at that period suspended in the atmosphere; and with the simultaneous "condensation" of its matter the Earth's diameter shrank to about 9,000 miles.

Only when the temperature had fallen well below the red-hot stage could the increasingly numerous floating blocks amalgamate into the Earth's first, still glowing, surface, which supposedly was composed of a continuous skin of granite and quartz flooded over with molten rock-salt. Thus developed a physical frontier between the Earth's body and the atmosphere, and the glowing skin stage set in. This may have lasted for more than 100,000,000 years, for the rate of the radiation of heat into space presumably continued to slow down, and also the enormously thick atmospheric envelope, with the fresh addition of carbon dioxide and ammonia, further inhibited rapid radiation. The pressure of the atmospheric gases on a square centimetre of Earth's surface must have approximated 270 present-day atmospheres.

Of course, the formation of the crust did not suppress or contain the hot, still predominantly gaseous interior of the Earth. What we nowadays call "vulcanism" must, for countless millions of years, have been a chaotic, seemingly perpetual state of affairs of which we can only form the faintest conception. But in spite of the titanic clash of armoured sheets of rock and the plutonic, turbulent gas-discharging depths, temperatures sank steadily and finally reached 1,000° C., at which stage the skin ceased to glow and the Earth was extinguished as a light-giving body. The glowing era had ended, and the dark era—the second main phase of the Earth's physical history, which continues up to today—had begun. Even the surface of the Earth was now wrapped in deepest darkness, eerily broken only by the reflections of eruptions of glowing lava and flashes of atmospheric lightning. The density of the atmosphere (being 98 per cent steam) shut out every ray of "visible" light from the Sun.

It will probably never be possible to reconstruct, even in the imagination, the exact geophysical conditions and appearance of the Archaean era which was now beginning. The diameter of the Earth continued to diminish; its density increased. The core was compressed tighter and tighter. The formerly gaseous under-layers turned increasingly into magma (molten rock). The original surface crust, after being wildly torn and crumpled, was now thickened with immense layers of lava thrown up by incessant eruptions, and finally, in certain areas that had become particularly stable, the crust at last proved impervious even to eruptions. Thus the "primal blocks" began to form—deep pedestals of rock, reaching far down towards Earth's centre; and these have existed with little change throughout subsequent history. Over and around all, weighed the ocean of air, convulsed by violent turbulent currents and electrical discharges. For the time being (and the "time being" may have continued for 280,000,000 years) water did not exist, since the atmosphere, perpetually heated

Geological Era	Duration of phases and Periods (in millions of years)		Chief geological and biological developments
CAINOZOIC ERA	Holocene		Holocene = present era
	Pleistocene	1 m.	Ice Age in Pleistocene
	Tertiary	70 m.	In the Tertiary, great development of mammals – Appearance of Man – Climax and end of Alpine mountain folding
MESOZOIC ERA	Cretaceous	65 m.	Principal age of the Reptiles. Mass extinction at end of Cretaceous – Development of plants up to the angiosperms – In the Lower Cretaceous vast sea incursions. Beginning of Alpine mountain-foldings
	Jurassic	45 m.	
	Triassic	45 m.	
PALAEOZOIC ERA	Permian	45 m.	Caledonian and Variscan waves of mountain-building – Permo-Carbon Ice Age – First vertebrates – Development of plants up to the gymnosperms – In the Devonian conquest of land by plants and animals
	Carboniferous	80 m.	
	Devonian	50 m.	
	Silurian	40 m.	
	Ordovician	60 m.	
	Cambrian	100 m.	
EOZOIC ERA	Includes: Torridonian Algonquin, etc.	1,000 m.	Dawn of life – confined to water, where temperatures continue to fall – several cycles of mountain-building
AZOIC OR ARCHAEAN ERA	Oceanic phase	2,000 m.	The period of first oceans without life. Temperature down to 173°C. First rains and first permanent, hot and intensely salt seas. High-temperature penetration of rocks by water and gas (gneissification). Formation of crystalline schist.

Main Geological Divisions in Earth's History

Geological Era	Duration of phases and Periods (in millions of years)	Chief geological and biological developments
AZOIC OR ARCHAEAN ERA (*cont.*)	Oceanic phase 2,000 m.	As a result of loss of water, atmospheric pressure drops to 8 atmospheres About 3,000,000,000 years ago, the Laurentian Revolution Start of continuous cycles of erosion and folding
	Anhydrous phase 300 m.	Temperature falls to 374°C. Granite and quartz "skin" covered with salt. Ammonia added to atmosphere. Atmospheric pressure: 250-260
' GLOWING ' ERA	Glowing-skin phase 100 m.	Temperature down to 500°C. First continuous granite "skin", covered by molten rock salt and subsequently a crust of rock salt. Further condensation and decrease of diameter to 8,200 miles. Atmosphere: 98% steam, the rest nitrogen, carbon dioxide, carbon monoxide
	Glowing-liquid phase 60 m.	Temperature falling to 850°C. First molten silicate forms. Atmosphere: steam, nitrogen, sodium chloride, carbon monoxide. Diameter about 9,400 miles
	Glowing-gas phase 120 years	The glowing state of the Earth after its birth – diameter at first about 13,000 miles(?). Density 1.6. Surface temperature sinks from 5,500°C. to 2,250°C.

Total age of the Earth about 4,000,000,000 years

Main Geological Divisions in Earth's History

by the warm surface of the Earth (still at temperatures up to 500° C.) was too hot for condensation. So this part of the Archaean era is called the anhydrous (the waterless).

It would certainly be a great help to our assumptions, and, more important, a confirmation of our guesses, if astronomy could find a corresponding state of affairs elsewhere in the universe. With reservations, the planet Jupiter formerly was regarded as the answer, since it was assumed that its present conditions resemble that of the Archaean Earth.

What do we believe we know about Jupiter?

First, it should be borne in mind that while it may be as old as the Earth, it may also possibly be considerably older. If, in spite of an equal or greater age, it is still so retarded in its development, such a state of affairs can only be attributable to its size, for its diameter is well over twelve times that of the Earth. In a sphere of that magnitude the cooling process would take place proportionately more slowly. Yet it is questionable whether "more slowly" could cover a period of almost 4,000,000,000 years. Moreover, the fact that Jupiter is composed of far lighter matter than Earth must be taken into consideration. Its average density is only 1.34 (compared to water). That requires very different yardsticks from those we use when considering the Earth. Furthermore, its considerably greater distance from the Sun means that it is also subject to different influences from outer space. Its very rapid period of rotation—only 10 hours—could be taken as an indication of its "youthfulness" (in its anhydrous period the Earth is believed to have rotated in about 5 hours), but also its great distance from the Sun means that the latter exerts less of a brake on its rotation than on nearer planets. These are some of the objections to comparing the early Earth with present-day Jupiter.

The surface of Jupiter itself is unknown to us, for it is hidden from astronomers by a dense, totally impenetrable and certainly very deep atmosphere, mainly composed of hydrogen, but also containing hydrogen compounds such as methane and ammonia (CH_4, NH_3). The lack hitherto of any definite evidence of the presence of water vapour and carbon dioxide does not mean that these chemical compounds are not present, since the dense enveloping atmospheric layer prevents observation to any depth. But should they both be present, as is currently assumed, then there is at least a resemblance to Earth's primal atmosphere. Jupiter's atmosphere gives a picture of instability and change. Its very apparent ribbon structure is the result of the planet's rapid rotation; its changing coloration is caused by equally violent turbulence which looks very like a heating up and consequent discharge of gas from the inner depths. We are only able to make a direct measurement of the temperature of the outer layer of its atmosphere, which is about − 150° C. This is a quite natural consequence of the diminished effects of the Sun's radiation and in fact tells us nothing at all about the actual temperature of Jupiter's surface.

On the whole, it seems that there is no real similarity with the Earth. There is even a theory that Jupiter is composed of a core surrounded by a mighty ice covering over which surges an ocean of liquid methane. It has also been suggested that the variegated coloration of its atmosphere is due to *free* chemical radicals, these being unchangeable groups of atoms which participate in chemical combinations but, not being molecules, do not consequently exist on Earth in a free form. Jupiter, however, according to this theory, *is* permitted these formations as free entities!

Another view of Jupiter is that it is a cold hydrogen-helium sphere, surrounded by frozen ammonia, methane oceans and an enormously dense atmosphere, the terrific pressure of all these reducing the hydrogen-helium core—already at a very low temperature—to an almost metallic consistency. This, of course, would present a totally alien picture, not corresponding in any respect to any stage of the Earth's development. So it seems that everything we try to discover about conditions so far removed in space and time ends up as more or less tentative speculations about probabilities, which admittedly are made more attractive by the inexhaustible charm of the unknown.

At all events, we feel confident that we know how the purely plutonic conditions upon the Earth were brought to an end by the appearance on the scene of their great antagonist—water. In order that the vast quantities of water vapour in the atmosphere should liquefy under the prevailing pressures of that early era, the general temperature of the air would have to fall below 374·2° C., the so-called critical temperature of water. One day, in one particular region of the atmosphere, this must have happened. The steam condensed to drops and swept down, in the first real, rain-like showers, on to the Earth's surface. Probably it required millions of years for conditions to reach the point where water first actually reached the rocky crust. Again and again the hot lower levels of the atmosphere must have vapourised the first water on its descent and driven it upwards once more. Tremendous disturbances, with shattering primeval thunderstorms, would have rent the whole atmospheric envelope. Localised but incessant variations in the atmospheric pressure must have set up chaotic turbulences which finally would have raged around the whole of the Earth's surface. As temperatures sank still lower, the rainstorms changed to gigantic cloudbursts, sheets of descending water, which finally—yet only here and there because of a favourable local lowering of air-pressure—would reach the surface of the Earth. And here again, of course, there began a further conflict with the hot surface of the Earth, producing new clouds of steam which must have shot upwards almost like explosions into the atmosphere, and then descended again and assaulted the hot rocks with further drenching torrents of water. Today we know who was the victor in this battle of the elements.

The next stage was the appearance of boiling-hot primal seas in the shallows pitting the Earth's surface. The effects of the water on the rocky face of the Earth was of a magnitude never equalled subsequently. It is, indeed, obvious that Earth's first mountainous features produced by subterranean forces should have been rapidly and completely eroded by the hot flood and washed away to give the primeval sediments (possibly the mica schists, para-gneiss, phyllites, etc.). The diminished pressure of the atmosphere resulting from the precipitation of its water content, would have produced fresh volcanic outbreaks of tremendous magnitude. The great jets of lava, like soaring fountains of fire, which fell back into the steaming waters, and the shafts of continually zigzagging lightning, were the only illuminations of the raven-black night that then reigned perpetually between Heaven and Earth.

Eons passed before the turbulence of the hydrous (water) era died down somewhat and a comparative calm set in. (The duration of this primal "frenzy" cannot even be estimated.) The water had conquered, and, as a primeval ocean, it now enveloped the Earth's sphere. It is not impossible that it did precisely this, and that only here and there a few high up-thrust rock points and volcanic giants broke the surface of the waters. Everything else was submerged. For this far-off period there are no discoverable traces of foldings of true sedimentary dry rocks. And it is extremely difficult (or impossible) to get at the original hard covering of the Earth which certainly formed the ubiquitous substratum for the later sediments. Where it is found today in the form of gneiss and crystalline schist, it has been heaved up by subsequent earth movements which began principally during the Laurentian Revolution.

If, among the staid terms used in the world of scientific research, the violent word "revolution" is found, it can only be because it refers to something that could not be described by any more moderate expression. And the later Archaean age started off, indeed, with a mighty, world-encompassing tectonic cataclysm never to be equalled in subsequent up-heavals. A wave of mountain-building of gigantic proportions persisted throughout millions of years. Practically all Archaean folds date from that epoch. It was as if the whole water-logged Earth surged into tectonic movement. From now on, through vast cycles of time, there continued the incessant alternation of erosion, sedimentation and folding—up to the present era. In this process the decisive role was played by the afore-mentioned primal blocks, strongly and deeply anchored masses of rock which stood in immovable opposition to the drifting, sediment-folding continental agglomerations.

In the case of Europe, for instance, one such block comprised Scandinavia, Finland and northern Russia. Geologists speak of a Finno-Scandinavian shield, a Baltic shield, a Russian platform, which, taken all together, are best described as the primal continent of Russia. In the case of Asia, primal blocks were formed by parts of Siberia in the region of the Angara River (Angaraland), the territory of the Tarim Basin (Serindia), North China (Sinia), and the Philippines (Philippinia). Other such blocks are West Australia, India, Arabia, and almost the whole of Africa (with the exception of the Atlas Mountains). In the New World, Southern Argentine, East Brazil, and Guiana, as well as North America around Hudson Bay, including Greenland, are primal continents. The Canadian shield is generally grouped together with Greenland and called Laurentia (a Latinised form of Laurence: the St. Lawrence River), from which this whole tectonic revolution received its name.

It was probably at this time that the relief profile of the world (including the floor of the sea) came into being, with its towering mountains, rivers, valleys, deserts, etc. Now the great game of endless variations could begin. What caused the revolutionary disturbance of the "sea-peace" of the late Archaean period is still not known. The Earth's crust started to move, and that was that; and with that fact we must content ourselves.

When, in point of time, the Laurentian Revolution came to an end, can only be estimated very roughly. The Earth's earliest eras are virtually inaccessible to more precise assessment. But to fit in with our general time-frame, this process must have ended about 2 to $2\frac{1}{2}$ thousand million years ago. By then about half of the Earth's estimated age had already been "used up", certainly no excessive lapse of time for the great events which had by then taken place in the life of our planet.

CHAPTER FIVE

Beginning of Life

A T this point, something must first be said about the chronological divisions and namings of the periods and eras of the so-called "historical" times which began with the Cambrian Period in the Palaeozoic Era. The table on pages 84 and 85 provides a general survey. There are a large number of different forms of nomenclature, coined at different times or even simultaneously in different places, many of which have continued to be used side by side. The reader will find in other books and works of reference treatments of geological eras which may partly correspond to those given here but which have been set out from different local viewpoints. Fundamentally, the course of Earth's history is divided first into eras, and these eras are then subdivided into periods. According to this scheme, the designation *pre-Archaean* indicates the world's "glowing era". That the following, extremely long time-period can quite simply be divided into anhydrous (waterless) and hydrous (watery) phases is obvious. But the latter is too generalised, so the absence or presence of life in the waters provides a criterion for further sub-divisions. One can therefore define an Azoic (or Archaean) Era, when no life existed and, after the appearance of life, an Eozoic Age (Archaeozoic, Proterozoic) which could be equated with the "springtime of life". The very nature of these designations shows that life in the animal world was given precedence in naming periods. Life in the early plant world has been somewhat neglected. To be just, therefore, one should write of the Aphytic, Palaeophytic, and so forth—which some palaeobotanists have done from time to time.

Subsequent divisions of later periods are generally arranged according to the series of sedimentary layers, which have proved a great help to systematic geology. But it is only with the Eozoic Era that they become clearer. It should be remembered that all strata formed earlier than the Cambrian Period may correctly be referred to as "pre-Cambrian"; it is only because of the vast thicknesses of rock involved, and the tremendous time taken for their information, that we try to sub-divide these pre-Cambrian beds. There is, as yet, no universally accepted system of classification for the pre-Cambrian.

In this chapter we shall deal with the rest of the Archaean Era after the Laurentian Revolution and also with the Eozoic Era.

Of the periods into which the Eozoic is divided, the Algonquin Period, recognised by American geologists, got its name from the group of American Indians speaking a language called Algonquin. Their earlier hunting grounds were in the neighbourhood of the Great Lakes, and here were found rock strata of the era in question, containing evidence of particular importance which could be most minutely investigated.

In Britain the Torridonian rocks, corresponding to the American Algonquin, are named after Torridon in Scotland. Many other terms are used in other parts of the world for strata which immediately precede the Cambrian.

At some time during the 1,000 million years assigned to the Eozoic Era, life must have begun on this planet. But only in the most recent Eozoic beds do we find fossil remains. Yet, though these are rare and very scattered, they are remarkably diverse in form.

In the course of this immense lapse of time a great deal, tectonically speaking, must have happened, though the details are completely unknown. There were probably endless cycles of erosion, sedimentation and mountain-folding. We know that there were frequent upsurgings of granitic rocks from the depths, and belching eruptions of basic magmas. An extremely interesting but scarcely explicable fact is that there are clear traces of ice action during the late Eozoic Era in North America and in Greenland, South Africa and China—i.e., in widely separated areas. This is deduced from the presence of smooth and round "planed" rock surfaces, with traces of smoothing and scratching such as are known, from experience, to be caused by the slow movements of glaciers. Although one must assume a steady, continuing decline in temperature, nevertheless the heat of the ground, the water and the atmosphere must still have been so high that it is somewhat hard to believe in a prolonged ice age. Even high mountains would scarcely have had the climatic conditions requisite to bring forth glaciers. Possibly these "Ice Age" traces are actually so-called "slickensides", caused by one layer of rock moving over another, which in the early Eozoic would have been under at least four atmospheric pressures and would therefore have produced a considerable effect. At any rate, that is one of the still unsolved mysteries of prehistory.

During the whole of the period in question the atmosphere was virtually impenetrable to sunlight, for it was dense with low-lying, high-reaching clouds. Only towards the end of the early Eozoic was there an appearance of twilight, due to the continuing lowering in temperature and the consequent decrease of steam in the atmosphere. Also the surface temperatures must gradually have sunk from about 170° C. at the start of this era to roughly 35° C. by the end. The same drop in temperature, of course, occurred in the case of the sea-waters, which still contained considerable quantities of carbon dioxide, ammonia, sulphuretted hydrogen, iron salts and other chemical compounds. At the same time the atmospheric pressure sank from 8 to 4·4 atmospheres.

The enveloping air now consisted predominantly of steam, nitrogen, and a very large proportion of carbon dioxide. In addition there were not inconsiderable amounts of methane, ammonia and cyanic compounds. What was completely lacking was free oxygen. During that earliest era of rock-building, particularly the formation of silicates, the available oxygen was completely used up, so the invisible ultra-violet rays of the Sun—which nowadays are intercepted by oxygen "buffers"—then penetrated unhindered to the surface of the Earth and even into the depths of the oceans. Broadly speaking, Earth's atmosphere at that time consisted of a mixture of gases which could hardly have been more inimical to life.

And yet, in spite of all this, conditions favourable to life eventually emerged—probably about 1,500,000,000 years ago.

This extremely important date is located at this particular point in the time-scale because in the preceding Archaean layers there are no signs of life, whereas the Upper Eozoic is very rich in them. In fact we may theoretically regard the first appearance of life on Earth as marking the start of the Eozoic. The oldest known, definitely identified, forms of life were discovered in the Algonquin magnetite layers on the north shore of Lake Superior in Canada. Here were found blue-green algae, lower fungi and a flagellate, already a transitional stage of development towards animal life. Its age, established with the help of the uranium-lead method, would be about 1·3 thousand million years, which corresponds very well with other conjectures.

10. Oldest blue-green alga hitherto discovered. Found in the magnetite strata of Lake Superior in Canada (magnification × 900)

How life originated is generally regarded as the greatest mystery of Nature. This problem of creation is enveloped in a whole tangle of myths with which great thinkers throughout the ages have wrestled. But myths only obscure the problem; they reveal nothing and at best only replace one riddle with another. The origin of life upon Earth—creation as we call this process—is exclusively a problem for the natural sciences and can only be solved by their own methods of thought and investigation. This view, admittedly, has been bitterly contested. Eminent thinkers have repeatedly maintained that this all-important problem lies in the domain of religion and metaphysics and not within the sphere of science. Obviously, in this argument, philosophical inclinations play their part, as well as age-old ingrained prejudices and those familiar, countless attempts, which have persisted throughout the intellectual history of mankind, to dictate to Nature precisely *what* her nature should be! This attitude produced the protracted, often bitter disputes which, while persisting continuously through the centuries and even right up to the present day, reached two great historic climaxes in the cases of Galileo and Darwin. The question of the origin of life was fundamental to all these arguments.

Scientific methods of thinking and working have a special place in mankind's intellectual researches. They represent an endless questioning of Nature, based on experiment and investigation. Any answers received, having been elicited by unprejudiced inquiry, are accepted and incorporated into the existing body of knowledge. When, as is inevitable, uncertainties arise, hypotheses have to be built in as temporary bridges and detours on the high-road of knowledge, until further, more searching, questions enable us finally to establish a solid causeway across this new territory. More of Nature's mysteries having thus been resolved, another forward base is now established for further scientific investigations. Essential to this process are absolute freedom of thought and conscious rejection of any disposition to regard any discovery as false merely because it does not agree with the hitherto proclaimed "laws of Nature".

It is certainly superfluous to stress that, by these means, knowledge has made immense advances. A classic example is the evolution of the theory of relativity. Its origin lies in Michelson's famous experiment, in which he attempted to prove, by means of the speed of light, an absolute movement of the Earth through an assumedly universal "ether". His experiment started from the simple and (in classical physics) firmly established assumption that the speed of a ray of light (absolute speed 186,283 miles per second) overtaking the Earth (whose own absolute speed through space is assumed to be 620 miles per second), would, measured from the Earth, only have a speed of 185,663 miles per second. Results, however, proved that the speed of light, irrespective of which direction it was coming from, was entirely unaffected by the movement of the Earth. In each and every case, light moved at a speed of 186,283 miles per second, no more and no less. This drove Michelson almost to desperation. He never realised that here he was telling Nature what she had to do, that in posing his question he also presented the answer which he expected. Einstein, however, accepted this apparently illogical phenomenon as a new *natural* answer which had somehow to be reconciled with reality. The absolute speed of light had been incontrovertibly established by experiment. If its nature defied all logic, then logic must be wrong; and so the standards used for measuring the apparent speed of light must also be wrong. And these standards were time and space. By this cold, bold conclusion the ancient conceptions of time and space were shattered once and for all, and a new relativistic view of the universe was born.

Planck, too, waged an almost equally fierce battle against preconceptions as deeply ingrained as those of Michelson. As a result of experimental researches into the behaviour of radiations he evolved a formula which would account for certain irregularities he had observed, but this formula appeared to him so absurd in its logical consequences that he, with his conservative scientific outlook, believed that it must somehow be defective. His formula required that the emission of radiations—a form of pure energy—should not be continuous, steady, unbroken, but should be in the form of a stream of separate particles, of a definite size but no further subdivisible—quanta of energy, atoms of energy. To the whole contemporary world of physics this was an absurd conception. Today we know—and Planck himself only realised it many years later—that the formula provides one of the profoundest keys to Nature. On it depends the system of quantum physics which is basic to scientific thought today.

Atomic physics, too, at the turn of the century, found itself faced with a similar crisis. The idea of the atom, a brilliant stroke of inspiration which occurred to the Greek thinker, Democritus, was, in the nineteenth century, virtually proved to be a chemical reality; but even the classical conception postulated that it must be the final, indivisible unit. No one doubted this, indeed, until, in 1896, the French physicist

Antoine Henri Becquerel discovered radioactivity, which provided disconcerting proof that at least one element—radium, which was discovered by M. and Mme. Curie in 1898—could disintegrate by means of radiation into another element—lead. So that meant the end of all ideas of the indivisibility of the atom, and the fundamental transformation of all experimentally acquired knowledge of Nature.

These are only a few examples of the game of questions-and-answers confronting scientists; they could be multiplied almost indefinitely. After the successes achieved by the use of such methods during the last few centuries, there is today no reason at all to assert that this or that problem can "never" be solved. How can one possibly know that? Mankind will always go on inquiring.

Even the mystery of the origin of life—a problem which many wise men have said cannot be solved—will one day yield up its answer. It is all a matter of posing the right scientific question in the right way.

And already the questions are being put very cleverly and effectively. The problem has been "fenced in", and there is all the time in the world to pin-point it even more precisely. Every generation after us will know more than we do. That is a commonplace fact generally ignored.

Everything described so far—the origin of the Sun and planets, the consolidation and cooling of the Earth—were chemico-physical processes; nothing more, strictly speaking, than changes in matter resulting from continuous loss of heat. But it was this very change from high to low temperatures that brought about the transformation of matter from ultra-hot simple elementary particles to the fantastic multiplicity of chemical combinations which eventually determined the composition of our Earth. The course of this transformation can be traced to a large extent by astronomical discoveries and laboratory experiments.

In the beginning was energy, of which we know that, in certain circumstances, it is capable of transforming itself into mass—of "freezing" into mass. This "freezing point" must, according to our mathematical estimates, lie somewhere around 100,000,000,000° C. At first only unstable mesons and positrons appear. A further lowering of temperature is needed to produce the more stable neutrons, which in their turn are able to transform themselves into protons and electrons. Going further down the temperature scale, neutrons and protons combine into ions, i.e. atomic nuclei. Therefore in the deep interior of most of the suns atoms must persist in an ionised state. In cooler stars, particularly in their atmospheres, atoms complete themselves with electron "envelopes". At this point occurs the first possibility of simple chemical combinations which are only one aspect of the "exchanges" of these electron envelopes. For instance, on red and therefore low temperature suns there are always more band spectra which are caused by molecules (carbon monoxide, titanium oxide, etc.). If a really effective cooling process takes place—as upon Earth— then the number and complexity of chemical combinations increases almost endlessly. With further lowering of the temperature, the conditions of aggregation change. Gases can become fluid and even solid. The original atoms and molecules become minerals, rocks and water, intermingled with and surrounded by gaseous elements in physical mixtures. After the simple molecules, consisting only of a few atoms (water and silicic acid), there follows the creation of larger, more complicated giant molecules, rather like Chinese boxes. Here a major role is played by carbon, which is perhaps the most important and versatile of all elements.

From the point of view of producing energy, carbon plays a vital part in the majority of all suns. Up till quite recently what the suns "lived on" was an unsolved mystery: how was it possible that with their immense outpouring of energy they did not cool off in a very short time? (For example, our Sun loses every day through radiation 960,000,000,000 tons in weight.) Today we know that the suns are atomic power stations in which hydrogen is continuously built up into helium. In this way so much energy is released that the loss by radiation is easily compensated for and even over-compensated.

This building up of an atomic nucleus can happen in two ways: either by direct impact of protons (of which hydrogen bombs are a hideous example), or indirectly by juxtaposition of protons with carbon atoms which through numerous transmutations add 4 protons to their own 6, transform 2 into neutrons and finally expel the intruders (2 protons and 2 neutrons) in the form of a compact helium nucleus. What remains is the original carbon atom which has merely worked as a catalyst. (This is the Bethe-Weizsäcker carbon cycle.) It seems that this second method of generating energy operates in suns of our type.

Now, what is the supreme importance of carbon in our world? It lies in its capacity to build up molecular rings and chains of almost endless variety. In this way extremely large and chemically complex molecules are formed. A particular example of this are the nucleo-proteins—the basic substance of all life.

Up to this point the line of evolution of matter is straightforward and fairly precisely known, and might be described as stretching "from the elementary particle to the giant molecule". Now these giant molecules cannot exist at high temperatures, so the heat of the Algonquin or Torridonian Period was probably about right for their emergence—just as, for example, 98.4° F. is, with slight deviations one way or another, the right temperature for life processes in the human body. And it was during the Upper Eozoic which, chemically speaking, was the stage at which giant molecules *must* occur, that life first appeared!

Up to this point the development of matter had proceeded steadily and uninterruptedly. Is one not therefore forced to the conclusion that life is but a further development of matter, just as matter was a further development of energy? Everything living is composed of matter, of the same elements as the spiral galaxies, the suns, planets and Earth. And of nothing else. Life consists merely of millions of differentiated forms and physical characteristics which do not appear in the inorganic world. It is, in fact, just one further stage of development. It is difficult to believe that chain development of matter throughout those hundreds of millions of years would suddenly reach its apotheosis in the giant molecules and then come to a dead end. That is what one would have to assume if life had first spontaneously begun with such highly organised beings as, for example, the fishes. This would imply a complete break which scientific logic could not bridge. But, indeed, such was not the case. Living macro-molecules were the first things from which life started, and they were the direct and immediate successors of inorganic matter at its culminating point.

This is not a mere assertion, for we are familiar with plenty of surviving macro-molecules. The genes, for example, the carriers of hereditary traits in the chromosomes, are such. Furthermore, the vast realm of sub-microscopic viruses, those vicious sources of diseases, represent a transitional state between non-living and living matter. Like the genes, they are protein molecules with a content of nucleic acid, and therefore chemically similar. But they crystallise like inorganic matter (a characteristic of no living cell); they are completely inert when not implanted in any acceptable host; but they immediately become alive and multiply when they can batten on to the right host. There is an almost magical awakening of dead matter to life, an amazing transition from inorganic to organic substance.

Now viruses are by no means the oldest form of life. Since they need existing living bodies to fasten on to in order to achieve their own live state, they must obviously have appeared later than their hosts. The viruses have been cited only to prove that in Nature there exist macro-molecules which can accomplish that jump, hitherto believed impossible, from the inorganic to the organic world. The investigation of viruses is now being intensively carried out throughout the world so that in a few decades we should know a great deal about them.

Thus the field of enquiry concerning the origin of life has now been narrowed down. There is no purpose in searching elsewhere than in the chemico-physical processes of the giant molecule. The very defining of this objective is a great achievement, and that the objective is the right one has been confirmed by the results of brilliant experiments in America. Once again experimentation, the direct questioning of Nature, came into its own. Once again the fundamental idea was as simple as all inspired ideas are. The geologists described what must have been the terrestrial conditions during the Upper Eozoic Period and they stated also that at that particular time life must have developed. Then, in laboratories, almost exactly the same physical conditions were recreated and the results observed.

This was the actual experiment. Sea-water, compounded of chemical ingredients believed to be of correct proportions for that period, was raised to a temperature of about 60° C. and brought into contact with a "primal atmosphere"—that is one without free oxygen—and then subjected to electrical discharges, simulating lightning, and powerful ultra-violet radiation.

What eventually happened was that substances began to appear which had not been present at the start of the experiment: these were porphyrines, the high-molecular basic constituents of haemoglobin, as well as chlorophyll, and numerous amino-acids, the basic constituents of living protein —all "created" under artificially arranged "Eozoic" conditions.

For a start no more could be expected. It was, indeed, only a start, using undoubtedly inadequate means. The boldness of attempting to reconstitute conditions which have not existed on Earth for 1,500,000,000 years was buoyed up on faith in the accuracy of the geologists' reconstruction of the world as it then was. But striking as the results of this experimental reconstruction are, one must bear in mind that it was largely guesswork and all the actual conditions prevailing at that far distant time are certainly not yet known. Indeed, it is conceivable that geologists might learn, from the results of further experiments, what those conditions really were, if one day variations in the experimental conditions should lead to better results.

Perhaps many would now protest that it is quite clear that life *began*, even that it began in the Upper Eozoic—but *how* did it begin? Even with the fairly powerful testimony as to the possibility of a purely chemico-physical process, there still remains the question: what next happened to these macro-molecules, so that they suddenly became endowed with attributes which they hitherto had not possessed, such as the power to feed and to reproduce?

These are, of course, the vital questions to which so far there are no answers.

But one must always bear in mind that even a "dead"

atom is an extremely complicated structure. Consider a medium-heavy element such as iron. Its nucleus is composed of 26 protons and 30 neutrons concentrated inconceivably closely together in the smallest possible space—26 positive elementary electrical charges held together by lightning-swift exchanges of unstable elementary particles between protons and neutrons at the critical verge between mass and energy, these exchanges occurring a thousand million times a second. Then imagine this fantastic structure enveloped in a cloud of negative electricity, 26 electrons revolving round it at incredible speed. Quanta of every imaginable energy-value dart about, are swallowed up by the electrons, vary the distance of the electrons' orbits from the nucleus, are emitted again as radiations with the electrons leaping back into their original orbits. Other electrons are forced out—liberated from—the community by the energy-laden quanta; then the atom becomes ionised, electrically active, radiating energy which attracts other electrons. A simple molecule, composed of perhaps 20 or 30 atoms, complicates this whole involved process to a scarcely comprehensible extent. But take now a giant molecule consisting of 100,000 atoms, and we have a structure of such labyrinthine complication that its internal interplay of energy cannot conceivably be analysed. It was this very complication which was of paramount importance in leading to the ultimate emergence of life. To speak extremely loosely, that "dead" molecule is already living in its immense multiplicity of movements, repulsions and attractions, combinations and equalisations of energy. Indeed, just like all living matter, it reacts most sensitively to the slightest upset. A single impact-ionisation, the expulsion of just one of the million electrons from the molecular community, affects the whole indescribably complicated structure and can completely transform a macro-molecule and even change its hitherto existing functions.

We know this with considerable certainty from biological experiments in mutation. Mutation—discovered early this century by the Dutch botanist Hugo de Vries (1848-1935)—proved for a long time to be an apparently inexplicable biological phenomenon. It involved the sudden, spontaneous appearance in plants or animals of heritable variations from the normal type. Welcome though the proof of the existence of this phenomenon may have been to natural historians, since it ultimately proved to be an important support for Darwinism in the battle about the meaning of variations in species, the actuating mechanism was totally unknown and therefore left the door wide open to all and every sort of vitalistic speculation. Modern atomic physics has helped to solve this problem and has shown mutation to be a chemico-physical process in the realm of the giant molecules. Investigations into heredity revealed that the genes within the nucleus of each cell (and, consequently, the chromosomes on which the genes are arranged) are the sole carriers of heredity. They alone determine the form and functioning of the living body which results from the union of parent cells. In order to alter an individual and its characteristics, it is necessary to alter its genes (or its chromosomes). These, working through the enzymes, decide the final form and life-characteristics of the creature in question. Now all genes are nothing more than giant molecules, subject to the interplay of the internal and external chemico-physical forces in the world of atoms. So if a radiation quantum scores a hit on a gene, one or more electrons will be torn out of an extremely sensitive structure, and the remaining constituents in the gene-molecule will then have to re-group themselves. As a result the gene itself changes its functions and now exerts its influence in a different manner. A mutation has taken place; the nature of the being has changed.

An immense amount remains to be investigated in this field. But countless artificially created mutations have been produced by radiation (as well as by heat, chemical stimuli, etc.) which have thus eliminated any remaining doubts about the phenomenon. It has been clearly *proved* that such things happen in Nature. So it is not too far-fetched to suggest that the actual source of life may be traceable to similar processes, particularly since the ultra-violet radiations from the Sun were almost unobstructed during the Eozoic Period. The Sun as the father of Life—is that such an extraordinary idea?

For the transformation of energy into mass we have the Einstein formula of $E = mc^2$. For the transformation of mass into life we have nothing comparable. The ultra-complicated world of the macro-molecule is still a closed one to us. For how much longer will it remain so?

At this point mention must be made of an hypothesis that the fructification of the Earth came from outer space. This theory originated with the Swedish astro-physicist Svante Arrhenius (1859-1927), who held that life had always existed in the universe and that spores driven by pressure of radiation from the Sun had colonised our planet after migrating through space. But when the deadly ultra-radiations in outer space were subsequently discovered, this theory became untenable.

So it seems that life originated on Earth during the early Eozoic Period, and quite possibly it may also have developed on other celestial bodies in a similar physical state to the Earth, for the laws of the evolution of matter must be the same throughout the universe. The apparently exceptional circumstances of the Earth are—from the cosmic point of view—no exception at all. The Earth is not even an exception in our planetary system. That beautiful, brilliant morning and evening star, Venus, may very well bear an astonishingly close resemblance to the Earth. Venus is practically the same size as the Earth (7,600 miles in diameter as compared to 7,927 miles), almost of the same density (4.86 as compared to 5.52), and she is surrounded by an atmosphere as impenetrable as the Earth's in pre-Cambrian times. For the latter reason it has proved impossible for astronomers to observe Venus's real surface. Of atmospheric gases only carbon dioxide has been detected, and that in very large quantities—a most important factor for maintaining life. No other gases have as yet been identified because of the high, dense clouds which envelop the planet. The presence of water, perhaps even in the form of oceans, was believed possible, which would mean that all conditions for the emergence of life would be present. However, this "wet" theory has had a rival, a "dry" hypothesis, which asserts that the planet is a glowing furnace enveloped in dust. Arguments in favour of either theory were equally meagre until astronomers interpreted the results of the first close-up view of Venus obtained by instruments aboard the rocket Mariner II in its rendezvous with the planet in

December 1962. These findings support the "dry" theory, as the surface temperature seems to be 800 degrees Fahrenheit —much too high for the possibility of the emergence of life.

However, the celebrated and much-discussed Mars is by no means entirely hostile to life, provided we do not apply to it the strict yardstick of conditions which exist upon present-day Earth. It is cold there; arctic temperatures are the general rule in most regions and at all seasons, although, especially near the equator, temperatures have risen above zero. The surface of Mars is predominantly desert-like. The grey-green regions have been explained as damp moorland areas, which is possible but also disputable. Free water is very scarce; the atmosphere is thin and only resembles the Earth's in very limited respects. So the place is not exactly encouraging for settling on. But hostile to life? No. And certainly not for a Martian form of life which could be quite differently organised from life on Earth.

It is now completely "taboo" to think that extra-terrestrial life must imitate our own forms of existence. It is well known what a vast number of differing forms of life have been produced on our planet. Every slight variation in environment lays down new conditions favourable to new forms of life, new anatomical structures and new possibilities of development. Mutation, on the contrary, changes things without purpose or object, and whether such a change is in fact favourable to the species concerned is only decided by its ability to survive in the world around it, by its capacity to exploit its environment, as is summed up in the frequently misunderstood phrase "survival of the fittest", by which Darwin certainly did *not* mean a merciless struggle to the death, but merely a general process of adaptation towards conditions most favourable to life. We shall come across enough cases, during the course of the biological development of the Earth, where the onset of unsuitable mutations led to the extermination of that particular form of life. The same rules must apply upon Mars. And if life does exist there, it must be so precisely adapted to Martian conditions—which are guessed at rather than known—that it must be quite different from life on Earth. Fundamentally, the same remarks apply to any planetary body which does not have the same physical characteristics as our Earth, such a similarity being quite possible, though likely to occur seldom.

However, the meaning of "seldom" in this context takes on a rather different complexion if a slight calculation is made. Our own galaxy consists of 100,000,000,000 suns. Assuming that every tenth sun has planets (a purely random assumption, and a far lower average than is probable) and assuming furthermore that in every tenth solar system just one Earth exists among a possible total of ten planets, then in our own Milky Way there would be 1,000,000,000 dark bodies capable of developing a form of life almost identical with that on Earth. Thus the heroic, overwhelming solitude of the creature called Man, who has emerged as the ruler of the third planet of the solar system orbiting through the dark depths of space, may one day, in the not too distant future, be ended by the discovery that there are an immense number of other inhabited worlds—an important thought which, rid of any cheap and sensational ideas about Utopia, could change our whole outlook on the future.

CHAPTER SIX

The Cambrian World

CONDITIONS on Earth in the later part of the pre-Cambrian Period were, by accepted standards, far from hospitable to life. If, a century ago, such a planet had been discovered in the neighbourhood of Alpha Centauri or Sirius, the possibility of life on it would most certainly have been denied. Since then we have learnt much.

One can only guess what the first living objects on Earth looked like. Unfortunately, fossils from that distant era have not survived. But they could only have been the most delicate, tiny agglomerations of protein, without skins or skeletons or hard chitinous coverings and therefore with no content of lime or silica which could survive in fossil form. Also, the frequent transformation (metamorphosis) of rocks under tremendous pressure and at very high temperatures must have destroyed any organic remains. The only possible indications are traces of graphite. Graphite is one of the forms of pure carbon, and is known to be the last stage of the carbonisation of plant life. Small lime deposits, too, could conceivably be of organic origin, but in any case this could only be the remains of algae which appeared as the first water plants. However, opinion is by no means definite, since such formations, under the particular conditions prevailing at the time, could also be of inorganic origin. There have indeed been meteorites in which graphite traces have been found, but it would have been quite wrong to assume that these traces were remains of life from some hypothetical exploded "world".

The earliest living organisms must have been able to synthesise their food from inorganic substances and hence must have been more like plants than animals. These primitive forms probably led to the simplest types of plants, similar to algae, which spread throughout the still-warm seas. Then

there appeared the first single-cell animals, which were probably represented by the flagellates. And thus the biological
"chain-reaction" developed at ever-increasing speed and in
all directions. But it must be borne in mind that hundreds
of millions of years were required for this primitive development to take place.

The upper beds of the Eozoic fortunately left behind much
clearer traces of life. Whole seaweed forests must have existed
in those days. The first reef structures of calcareous algae
appear; and the animal world is dominated by the innumerable single-celled protozoa. Together with the flagellates there
swam in the seas amoeboid Globigerina as well as Radiolaria
with their beautifully constructed siliceous skeletons, and
tunicate Foraminifera in vast variety. In the realm of higher
life were the sponges, molluscs, and the first brachiopods.
Tracks in rocks also indicate the existence of worms. It is
impossible to suggest fully how rich were the forms and
variations of life; for the Upper Eozoic, in spite of its comparative nearness in time to us, is a riddle that is still proving
difficult to solve.

At the end of the Eozoic we come well below the magic
number of a thousand million years, for, according to our
table, that period came to an end about 600,000,000 years
ago. The legendary early "time" which lasted over the
gigantic eons of the pre-Cambrian Era, has now reached a
"historical" stage which, as a whole, can be conveniently and
conventionally divided up into early, middle and modern
periods.

(Although our radio wave is still speeding through space,
and has covered 3,460,000,000 light years, it is still immensely
remote, far on the other side of the Milky Way.)

The Palaeozoic Era, as the early part is called, begins with
the Cambrian Period, the formations of which were first discovered in Wales (Cambria being the Latin name for Wales).
Its duration is generally estimated at 100,000,000 years; and it
is subdivided into three parts: Lower—Middle—and Upper
Cambrian.

From the geophysical and tectonic point of view much had
been happening in the slow transformation of conditions on
Earth. The seas had grown perceptibly cooler, with a corre-

sponding effect on the ocean beds. The waters had long since ceased to steam and the atmosphere had therefore become much clearer. The first blue sky appeared during the Cambrian Period. The powerful sunshine—the "visible" parts of which had hitherto been intercepted by the thick atmosphere—now began to penetrate to the land and the surface of the seas.

Another process most important for the future development of life seems to have first taken place during the Cambrian —the formation of free oxygen in the atmosphere. Until quite recently it was assumed that the present oxygen content in air dated from a much more recent period, from the time when the plant world had finally conquered the dry land and had largely "assimilated" the carbon dioxide in the atmosphere. (By means of their chlorophyll the plants were enabled to absorb the carbon and discharge the oxygen into the air.) To a certain extent this assumption was correct; for today, of course, this process of assimilation continues to provide our atmosphere with considerable quantities of oxygen. But investigation into the upper atmosphere has revealed pockets of ozone (molecules consisting of 3 atoms of oxygen) and ionised layers of free oxygen whose origin and existence must give rise to new lines of thought. The powerful ultra-violet radiations from the Sun which, in Archaean and Eozoic times, penetrated unimpeded to the surface of the Earth because of a lack of oxygen in the atmosphere, could have broken down the steam molecules (photo-dissociation) and liberated oxygen in the lower layers of the atmosphere even then. But it would not have been stable; for this element which is so essential to life easily enters into combinations, and such oxygen as there was played a part in the building and weathering of rocks, and was also involved in all molten magmatic processes throughout the Archaean. Consequently any free oxygen molecules resulting from the dissociation of steam were very soon absorbed again in the tectonic processes. It could not have been until the great tectonic age was nearly over that a modest quantity of pure oxygen made its permanent appearance in the lower atmosphere. Once this happened, an immediate consequence was that the oxygen in the atmosphere began to intercept the ultra-violet rays from the Sun, and did so with increasing efficiency as the proportion of oxygen in the air rose. Today—and perhaps also in the Cambrian Period—the process of dissociation takes place mainly in the upper atmosphere, which thereby acts as a defence against cosmic radiation. There is thus a perpetual cycle of rising water vapour and descending free oxygen, so that the high oxygen content of the atmosphere is certainly not *solely* attributable to the plant assimilation process.

A geophysical picture of the world in the Cambrian Period would closely resemble the world today, the only exception being that the proportion of carbon dioxide in the atmosphere must have been much higher. Yet in this respect, too, there was a gradual cleansing of the air, which later favoured the development of lunged animals, though matters had not yet proceeded so far in the Cambrian Period. Still, the lime-depositing plants and creatures in the sea took so much carbon dioxide from the air that the atmospheric pressure, which to start with was extremely high, dropped to almost its present value.

The actual surface-appearance of the Earth was very different from what it is today. To all intents and purposes, the only land-surfaces were the primal continental blocks already mentioned, which rose up out of the two world-wide oceans —the Pacific and the Tethys. The Pacific seems always to have been the greatest expanse of water in the world. During Cambrian times it extended over North and Central Asia and inundated the whole area of what is now the cordillera chain of both North and South America. Parallel to the equator, but somewhat to the north, stretched a circumferential sea which has been given the name of the Tethys Sea (after the wife of Oceanus in Greek mythology). Throughout almost the whole of Earth's history the Tethys separated the northern and southern blocks of mainland. A primeval traveller coming from the east would have found nothing but blue sea in the region of the Himalayas, could have sailed through a channel north of the Indian block and south of the Turkestan block of Serindia, after which he would have been able to voyage freely across present-day Europe as far as the near end of the Pacific in the region of Central America. To the south of this semi-circumnavigational voyage, there would have been no way through. Neither the Indian Ocean nor the South Atlantic Ocean existed. Instead of these there stretched from West Australia, via India, Arabia and Africa to Brazil and Argentine, one single vast continental block which probably reached far down the world and may even have joined up with Antarctica. This great primeval continent has been named Gondwanaland after the Indian race of the Gonds.

The northern land hemisphere had meanwhile taken on a

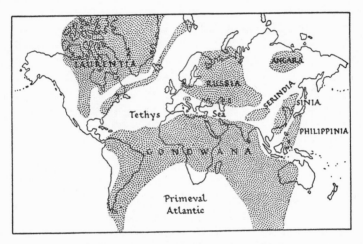

11. The Earth in the Cambrian Period

pronouncedly insular character. Parts of North America and Canada (the North American shield) remained solidly connected with Greenland and formed the continental block of Laurentia. To the east of Laurentia, and separated by a narrow arm of the sea, there was a long solid ridge stretching as far north as Iceland. Europe, apart from some possible island groups, consisted mainly of the Finno-Russian block called Russia. Beyond that, there began again the great world of the Pacific Ocean with a few scattered clumps of islands— Angara in Siberia, Sinia in Eastern China and Philippinia opposite it. A very strange picture of the Earth's surface, and in many aspects an uncertain one, too. One cannot expect to draw a precise map of the world as it existed 500,000,000 years ago. But palaeogeography is still young as a study and there is plenty of time to improve on this first tentative lay-out.

We know even less about the actual surface-appearance of the Cambrian continents. One can assume the existence of tall mountain chains, and, probably, the formation of ice and glaciers—but only in the highest regions. These could have been the cause of those numerous glaciation traces which occur in geographically widely separated areas; but the extraordinary thing about these glaciation traces is that they must have been made in a period when, it is almost certain, a warm climate extended over a very wide latitude from north to south. We will return to this problem later.

There is one thing we know definitely about the Cambrian Period: all continents and islands were dead rock, completely without land plants. Life was still exclusively confined to the open seas. Whether, in the later Cambrian Era, life developed in enclosed seas is so far not known.

The plant world flourished, dominated by the luxuriant spread of the lime and silica-depositing algae which created endless reefs in the seas. The animal world, having appeared in the late pre-Cambrian almost instantaneously in a considerable number of variations, had diversified itself by the Cambrian Period into nearly 2,000 varieties. And, of course, the evolution of life had already proceeded further. There now existed representatives of many important invertebrate groups. Lamellibranchs, gastropods, brachiopods and arthropods were all to be found. An important development which helped to leave a record of primal forms of life was the fact that the early, predominantly soft types were now giving way to those with hard skins, skeletons and armament. Their soft parts generally rotted away after death and disappeared very rapidly, but the shells and structures formed hollow spaces which were filled in by mineral substances which then hardened and retained precise impressions of the original creature. Any preservation of soft portions of an animal was mostly a matter of chance, such as sudden envelopment by a mineral substance which served to exclude destructive oxygen, another important factor being the fineness of the

enveloping mineral—e.g. lime. Just such a lucky circumstance occurred in British Columbia at the Burgess Pass.
There schistose rock of the Middle Cambrian was found
containing, among 1,200 identifiable species of invertebrates,
the impressions of jelly fish, worms, early echinoderms, and
the entrails of primitive crustaceans, which are rarely fossilised
normally.

From the Cambrian onwards, the trilobites play a most
important role for a very long period in the life of the world.
Trilobite means "three-lobed", and the creature was so
named from the triple overlapping armour on its back which
was divided into head, thorax and tail portions. This
"armour" was formed of chitin, a horn-like extrusion of the
skin which, with the addition of calcium carbonate, solidifies
and provides a very favourable substance for preservation.
These trilobites were, generally, tiny animals, up to a few
inches in length, but they have been found in giant forms
over 2 feet long. Their variations and distributions are quite
astonishing. Trilobites accounted for roughly 60 per cent
of all Cambrian forms of life. Some existed by crawling and
digging into the mud and slime of the ocean bed. Others
must have been good swimmers or even floating animals
resembling plankton. It is known that they lived in the oceans
at very varying depths, for this can be deduced from the
range of development of their eyes. The blind trilobites must
have lived in the black abysses of the sea; while those with
tremendously developed eyes—some sticking out on stalks
with about 15,000 lenses—dwelt in regions of extremely
faint light, say at a depth of between 200 and 600 fathoms.
Undoubtedly, these were the most highly developed creatures
in the whole Cambrian, and their predatory way of life must
have made them the almost unchallenged first lords of the
Earth. They continued to exist and flourish over the immense
period of 320,000,000 years, until, in the Permian, unable to
cope with changes in the environment, they died out. Because
of their world-wide distribution and prolonged existence as
a species, they are especially important as zone fossils for the
Cambrian Period.

Trilobites are now only known as fossils, but a related group
of arthropods, the Xiphosura (sword-tailed), have survived

from those distant ages right up to the present day. In the present biological scene they are represented by the extremely ancient king crabs (*Limulus*) which occur as mud-borers along the Asiatic coasts and on the south-eastern coast of North America.

CHAPTER SEVEN

Life Takes to the Land

AFTER the Cambrian Period came the Ordovician, so-called from discoveries made in Welsh territory once inhabited by the old Celtic tribe of the Ordovicii; and then the Silurian, similarly named after the Silures.

Some geologists have treated the Ordovician and the ensuing Silurian as one, but the distinction between the two is generally accepted and for the purposes of this book they will be regarded as being quite separate. The duration of the Ordovician is now agreed as being about 60,000,000 years, and that of the Silurian 40,000,000 years.

Climatically the Ordovician and Silurian Periods present no particular problems. The presence of coral reefs—even in high latitudes (Greenland, North Canada)—which, as we know from their present-day distribution over the Earth, are associated with the warmer seas, bears evidence of a very widespread and constant temperate climate. Tectonically there was not much change. Towards the end of the Ordovician a weak wave of mountain-building set in, one of the results of which was a first version of the present-day Appalachians of eastern North America. It was only towards the end of the Upper Silurian Period that there started an enormous process of mountain-folding, of a magnitude that has, so far as is known, very seldom occurred in the whole of Earth's history. Those areas primarily affected were Europe and the North Atlantic, in the geosynclines of which, during the course of many millions of years, vast quantities of sediment had piled up. A gigantic chain of mountains, about 4,000 miles long, stretched from Ireland and Scotland, to Norway, Spitzbergen and Greenland. Traces of this great range are still to be found in Wales, Norway and Scotland. The ancient word "Caledonia" for Scotland has given to this folding period the term *Caledonian Mountain-Folding*. A lesser mountain chain arose, at the same time, running from the Ardennes down to the vicinity of Vienna. Probably there were also foldings in the areas of the Sahara and the South African Cape. At the same time there occurred almost everywhere, as evidence shows, upsurging of magmatic rock which wedged itself in between the overlying layers (intrusions). Throughout both periods there was much volcanic activity in many parts of the world.

Obviously such widespread folding must result in considerable changes in the Earth's surface. Laurentia and Northern Europe were now connected by newly created land-bridges; and for a while the Tethys Sea was closed in by solid land connections stretching southwards to Gondwanaland from the regions of Panama and the present-day Balkans. Yet, on the other hand, upliftings of the Earth's surface resulted in an overall enlargement of the areas covered by water. Immense stretches of land were flooded, in marine transgressions, to an extent which led finally to the greater part of the Earth's surface being submerged.

In the living world, plants had hitherto made astonishingly little progress. In the course of about 100,000,000 years, they had scarcely transcended the alga stage. This is quite extraordinary, for the animal world had proved incomparably more fruitful and had far surpassed the flora in evolutionary progress. Obviously the plants had to achieve a fundamental change, and for this they required a completely new environment, i.e. the land. It is clear that the conquest of land must have been achieved by the early stages of an amphibian life in gradual progress from the sea-shore, and this has indeed been confirmed. Yet it remains a major mystery why this should have taken place so late, for in the world there are innumerable coastal areas and river banks offering countless millions of opportunities for the development of a land flora.

Yet this development may not, in fact, have taken place as late as has been believed hitherto. For, recently, reports have been accumulating, principally from Indian and Russian palaeobotanists, that in the Cambrian rocks of their respective countries there have been discovered spores and woody fragments of land-dwelling vascular cryptogams, such as primitive club-mosses. If this is so, it means that the invasion of land by life would have to be considerably pre-dated.

Clearly, the answers to questions such as these can only be provided by fossil discoveries, and then only in so far as it is possible to identify definitely the layer in which the fossils are found as (in this case) Cambrian. It is thus that we have traced the developments which have brought us now as far as the Upper Silurian; and we can carry the story onwards by the same method. But at this point it should be mentioned that new discoveries and techniques in the future may very well alter our present picture of the evolution of life. If these latest reports from India and Russia are confirmed—which cannot be done overnight—thus establishing the correctness of the new dating, then we are no longer confronted with any mystery, for the transition of plants from the sea to the land evidently took place over an immensely long period and was, quite naturally, attempted at widely differing places on Earth and at very different points in time. After countless failures, there must have been certain local successes followed by an inevitable general line of development which caused them to flourish everywhere during the Upper Silurian Period. The first land plants had now arrived and had begun at last to "settle" the mainland. These plants, the psilophytes, were leafless and without actual roots. But they represented an immense step forward, the great prelude to a rapid evolution towards higher forms which took place during the following Devonian Period.

In the animal world of the ocean, development went on apace. All the major animal groups were now represented, the first vertebrates having appeared late in the Ordovician. The trilobites had not yet reached their highest point of development, and their immense importance as zone fossils still persists during this period; but already they have been overshadowed by the graptolites, a singular, rather mysterious group of animals, restricted to the Ordovician and Silurian Periods in the course of which they appeared and also vanished. Their name, which means "stone-writing", was propounded by Linnaeus, who discovered their bizarre, convoluted and branching saw-like impressions in dark slate-stone. As palaeontological specimens they have, therefore,

Period	Principal Biological Developments
CAMBRIAN 600-500 million years ago	Life confined to water. Lime-depositing algae. Animals all invertebrate: molluscs, trilobites, Bryozoa, brachiopods, worms, holothurians and coelenterates
ORDOVICIAN 500-440 million years ago	Plant life: marine algae only. Most important animals: graptolites, trilobites and brachiopods. Also siliceous sponges, sea-urchins, primitive cephalopods and first vertebrates (ostracoderms, i.e. armoured fishes)
SILURIAN 440-400 million years ago	In addition to algae, first land plants (Psilophytales). Reef-building corals, Bryozoa, crinoids in warm shallow seas, with abundant brachiopods, trilobites. Dominance of eurypterids. Graptolites. First air-breathing animals (scorpion-like forms)
DEVONIAN 400-350 million years ago	Further development of Psilophytales, also ferns, horse-tails and pteridosperms. Goniatites appeared, but grapto-lites almost extinct. Corals and brachiopods. In addition to ostracoderms, bony fish, including first crossopterygians and lung-fish. First sharks. Earliest land vertebrates (primitive amphibians)
CARBONIFEROUS 350-270 million years ago	Very rich swamp flora: lycopods, horse-tails, Cordaitales, ferns and pteridosperms. First conifers. Brachiopods and crinoids abundant. Limestone-forming Foraminifera. Grap-tolites wholly extinct, and trilobites almost so. Scorpions, millipedes and numerous winged insects (including giant dragon-flies). Fresh-water lamellibranchs. Ostracoderms extinct, but numerous sharks and bony fishes. Labyrintho-dont amphibians, and first reptiles (cotylosaurs)
PERMIAN 270-225 million years ago	Lycopods and horse-tails decrease, but conifers more abun-dant. *Glossopteris*-flora in southern hemisphere. Lime-stone-forming foraminifera, and reef-building Bryozoa. Brachiopods numerous Extinction of tetracorals and trilobites. Modern insect groups appear, including those which pupate. Labyrintho-dont amphibians. Cotylosaurs. Therapsid reptiles start evolutionary line in direction of mammals.

The Last 600,000,000 Years

Period	Principal Biological Developments
TRIASSIC 225-180 million years ago	Relatively poor flora of conifers, cycads and ferns in the northern hemisphere, continuation of *Glossopteris*-flora in the south. Appearance of hexacorals, ammonites and belemnites. Crinoids. Brachiopods. Labyrinthodonts. First ichthyosaurs. Appearance of Rhyncocephalia, theropod reptiles and turtles. Predecessors of crocodiles (thecodonts). Therapsid reptiles disappear from fossil record after evolving into mammal-like forms
JURASSIC 180-135 million years ago	Rich land flora of conifers, cycad-like plants (Bennettitales), maidenhair-trees, and ferns. Possibly the first flowering plants. Rich marine fauna, with very abundant ammonites and belemnites. Crinoids and other echinoderms. First crabs. With decrease in amphibians, reptiles become more important: ichthyosaurs, plesiosaurs, theropod and sauropod dinosaurs, first true crocodiles, bird-lipped dinosaurs (Ornithischia) and flying pterosaurs. First lizards. First true mammals.
CRETACEOUS 135-70 million years ago	Definite widespread expansion of the flowering plants. Abundant sponges and lamellibranchs. Great variety of ammonites and belemnites, which however become extinct at end of period. Many large dinosaurs, mosasaurs and pterosaurs, all becoming extinct at end of period. First birds (with teeth). Mammals still small and inconspicuous, evolving slowly. First placentals.
TERTIARY 70-1 million years ago	Great variety of flowering plants. Rich warmth-loving flora in more northerly latitudes. Abundance of nummulites in Eocene and Oligocene, other marine invertebrates very similar to those of present day. Abundant sharks and bony fish. Early whales (zeuglodonts) and sea-cows. Crocodiles, turtles, tortoises all frequent. Rapid dominance of mammals on land, all main groups existing during the Eocene, including first primates. Man's evolution traced via apes of Miocene, from which anthropoid apes evolved separately
PLEISTOCENE 1 million to 10 thousand years ago	Fauna and flora very similar to present day, but cold-loving forms in Europe, many of which (mammoth, cave-bear, woolly rhinoceros, sabre-tooth tiger) are now extinct. Man evolves to *Homo sapiens*. Divergent Neanderthal man and australopithecines become extinct
HOLOCENE 10 thousand years ago until present day	Man dominates life on earth

The Last 600,000,000 Years

been known for a considerable time and have been studied
in great detail, especially because of their abundance throughout the Ordovician and Silurian rocks. They are definitely of
horny, chitinous origin, so there is no possible doubt that
they are the remains of animals, since chitin is formed only
from animal skins. The graptolites appear most frequently as
light membranes on a dark background of slate or mudstone.
Very rarely they are to be found, also, in a more solid form
in limestone or marl. These were colony-building creatures
whose gas-filled "cysts" or bladders enabled them to float
freely in the plankton. Others may have been attached to
submerged objects on the sea-floor. Their place in the animal
world has been disputed for a long time. It was even believed
that they were a specialised form without any recognisable
ancestry. Nowadays it is generally assumed that they must be
included among the coelenterates, a group of predominantly
marine animals which include the sea-anemones. The pronounced frequency of graptolites in alum schist (alum being
a sulphur compound) leads to important conclusions about
the constitution of the seas in which they lived. These may
well have been stretches of water covered by rotting slime
which caused the ocean-bed to be continually poisoned by
sulphuretted hydrogen, a phenomenon that still occurs today,
as in parts of the Black Sea, where the tolerable zone of
existence for most living creatures ends at a depth of about
800 feet, any life below that consisting purely of anaerobic
bacteria and yeast-fungi which are able to survive in the
absence of free oxygen. This state of affairs provides an interesting picture of conditions of life at a time when graptolites
were dispersed throughout the ocean waters of the world.
And it was this very wide dispersal and their rapid evolution that made them the ideal zone fossils for the Silurian
Period.

With ever-increasing variations, and embodying lime to a
greater and greater extent in their shells, the brachiopods,
which had already existed in the Cambrian Period, now
evolved into a considerable number of new forms. Their two-
valved shells became properly hinged and the short stalk (by
which the animal was attached to rocks) emerged from a
well-defined round hole. The Brachiopods did not suffer

extinction at the end of the Silurian, but lasted right over to the present day, though now very depleted in numbers.

Among the numerous arthropods, the eurypterids stand out—and in the most literal sense of the word—for they grew to as much as 6 feet in length. These were relations of the scorpions and spiders, being equally predatory, and were certainly among the most horrifying manifestations of primeval life. Undoubtedly they also existed in fresh water.

Among the soft-shelled creatures, the cephalopods were of great importance and—after a modest start in the Cambrian Period—they played a predominant role for a long time thereafter. They were the predecessors of the present-day squids and the oceanic nautilus. Characteristic of them was their snail-like shell which was their "living-room", protecting their soft body and also providing a number of gas-filled swimming chambers which gave them buoyancy and mobility. This shell-housing took the form of tubes, straight, coiled or spiral. The cephalopods, too, attained giant forms, some being up to some 6 feet in length.

The first corals which lived in the warm Ordovician seas were characterised by their four-rayed symmetry. The Echinodermata, especially the sea-lilies, flourished in great profusion and variety and enlivened the shallow water beds with their aesthetically beautiful forms closely resembling rooted plants and flowers.

We assumed as a climax of the late Silurian Period the emergence of the first plants which, as psilophytes, began to grow along the banks of backwaters. A second, equally important event came with the appearance of the first land-living animals of arthropod descent, the primitive scorpions, spiders, and millipedes.

But what about the vertebrates? The earliest vertebrate remains that have been discovered belong to the Ordovician, but the point in time when Nature began to experiment with a backbone running the length of a creature's body to anchor and protect the soft organs and their functions is impossible to estimate within 50,000,000 years. An approximate notion of how those first creatures may have looked can be gleaned from the appearance of *Amphioxus*, the common lancelet. This small fish about 6 inches in length is a delicate, almost colourless denizen of the sea-floor, where it burrows into the sand. The distinguishing feature of the lancelet—which even today is still without jaws—is the notochord, a cartilaginous rod which is a primitive precursor of the spinal column. It is known from embryological research that the higher vertebrates have similar notochords when still in the embryonic stages and that subsequently these develop, with the growth of vertebrae, into an articulated spine. Here is an application of Ernst Haeckel's "Basic Biogenetic Law"— today regarded as an over-simplification—which states that the development from embryo to adult follows exactly the evolutionary course of development from the primeval cell to the modern individual, a process which took place over thousands of millions of years. This is one of the greatest puzzles of Nature, and much use has been made of it in tracing our origins back through ancestral animal stages.

Now, this very primitive lancelet fish is probably not a present-day descendant of the first vertebrate types, but it must be somewhat similar to those earliest fish-like creatures which needed several million years to develop into orthodox fish. All those earliest fishes lacked jaws; and they are therefore called collectively the Agnatha. In this they resemble the lampreys and hagfishes—the only members of the group to survive to the present day. Many differed, however, in having a dense external armour of bony scales and plates which, even though they themselves were predatory creatures, gave a much-needed protection from such aggressive animals as the trilobites and eurypterids. Some even, like Cephalaspis, may possibly have been equipped with "electric batteries", those quite extraordinary organs such as are to be found nowadays in electric eels, which are equipment both for defence and for catching prey. We know that the blind electric eel also possesses some sort of "radar" equipment by means of which it emits and receives electrical impulses, thus enabling it to orientate itself in its world.

Earliest traces suggest that these armoured fish first appeared in freshwater areas; only towards the end of the Silurian Period are they in evidence in salt-water regions. At this time a new group of fishes seems to have developed—the gnathostomes, equipped with primitive jaws. Many of these also bore coats of armoured plates, and creatures such as *Dinich-thys* (from the Devonian of North America) grew to be as much as 18 feet long. These armoured jawed fish did not, however, survive the Devonian.

Other armoured fish, such as the *Pterichthys,* were equipped with stilt-like front limbs which would have been entirely adequate for them to make temporary crossings of dry land. All in all, we have here a picture of a highly organised, well-equipped groups of animals through whom Nature embarked

12. Some types of armour-plated fish.
In the middle, *Cephalaspis*; lower right, *Pterichthys*

on a large-scale attempt to combine the hard external protective casing of their former mode of life with the novelty of a "spine".

But simultaneously, after the close of the Silurian Period, there were several other "attempts" of this sort. Thus, for example, there appeared the elasmobranchs, predecessors of our present-day sharks and rays, fish whose internal skeleton is composed of hard cartilage rather than bone. The primal sharks were, admittedly, small, only a little over 2 feet long. They were predators just as they are today; but as menaces in the animal world they were only comparable to such present-day fish as pikes. Still, they probably fell victim often enough to the armoured fish, though possibly superior to the latter in speed of movement and agility.

If we now mention that scorpions were probably the first animals to climb out of the waters and explore dry land as a possible, hitherto unknown habitat, we have then rapidly covered the developments of over 100,000,000 years and we can turn to the ensuing Devonian Period.

(Interim report from the universe: our radio wave is now 350,000,000 light years away, and so has still to cover 2,087,000,000,000,000,000,000 miles.)

The Realm of Psilophytes and Fishes

T H E Devonian Period (duration 50 million years) derives its name from extensive geological formations found in Devon in England. It is subdivided into Lower, Middle, and Upper Devonian.

The vast sea inundations of the departed Silurian Period persisted for some time, but then yielded to a steady increase in land building. The transgressions chiefly affected the Sahara areas of the Gondwana continent which was still firmly connected to Laurentia by an immense land-bridge. This bridge separated the Tethys Sea from the Pacific, which had penetrated far into North America in the form of a gigantic ocean bay. Very characteristic geologically is the northern continent which was joined to North Europe by the Caledonian mountain folding (see map on p. 126). We speak of this as the "Old Red" continent, in reference to the old red sandstone which at that time was deposited in strata of great depth. It is evident that the northern continent, whence all this sedimentary material came, must have consisted largely of quartz-sand deserts which, as a result of the admixture of iron oxide, "rusted" and thus acquired its reddish colouring. A parallel example of this process is perhaps to be found on Mars, where a similar condition prevailed over wide areas of the planet's surface, giving it its red appearance. Mars could possibly be in a period corresponding to the Devonian on Earth, particularly since it has been suggested that on Mars there are damp, marshy areas supporting the lower forms of plant life. However, one has to be cautious with such analogies, for cosmic circumstances change, and physical courses run parallel only to a very limited extent. Thus a certain part of the apparent picture of Mars may be effectively comparable, whereas the whole is definitely not, particularly since it can be assumed that our terrestrial Devonian "deserts" had a heavy rainfall and were frequently covered with inland seas.

Further to the south of this northern continent there stretched extensive shelf-regions, shallow-water depressions where sediment was deposited. The Old Red continent itself spread as far east as Russia; but there it was separated from the Siberian Angara by an immense arm of the Tethys Sea.

As in the preceding period, the climate remained warm right into high latitudes. It has not been definitely proved that a high carbon dioxide content in the atmosphere contributed to this warmth. Certain scientists (such as Arrhenius)

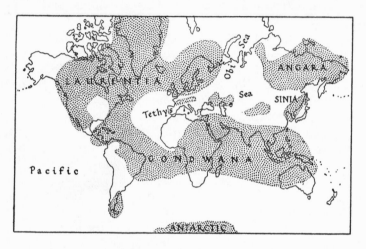

13. Land Map of the Devonian Period

attribute a glasshouse effect to the carbon dioxide, in that it let the sunlight penetrate and at the same time contained the quantities of heat reflected back from the Earth's surface. Like much else, this theory is very debatable. But it is quite probable that there was then a higher proportion of CO_2 in the air, especially since incessant volcanic activity would have continually produced carbon dioxide which, in the beginning, would not have been used up in appreciable quantities by plant life.

Tectonically, the Devonian Period was peaceful, predominantly an age of erosion and sedimentary layering. But from this it must not be assumed that practically nothing of a volcanic nature occurred. Forty million years is far too long a time for any such perpetual quiescence. Here and there eruptions burst from the depths, with the consequent upheavals and subsidences of land. In the German areas of Lahn-Dill alone there occurred outpourings of diabasic magma which formed rocks 600 yards thick. But there were no revolutionary phenomena such as the massive Caledonian foldings. A cataclysmic event of this kind only set in again towards the very end of the Devonian, and reached its main phases and climaxes during the following Carboniferous Period. This was the Variscan mountain folding process, which will be described later. During the later Devonian Period, just as in the Silurian, it was chiefly the Appalachians that were affected. They must have been comparatively quickly washed away and levelled down. Their sediment exerted tremendous pressure on the floors of the geosynclines in their own area, and these floors sank down and triggered off that mysterious mechanism that leads to the beginning of a new folding movement which ultimately extends into other areas.

The most important events in the Devonian, however, lay in the biological realm. These culminated in the final conquest and settlement of the land by plants, in the development of vertebrates in the form of fishes, and finally in the appearance of the first land vertebrates.

Of the psilophytes, the first land plants, we know that in the Upper Silurian (and perhaps earlier) they had already settled along the banks of seas and rivers. From the Devonian schist in Bohemia and the Rhineland have come valuable finds which provide us with fairly clear pictures of their further development. These stages of evolution beyond the hitherto predominant algal stage led to numerous new "discoveries" of powers of development. Whereas simple organs of nourishment and reproduction were perfectly adequate for the algae growing predominantly in water, much more complex structures were necessary for life on dry land, where the plants were no longer surrounded by water. From now on water and minerals must be drawn from the soil and incorporated into the plant's tissues above ground, whilst for the exchange of gases, such as oxygen and carbon dioxide, pores (stomata) developed in the epidermal cells. At the same time lignin made its appearance as a strengthening substance in the now woody aerial stems, and genuine roots were evolving.

For purposes of classification these psilophytes are nowadays regarded as the forerunners of the ferns, since real ferns developed from them subsequently. But to begin with they had no real roots. At the end of the vegetative twigs there were bulbous swellings which contained the asexual spores by means of which they propagated. These minute and very light spores were probably blown considerable distances by the wind. Of course those carried out to sea would fail to develop, but those encountering moist, rich ground inland

14. Psilophyte flora in the Lower Devonian

could immediately grow into new plants. That meant the end of the primal desert. The Earth began to acquire a covering of green wherever the soil proved favourable.

This first, tremendous development in the new realm of life led to rapid changes of form. The psilophytes of the Middle Devonian are already very different from those of the Lower Devonian; and those of the Upper Devonian are even more advanced. The herbaceous, leafless types rapidly developed into yard-high stalks. Then they became man-high bushes and finally regular little trees, displaying by the end of the Middle Devonian rudimentary leaves. It is not known whether the first, real primeval forests appeared at this stage; but it is in fact quite probable that they did in favourable, moist areas close to water. It must have been a strange wilderness of herbaceous growths, almost shadeless, with stalks, spikily forked and looking rather like antlers. There would be not the least suggestion of the endlessly rich variety of our luxuriant present-day forests. And only trilobites, giant crabs, scorpions and other primeval adventurers would be scrabbling over the swampy ground between the plants.

By the beginning of the Carboniferous Period the psilophytes had already disappeared. Whether, in this case, one can say that they "died out" is questionable; for it seems that there is a direct line of descent from them to the flora of the Carboniferous. Towards the end of the Devonian there were indeed no longer any psilophytes, but there were already forms which later developed into ferns, horse-tails, lepidodendrons, etc. A perpetual steady process of change, like a process of growth, was taking place. The original, helpless baby is now unrecognisable in the adult.

Among the invertebrates of the Devonian the graptolites had vanished completely, victims of a fate frequently met with in the biological world and not always explicable from any clear cause. The trilobites, too, exhausted the possibilities of their forms of life by developing exaggeratedly bizarre shapes, something which, in the history of the animal world, has frequently presaged final extinction. In their place there flourished abundantly echinoderms, corals, lamellibranchs, gastropods and brachiopods. Included among the echinoderms were the sea-lilies (Crinoidea), which proliferated over extensive areas of the shallow seas. The early cephalopods had developed by this time into a great variety of nautiloids and the wide-spread group of ammonites. The eurypterids gradually diminished in importance, a trend which possibly had some connection with the prevalence of the armour-plated fish who undoubtedly decimated them.

The vertebrates were now represented by the fish. The Devonian was indeed the golden age of their development, for more advanced fish now appeared alongside the great group of armour-plated fish. (The emergence of such cartilaginous fish as the sharks has already been mentioned.) A further historical stage of evolution was the appearance of the bony fishes (Osteichthyes), which gradually lost all defensive armourplate. The first members of this group, still of the armoured

type and covered by thick scales which were coated with a
hard enamel-like layer composed of ganoine, are today still
represented by the sturgeons, gar-pikes and mudfish. But
now the path of evolution to the ultimate fish form had been
clearly laid down and led, very gradually, via the Holostei of
the Mesozoic up to the Teleostei of the present day, with
their enormous profusion of species.

The soil composition of the Old Red continent, in conjunction with the warm climate, must have largely contributed to
the extensive inland seas becoming much shallower through
evaporation, thus threatening the existence of the fish inhabiting them. Mass extermination may have occurred countless
times until eventually, somewhere, some groups managed to
survive because they could absorb the life-giving oxygen not
only by means of gills when in water, but also by means of
lungs when the water dried up. Thus there arose the lung-
fishes (Dipnoi) whose air-bladders were suitably adapted for
the purpose. Of all the numerous forms of Dipnoi that once
existed only three types are recent (recent means still living
today, in contrast to fossils). The best known is *Ceratodus,*
which lives in a few streams in North-east Australia. The
second type is represented by the African lung-fish, and the
third by the South American *Lepidosiren.* All three, it will
be seen, live in regions which belonged to the old Gondwana
continent. Lung-fish have the habit of aestivation—the counterpart of hibernation—whereby, when their watery surroundings
dry up, they burrow into the mud and survive through the
dry season, unharmed. They thus represent the first attempt
by Nature to create a further higher class of vertebrates—
the amphibians (batrachians). This step, however, was not
achieved by them, but by members of the related family of
lobe-finned fishes (the Crossopterygii) whose fins, arranged
in pairs and projecting from the body fore and aft, look very
much as if the animal could walk "four-footedly" over the
ocean floor. If they could do that, then why not—with a lung-
breathing apparatus—walk over land to escape from an old
evaporating sea to some other more favourable to existence?
The possibility that this may have occurred is supported
by anatomical skeletal characteristics which appeared somewhat later in exactly the same form in the Stegocephalian

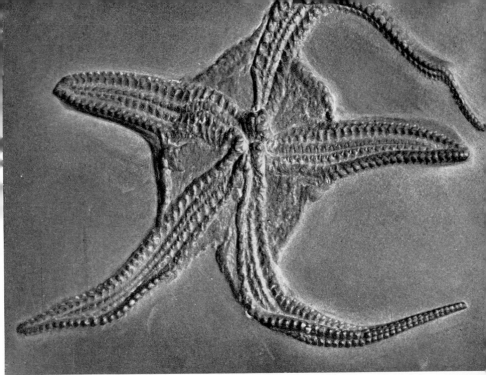

9. (*Above*) Starfish from the Lower Devonian slate.
(*Below*) Trilobite from the Silurian.

10. (*Above*) Graptolites from the Silurian.
(*Below*) Sea-lily from the Muschelkalk.

11. (*Above*) Psilophyte flora of the Devonian Period.
Chicago Natural History Museum.
(*Below*) Bark of *Lepidodendron*, showing pattern of scars of leaf bases.

12. The coelacanth *Malania ajouanae*, the surviving lobe-finned fish—
a photograph of the sensational capture of 1952.

13. Impressions of ferns (*above*) and twigs of *Lepidodendron* (*below*); from the Carboniferous.

14. (*Above*) Mammal-like reptiles from the Triassic in South Africa.
(*Below*) Pictorial reconstruction of the Upper Jurassic with primaeval
birds (centre), *Rhamphorhynchus* (on the tree-trunk and flying), and
Compsognathus (lower left).
Murals by Charles R. Knight. Chicago Natural History Museum.

15. (*Above*) Fossilised ammonites.
(*Below*) Fossilised belemnites.

16. *Ichthyosaurus* from the Lias of Holzmaden; (*above*) showing parts of skin preserved, and (*below*) showing fully developed foetus of young about to be born.
Natur-Museum Senckenberg, Frankfurt-am-Main.

amphibians, the first real land vertebrates. It seems very likely that these amphibians did in fact evolve from the crossopterygians, probably beginning in the Devonian Period. Another lobe-finned line of crossopterygians gave rise to the marine coelacanths, an interesting group which has recently fulfilled the secret but seldom expressed desire of the palaeontologists to observe for once, alive and kicking, a long-extinct fossil animal.

Coelacanths had long been known as fossils. From their remains, it was evident they must have become extinct at the latest by the end of the Cretaceous Period, about 60 million years ago. But apparently the ocean is conservative in maintaining its inhabitants. For in 1938, off the South African coast near East London, a trawl-net was raised filled with sharks, and among the sharks was a fish about 5 feet long which was completely unfamiliar. Finally, in the Rhodes University College of Grahamstown, Professor J. L. B. Smith was able to identify this creature—an identification which rapidly produced a sensation, for the fish was without doubt an "extinct" coelacanth, and was assigned to the genus *Latimeria*.

Publication of this discovery aroused great excitement, amounting almost to incredulity. But the concrete proof was there. Unfortunately the animal was in a very poor condition, since steps to preserve it had inevitably been taken too late. Smith, however, was convinced that this specimen was not the last of the Mohicans, but might well have numerous living relatives. The fact that it had remained hitherto undiscovered was explained by many scientists as being due to the fact that the coelacanth had probably been living in retreat in the profound ocean depths. Smith, on the contrary, expressed the opinion, based on practical knowledge, that these animals live on and from the rocky floors of shelf-reefs which exist particularly around Madagascar and certain other islands in the Indian Ocean.

To organise a full-scale search-expedition would be too expensive; but it proved possible to mobilise the fishing population of most of the East African coastline by means of multilingual leaflets carrying a picture and detailed description of the coelacanth and offering a reward of £100 for the capture of the next two specimens. These leaflets were then distributed with the help of Madagascan and East African officials. But it was not until 1952 that another catch was made. Great credit for this is due to Captain Hunt, who was trading with the Comoro Islands, a group lying between Madagascar and Mozambique. By means of the leaflets he kept drawing the natives' attention to these fish. But his gallant efforts nearly went for nothing, since the fishermen who netted and killed the second coelacanth over a shelf off the Comoros, at a depth of nearly 60 feet, were bent upon selling it next day. It was only at the market that another fisherman recognised the wanted beast and brought it, together with its captors, into touch with Captain Hunt. The latter immediately telegraphed Smith and asked him to collect his booty. Unfortunately the distance from Durban to the Comoros is about 2,000 miles, and there was no money available to charter an aeroplane. Therefore the inevitable lapse of time threatened the complete disintegration of the precious prize. At this point the South African Government produced a military plane. Thereafter all went rapidly, though not without difficulty, for the return flight was endangered by very bad weather.

This may seem a lot of fuss about a mere fish. But gratitude is certainly due to all concerned for a fine example of unselfishness and co-operation in the service of pure science.

A windfall such as the finding of the coelacanth is naturally rare. Even fossil discoveries of any importance are largely the result of luck. Yet it happened that at just about the time when the Crossopterygii were acclaimed as the ancestors of the vertebrates to come, a Danish expedition discovered, in the Upper Devonian layers of East Greenland, the remains of probably the oldest fossil amphibian. From the reconstruction of such remains as were unearthed, it appeared that this was an "improved" form of lobe-fin, having almost the same skull structure. But in the case of the *Ichthyostega*—as this primeval amphibian was named—fins had turned into feet, possessing four toes in front and five behind. To judge by tracks found long before in the Upper Devonian of North America, this must have been a clumsy beast, crawling and slithering about, with a stomach still dragging along the ground like a salamander. Probably the short, squat limbs merely served to prop up the body, and proper walking was only "discovered" later.

In the Middle Devonian layers, also, were found the first wingless insects, from which developed the most prolific branch of the animal kingdom.

Thus, in the Devonian Period, flora and fauna seem to have made a sudden jump forwards; but it only seems so, because we have covered the whole complex with one quick

15. Primeval *Ichthyostega* from the Upper Devonian of East Greenland

glance and been able to take only the briefest note of what happened. And of course in terms of time the sequence of these events was not nearly so rapid. Is there, indeed, any human being, however brilliant, who can comprehend all that has happened in the course of just one million years—the development of generations of plants and animals, the tremendous erosions and mountain folding? And the Devonian Period covered 50 million years! For us, with our minute span of human existence and consequently limited powers of comprehension, that is an almost inconceivable length of time.

The numerous difficulties—more psychological than actual—
of comprehending the development of life as a physico-
chemical process is due, not least of all, to our mental inability
to break out of the narrow limits of our conception of time.
How is it possible, considering all the interplay of mutations
and the forces of environment, that certain enzymatic and
hormone deviations occurred, that legs developed from fishes'
fins, that psilophytes turned into fern-trees, that egg-laying
reptiles became mammals? What was it that made a fish
capable of living upon land? It was not only the transformation of fins into legs and the absorption of oxygen through
lungs. That was not enough. For seeing on land the eyes,
too, need a different structure from that required for seeing
in the water. The senses of touch and smell must function
differently. The muscular system has to be otherwise arranged.
All this means a vast amount of important and complicated
transformation. The trivial variations which we can observe
in the laboratory and in Nature give us only the most limited
clues to the fundamental mechanisms of evolution. But these
indications have made valuable contributions to the total
knowledge of experimental zoologists and physiologists. Some
most interesting discoveries on the subject of radical change
have been made by the zoologist J. W. Harms in his studies
of mud-hoppers. The mud-hoppers are fish with a strong
inclination towards amphibious life. Their pectoral fins look
like splayed frog's feet and are employed by these adventurous creatures for fairly nimble, step-like progress on land
and for climbing about in the mangrove swamps where they
live. Their stomach fins also have developed into a means of
gripping, and their ability to jump like a frog enables them
to cover a distance several times their own length (5 or 6
inches). The adaptability of the various types to their surroundings differs greatly, which suggests that here is a whole
family of fish in the process of transformation into land
animals. Harms speeded up this natural process by injecting
thyroid hormone and promptly brought about an accelerated
development of the organs vital to living on dry land.

Thus we already know, basically, how Nature works. But
the fact remains that she only progresses by tiny steps, and
for major developments she needs such immense spans of

time that we are left completely helpless. We have been study-ing the process of mutation closely for roughly the last 50 years, unconsciously perhaps for the last 4,000 years. If we had been able to do it for the last 40,000,000 years we might perhaps be able to understand fully the wonders of the Devonian Period.

The Carboniferous Period

THE great economic importance of coal—not in the least diminished by the onset of an atomic era—has evoked a sort of popular interest in the Carboniferous Period. The thought of gigantic primeval forests, which sank and turned into coal, makes a powerful and unforgettable impression on the imagination. However, the process of coal-making was by no means restricted to the 80 million years of this period: nor was it, indeed, its most important geological phenomenon. Nevertheless, it was a striking enough event to give its name to the whole of the period. The Carboniferous, like other periods, is divided into Lower, Middle and Upper.

In order to understand the process leading to the formation of coal, particularly in the Carboniferous, a brief survey of conditions prevailing at that time is essential. Tectonically, the chief event was the Variscan mountain building, one more long-lasting era of huge crustal movements and foldings. This had already begun in the Devonian Period in the Appalachian area of North America, and it reached its climax in Europe in the Upper Carboniferous. Since the far, far distant Caledonian foldings, those mountains had been eroded, deposited in the peripheral continental seas, and then been pushed up again in successive phases. And a corresponding process took place in the territory of the remaining Caledonian mainland against which these new mountains were pressing. The results everywhere were long continental mountain chains. The Armorican Range stretched in a north-westerly direction from the French central plateau, across Brittany, south-west England and Ireland, as far as Greenland. A second mountain chain ran from southern France, across southern and central Germany as far as the source of the Oder. And a third chain seems to have been even more extensive, stretching from the neighbourhood of Berlin, across Westphalia, Belgium and southern England, here probably linking up with the Armorican range, and then extending as a land-bridge as far as the Appalachians. Of other known terrestrial formations the Urals were certainly created from the sediment of the Obi Sea. Simultaneously there were tremendous eruptions of granite and porphyry, and widespread rock upheavals. As a result of mountain formation in central Europe, the Tethys Sea retreated. Only a shallow arm now stretched from England over Belgium, Westphalia and Berlin as far as Upper Silesia and continued to exist for a very long time with a varying depth of water. Its flat and perpetually swampy coastal areas were the regions which eventually produced the greater part of Europe's coal deposits.

The actual chemical process of coal formation is well understood. It is, in fact, nothing more than the continuing enrichment of the carbon content of dead plants after air has been excluded, in a process which requires certain special conditions. In normal conditions plants, after they have died, are ill-suited for preservation, for they are rapidly decomposed by the oxygen in the atmosphere; so one essential is a swampy ground into which the plants can quickly sink to a considerable depth and be sealed off from the air by layers of sand or mud. In these circumstances, and as a result of heat and pressure, disintegration takes place with the release of water, oxygen and hydrogen, with corresponding enrichment of the remaining carbon. The first stage of carbonisation produces peat, which has a carbon content of 40 per cent. Under continuing favourable conditions, the next stage reached is brown coal, which has a 45 per cent carbon content. Then for a while nothing further happens; indeed, the brown coal can survive in its own state for a practically indefinite period unless quite extraordinary tectonic circumstances intervene. A proof of this are the brown coal deposits in the Moscow area which are certainly of Carboniferous origin but have never turned into real coal. In order to complete the process, immensely increased pressures are necessary, such as, for example, mountain foldings. Only then does there occur the final transformation into coal with a carbon content of about 72 per cent, rising to 94 per cent in anthracite and 100 per cent in the case of graphite.

From this it must be clear why coal is such a typical con-
stituent of Carboniferous deposits, though only in strictly
limited areas. Coal could occur only in regions of extremely
luxuriant swamp flora which later was subjected to the pressure of a mountain folding process. The Carboniferous Period
fulfilled both conditions. Therefore the richest and most important coal seams are embedded in Carboniferous sediments
and in the outskirts of the Variscan mountains. Other, later,
examples are rare; and their situation in the region of comparatively recent folding areas proves that they must have

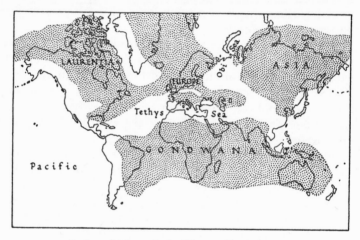

16. Land Map of the Upper Carboniferous

been produced in the same way as coal in the Carboniferous
Period. Since, after the rigidification of the primal crustal
land mass of the Russian continent, no considerable subsequent movements took place, the carbonisation of many
primeval carboniferous forests remained at the brown coal
stage although the raw material was just as old as that which
elsewhere produced fully developed coal.

With reservations, it is possible to reconstruct fairly precisely the appearance of such a carboniferous forest. Layers of
clay and sandstone, which surrounded the coal seams, have
preserved for posterity a wealth of impressions of plants of
the period, to such an extent that, compared with extinct

forests of other ages, a relatively great amount is known of their size and variation in form. In contrast to the almost oasis-like local patches of the Devonian flora with its arid, scrub-type growths, in the Carboniferous Period there were actual, extensive forests. At first, they flourished always in the immediate neighbourhood of water, which explains their predominant character of swamp forests. So we must imagine the Earth of that day as being only garlanded in green. In between widely separated forested islands vast areas of the land remained for the time being without any vegetable covering.

Characteristic classes of the Carboniferous were club-moss, horse-tails and ferns of immense variety. Among the club-moss were *Lepidodendron* and *Sigillaria*. Both grew to gigantic heights: *Lepidodendron* to 90 feet with a trunk diameter of 6 feet, forking at the top into a modest crown; while *Sigillaria*, in contrast, had at the summit a corn-like tuft of narrow leaves. The leaves discarded during growth left behind on the stem hexagonal or roundish scars which look as if they had been impressed with a seal. *Sigillaria*, like *Lepidodendron*, sprang from rhizome-like creeping roots which provided the necessary supports in the swampy ground. Both forms died out in the ensuing Permian period.

The horse-tails, too, whose present-day descendants appear only as low-growing herbaceous plants, were in the Carboniferous giant trees—*Calamites*—also soaring up to 90 feet. Plainly, this was a 'norm' of growth in that period. But such plants did not survive the Permian period.

The most luxuriant growths were the ferns. Apart from forming undergrowth, they frequently grew into full-sized trees. Many types crept, liana-like, around the trunks of the forest giants, veiling them in green.

All these classes of plants belonged still to the vascular cryptogams, flowerless plants which multiplied by means of spores. They formed the greater part of the Carboniferous flora and it was thus from them that coal was later formed. At the same time, the constant, steady development towards higher forms continued unabated, and next to appear were evergreen plants with naked seeds, the gymnosperms. As ancestors of our present-day conifers their particular importance (for the Carboniferous Period) lay in their ability to root on drier ground, well away from the marshy regions, and therefore to settle as pioneers in those territories that hitherto had been devoid of life.

Transitional to the gymnosperms were two groups which we have come across previously. The first were represented by the seed-ferns (Pteridosperms), still true ferns in their general habit, yet with the fundamental difference that they now propagated by seeds instead of by spores. The second group were the Cordaitales, which had tall, slender stems (also attaining up to 90 feet in height), surmounted by now impressive crowns of narrow parallel-veined, strap-like leaves which grew to a length of as much as 3 feet. They appeared for the first time in the Lower Carboniferous and for the last time in the Permian.

All in all, it was a luxuriant world of plants that, in the course of 70 million years, conquered the dry land. Naturally, those early forests possessed some very strange characteristics in comparison with forests of today. To begin with, there were no cool shady depths. There were no flowers or colourful foliage. The predominant impression was of almost endless swampland swathed in mist. Morass-like lagoons, intersected by labyrinths of water channels, marked the areas of brackish water intervening between the shallow open reaches of the sea and the land sites of the great forests.

Within these forests lived an animal world that was no less strange and weird. Insects, existing in the Devonian, had now proliferated in bewildering variety, at least 1,300 species being known from the Carboniferous Period. And, most important of all, they had discovered how to fly. After the conquest of water and land, began the conquest of the air. All flying creatures in the Carboniferous could still only flap their wings vertically up and down, and the folding of wings was something as yet unknown. There existed giant forms of startling sizes such as are no longer known today. So far the record seems to be held by *Meganeura*, an insect with a wing-span of $2\frac{1}{2}$ feet. Primeval forms of the present-day Ephemeroptera (May-flies) attained a hand's-breadth in size. And roaches of that era were four or more inches in length.

Among other arthropods, there crawled through the vegeta-

17. Carboniferous flora. In foreground the giant insect,
Meganeura

tion millipedes several feet long, spiders, and giant scorpions. Snails, too, left their traces on the land.

Land vertebrates in the form of amphibians were now represented in various forms. Apart from the primeval forms which seem to connect with the crossopterygians, the scene was dominated by the Stegocephalia (armour-plated heads), whose low, flat, unarched skulls were now completely closed—so to speak roofed-over—with tiny openings for nose and eyes. To judge from their numerous foot-prints they must have been, for a long time, clumsy crawlers like their proto-type, *Ichthyostega*.

The step up to the next higher class of vertebrates, the reptiles, is not a great one and took place within the Carbon-iferous Period. Apart from the variations of form within a class, the chief distinction between amphibians and reptiles lies simply in their different modes of development in early life. The batrachians still continue to lay soft-shelled eggs in the water which is absolutely vital for their hatching. The young then undergo a metamorphosis, in the course of which they change from their larval stage of breathing through gills and emerge on land as fully developed animals breathing by means of lungs. The reptiles, on the other hand, have made themselves independent of water. Their eggs have become hard-shelled, are laid on land, and hatch out fully developed young which, being genuine land animals, start straightaway to breathe with lungs. So here is a very clear example of adaptation to land-dwelling. Furthermore, in the case of the cotylosaurians, which were the stem reptiles, the sense organs developed further to meet the requirements of living on dry land. Their sight grew more acute; their skulls became more domed; their brain functions assumed greater importance. Their powers of mobility also increased, an important factor for the future of animal forms already slender and lizard-like. A new animal group was evolving which was to play an immensely important role in the future course of Life.

The sea fauna, on the whole, remained somewhat more conservative. The prevalence of armour-plated fish was sharply reduced, but the sharks and electric rays among the cartilaginous fishes and numerous forms of ganoid fishes all survived the Carboniferous. The tetracorals were still varied and widespread. So were the tabulatae, coral animals known since the Silurian Period, which lived only in colonies composed of conglomerations of tubular dwellings. The brachiopods developed to an exceptional size with *Productus*, the hard shells of which were armed with long projecting spines. The Echinodermata were represented, as hitherto, solely by sea-lilies. The trilobites, which by now had become very "dated", were considerably reduced in their varieties. Only 15 varieties are known from the Carboniferous as against more than 1,000 from the Cambrian. Their giant forms, too, had vanished. Only tiny trilobites now continued to maintain their precarious existence. Among the cephalopods, the goniatites continue to be the zone fossils of the Period. These predatory types had still an important future before them. The Protozoa, those one-celled animalcules from earliest times, re-appeared in almost unimaginable multitudes—a sporadic phenomenon that crops up in astonishingly varied periods. This time they were represented by Fusilina and Valvulina (forms of Foraminifera) which—extraordinarily increased in size (some as large as a pea)—became limestone builders.

The description so far of the Carboniferous Period—tropically hot regions of swamp-forests and coral reefs stretching as far north as Spitzbergen and Northern Canada—tempts one to assume that the whole surface of the Earth enjoyed a uniformly warm climate; and even if the southern parts of the Gondwana continent were, possibly, largely rainless, dry, desert-like regions, that still does not alter the general climatic picture. So it is all the more astonishing to learn that, from the Upper Carboniferous to well into the following Permian Period, extensive areas of the present-day East Indies, South Africa, Togoland, Australia, and South America passed through an Ice Age that, at least in its duration, exceeded any Ice Age which may have occurred before and all Ice Ages which to our definite knowledge occurred afterwards. Such a tremendous natural cataclysm is tantamount to an attack, an onslaught on life itself. Imagine millions of square miles of land being covered by slowly forming, onward creeping glaciers, towering up to a height of 3,000 feet above ground level. Such a scene is known today only in Greenland and Antarctica, two of the most inhospitable quarters in the world.

And here it occurred in regions which today are tropical or sub-tropical! While the (comparatively) recent Pleistocene Ice Age through which the world has just passed lasted, with sporadic warmer intervals, for about 600,000 years, the Permo-Carboniferous Ice Age extended over a period of very many millions of years. Pre-Cambrian ice traces are still regarded with some dubiety, but here there is no doubt at all: traces of glacial grinding and drift-blocks carried great distances provide unmistakable evidence. There is no doubt that Gondwana was covered with ice. How is this mysterious fact to be explained?

To tell the truth, there is as yet no incontrovertible explanation. Once more, one can only suggest hypotheses of a more or less plausible nature. Any possibility that the present-day glaciation of our polar regions is a condition that has existed for a very long time is completely out of the question. Its impossibility has been proved absolutely by the discovery of the remains of warmth-loving plants and animals in both the extreme North and the extreme South. It has already been mentioned that, in the course of Earth's history, the tilt of the polar axis must have undergone considerable variations. There are no tropical growths which will survive the six-months polar night which now prevails as a result of the present polar inclination; but such plants would be likelier to accept a more rapid alternation of day and night such as certainly prevailed during the Carboniferous Period. Therefore, in earlier times the polar inclination must have been much less; or else—the poles wander.

This latter is a daring and unprovable speculation. But its very simplicity is attractive. Assume (and it is assumed by many) that in the Permo-Carboniferous Period the North Pole lay in the northern Pacific. Then its opposite, the South Pole, would be somewhere in the region of South Africa. Polar icing of the north Pacific can naturally no longer be confirmed, but there are very definite glacial traces to suggest that the South Pole may have been located in South Africa. In that case the line of the equator, too, would have run differently, roughly through the warm regions of the coal areas. But then why were there glaciations in such widely separated areas as Tierra del Fuego, the Falkland Islands, India and Australia?

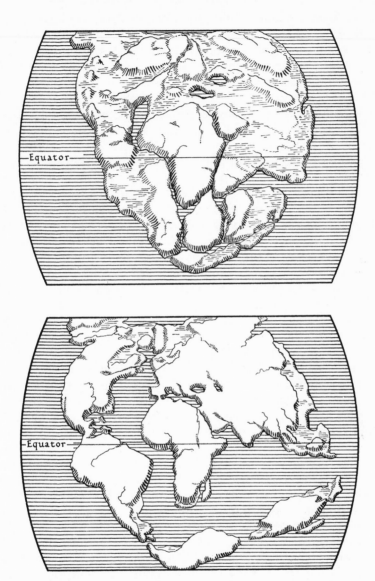

18. Two phases of Alfred Wegener's conception of the
disintegration of a primal continental mass

Now we come to a bold idea, but one which is at least conceivable: in the mind's eye push South America and Africa together, push India towards Africa, with the southern tip of India in the region of Madagascar, and finally push Australia west and Antarctica north-west—and the result will be a massive land block in which all the areas of Permo-Carboniferous glaciations are grouped together in a polar cap.

This result is certainly startling. The suggestion that this state of affairs once existed remains still no more than a suggestion. It was put forward by Alfred Wegener (1880-1930; perished on an Arctic expedition), who then proceeded to construct on these premises his much-discussed Continental Drift Theory. A somewhat closer examination of the outlines of the continents and islands on a globe reveals the astonishing fact that in very many places the coastlines of land masses lying opposite one another do fit into each other. Most obvious is the example of South America and Africa, and it is not difficult to imagine a conjunction of Africa-Madagascar, Australia-New Guinea, Borneo-Celebes and many other combinations. Wegener accordingly asserted that originally there were not a number of spatially separated primal continents, but one single, immense land-mass which continued in existence up to the Carboniferous. He then went on to assume that this mass—probably as a result of the Earth's oscillation—broke apart into pieces which we still recognise today and that these pieces drifted away from each other like floating ice-floes until, after hundreds of millions of years, they reached their present positions.

He elaborated this hypothesis extensively and offered, in rather tempting form, apparent solutions to a number of geological problems. He even explained the folding of the South-North American Cordillera chain as a result of the piling up of the westerly drifting land-mass.

Of course, by making such assumptions he stood the whole of primal geography, as hitherto accepted by geological teachings, on its head. In itself, that would have been nothing to worry about. For the sake of greater knowledge, anyone would have been ready to learn afresh. The important thing is how far this hypothesis is tenable and how well can it be fitted in with all our other knowledge about primal epochs? And here, unfortunately, objections mount up apace and amass.

It is proved and accepted that whole continents can drift on the sima. Greenland floats 30 yards a year towards North America. Recent work on the directions in which these early deposits were magnetised also supports the idea of some continental drifting having taken place. Wegener may have been rather over-dogmatic and naïve in his views, which have been vigorously opposed by many geologists. It is still not possible to decide for certain for or against Wegener's theory—modifications of it (such as that put forward by Du Toit) prove more acceptable to geologists. In view of these conflicts in opinion, there is probably little point in pursuing this matter further, and we may turn to other solutions to the riddle of glaciation during the Permo-Carboniferous Period.

The idea of a migration of the poles is still eagerly canvassed, although it can scarcely be made plausible geophysically. Above all, it tacitly assumes that the polar regions were always covered by ice-caps, in a way that they are today. But were they—even in the distant Cambrian Period, or the pre-Cambrian? What if the present glaciation of the poles were nothing else but the remains of the Pleistocene Ice Age which is only just reaching its end and which, naturally, with the present inclination of the axis, would survive longest in the most climatically inhospitable regions—the poles—but one day will vanish entirely? It is a meteorological fact established over the last few decades that the arctic region is steadily growing warmer. (This, also, is one cause of the unsettled, quite abnormal weather which has been afflicting Europe.)

It is by no means certain that the Earth's poles, even at the most favourable inclination, would necessarily be covered by ice. On the contrary, it is quite certain that over vast periods of time they have *not* been ice-capped. The movement of the poles is, therefore, no more than an idea, with no sort of proof behind it. Yet, on the other hand, the Ice Ages were facts which have to be explained.

What, then, were the climatic conditions during the Carboniferous? Obviously, they could not conceivably have been anything other than tropical in the present sense of the word, and possibly even warmer. And this must have applied to most parts of the Earth, for most of the duration of the Carboniferous Period. The atmosphere must have contained a considerably higher quantity of carbon dioxide than today, and, as has been previously mentioned, this would have acted like a built-in greenhouse window, retaining the sunlight in the form of warmth. Now this suggests another theory: in the Carboniferous, for the first time on Earth, the wildly luxuriating plant-world began to play its part as an additional consumer of carbon dioxide; the plants absorbed immense quantities of that gas from the air and they transformed its carbon content into coal; as a result, the CO_2 content in the atmosphere decreased, its "greenhouse" action was diminished, the temperature fell, and an Ice Age was the consequence of this atmospheric metamorphosis.

This conception originated with the Swedish scientist Arrhenius. It sounds almost too convincing, particularly since it is equally applicable to the Pleistocene Ice Age which was preceded by the excessively luxuriant vegetation of the brown coal forests. Unfortunately, questions arise here which cannot be answered. Why did only the equatorial regions of Gondwana become covered with ice? How did an Ice Age occur in the Cambrian when there were as yet no land plants? How does this hypothesis explain the completely irregular recurrence of Ice Ages while the diminution of carbon dioxide in the atmosphere was a consistently steady process? Every Ice Age we know of was far from being an enclosed process of simple glaciation and melting; instead, it was broken up into a number of main advances and numerous retreats. In the Permian Period, Australia alone was subject to six major advances. But between each there were very long warm periods (Interglacial), during which the ice retreated far back or else disappeared completely. The old sub-tropical regions were restored until a fresh advance by the glaciers drove them back once more. This bitter to-and-fro battle becomes very plain in the Pleistocene Period.

The problem of this phenomenon caused a great deal of brain-racking, generally in vain—until suddenly it was recalled that the Earth is a member of the solar system and completely dependent on the Sun. A slight diminution in the intensity of the Sun's radiation would suffice to produce overwhelming climatic effects. The lowering of the Sun's surface temperature by 100° C. would bring about an Ice Age through an average decline of temperature on Earth of about 8° C. (*no more is necessary*). So the question was put to the astronomers: could this happen?

The immediate answer is comforting. We know of variations in temperature and radiation in the so-called "variable stars", which are predominantly unstable, pulsating suns with periodic change of light intensity, but our Sun is not one of these. Even though it is probable that the Sun is slowly losing heat this decrease is so gradual that it could not possibly have played any part in the irregular glaciation periods on Earth. Yet now comes a "but". In outer space, probably in the majority of galaxies, there are vast areas containing conglomerations of dark matter. These dark clouds are certainly very tenuous, but we know that they are so great in extent that they diminish considerably, and even extinguish totally, the light of numerous suns situated in and beyond them. Even in those regions of the Milky Way richest in stars, astronomers are continually discovering completely inexplicable "holes" which are nothing more or less than dark clouds concealing any view of the suns behind them.

It has already been mentioned that our Sun, together with its covey of planets, orbits about the centre of the Milky Way in one of its spiral arms. Its actual orbit is immense, taking 240,000,000 years to complete, although it moves at 175 miles per second. It can be taken for certain that some time during this cosmic year the path of the Sun will pass through a realm of dark clouds. With what result? Undoubtedly a fine layer of dust will intervene between the Sun and its planets. Dust fine, indeed, beyond conception, imperceptible to the human eye, but quite sufficient to diminish considerably the radiation power of our "day star". Such an effect is only to be expected, for the gravitational attraction of the Sun as it swept through the dust belt would cause surging and agglomeration of the dust. This theory provides an easy explanation for almost all Ice Ages, for any variation in their development and for differences in their durations, all factors being dependent on the position, in space, of the dark clouds and the density of those clouds, which must certainly vary.

The inevitably speculative character of this hypothesis takes on a very different aspect when one examines it somewhat more closely. It is possible that the dark clouds as a whole do move in space; but there is no evidence of this, so there is no reason to regard them as other than static. That being so, the Sun in its course must repeatedly travel through these clouds at roughly the same intervals in time. So let us look back 480 million years. The Earth was then right at the end of the Cambrian Period, from which frequent glaciation traces have survived. The result is equally startling if we go forward from there through 240 million years towards the present. We should then be at the end of the Carboniferous. And yet another 240 million years on takes us almost into the Pleistocene—the latest Ice Age. Even if the dates are out by ten or a few more million years, this correspondence seems to provide striking proof in favour of the hypothesis. Any small differences in time can be attributed to the variations of conditions and movements within the dark clouds themselves and also to our uncertainty as to the exactness of our geological time-scale. Even the great difference between the durations of the Permo-Carboniferous and the Pleistocene Ice Ages is completely unimportant. For who can say that the last Ice Age has finished? What if the past 12,000 years since the "final" retreat of the glaciers is only part of an interglacial warm period? The duration of the last three interglacial periods in the recent past were 70,000, 90,000, and 62,000 years. A further proof of the hypothesis is provided by the astronomical fact that at the present time our Sun is moving between two gigantic dark clouds, one of which was left behind in the Pleistocene. The other we may reach in about 50,000 years. That would mean a fresh glaciation or, more accurately, a continuation of the old one, so that the period from now on until 50,000 years hence is nothing more than an interglacial interval. This alternation can last for another several million years, so that the Pleistocene glaciation could finally prove to be as long as the Permian. This very conception shows again how helpless we are vis-à-vis geological time-spans. To us, a mere 10,000 or so years is such an immense period that we boldly state that the latest Ice Age as a world-wide manifestation is past and that it has lasted an incomparably shorter time than the Permo-Carboniferous Ice Age. But—from the geological point of view—we may be still at the starting-post!

In spite of the probability of cosmic influences being a contributory cause of Ice Ages, all problems concerning the phenomenon of glaciation are far from having been solved. The only thing that astronomical discoveries can definitely explain is why there should be a general lowering of temperature under the particular circumstances described. What happened on the Earth thereafter, why this particular area was covered by ice and that not, involves a series of problems which are still a cause of scientific headaches. In the last Ice Age, the centres in Europe and North America from which the glaciation spread were the Scandinavian, Scottish and North American mountains, as well as the Alps. It is therefore possible that in the Permo-Carboniferous there existed, in the regions affected, particularly high mountain ranges which became the sources of the formation of massive glaciers. This would presuppose very considerably increased rainfall, which most probably did occur as a result of the drop in temperature. Perhaps, in fact, only the mountain heights were responsible for localising the glaciation. It must be borne in mind that a sudden but steady spread of ice would of itself continuously affect the climate of the areas concerned and bring about conditions conducive to an ever-increasing reinforcement of the ice-masses. Cold air must have collected over the icefields, " polar fronts " must have arisen, which would have exerted an influence on the general weather situation, much as they do today. The disappearance of the tropical Carboniferous flora in the following Permian Period is closely connected with this. Let us hope that one day a theory will emerge which will explain all the unsolved riddles of the Ice Ages.

CHAPTER TEN

The Earth in the Permian Period

THE events just described have, in fact, brought us deep into the Permian Period which followed the Carboniferous. There are now only 240,000,000 years to the present day—strangely enough, a cosmic year for the Sun. Our radio wave at the beginning of the Permian Period, was 270 million light years off, somewhere deep in the realm of the spiral galaxies on the far side of the Milky Way, still some 1,600,000,000,000,000,000,000 miles away.

The Permian Period itself—its sediments were first identified by Murchison, an Englishman, in the Russian district of Perm—lasted 45,000,000 years. With it ended, from the geological point of view, the Earth's primeval era, the Palaeozoic. The two great sub-divisions of the Permian are the New Red Sandstone and the Limestone.

Tectonically, much happened throughout the whole Permian Period. The Variscan mountain-building at last came to an end. The glacial invasions of the Carboniferous Ice Age, with all their consequent effects, continued far into the Permian. In New Red Sandstone times there occurred widespread eruptive outbursts of quartz-porphyry and tuff. Sediments consisted of sandstone, clay and dolomite.

The climate underwent a considerable change from that of the Carboniferous. The ice masses in the Gondwanaland continent stored up immense quantities of water, so that the seas retreated in other areas. The surface water level must have sunk, resulting in pronounced tendencies towards the emergence of land; in particular, the northern land masses became drier, and more desert-like. In the Limestone phase once more there occurred extensive flooding of areas in Central Europe and North America, and the formation of the Permian Limestone sea. This flooding was particularly important in creating the deposits of rock-salt and potassium-salt which we exploit today. The Limestone sea can be regarded as the product of enclosed inland seas evaporating in the desert heat and depositing their salts. The immense accumulation of salt cannot have resulted from just one evaporation of a sea basin. Throughout millions of years the oceans must have trickled through to the Limestone sea by narrow and shallow channels, so that unfailing supplies of salt water continually compensated for the steady process of evaporation. Probably the Limestone sea was entirely lacking in freshwater supplies from rivers emptying into it; and very likely there was an almost total absence of rain. A whole number of factors must have combined to produce salt deposits of such vast extent.

In every respect the flora showed a considerable change. The almost unimaginable luxuriance of the Carboniferous forests rapidly disappeared. The drying earth favoured the development of gymnosperms. The distinctive representatives of the Carboniferous forests died out. Gondwanaland for the first time produced an indigenous flora in the shape of *Glossopteris* which later migrated into the northern hemisphere. The trees of the southern continent show rings which suggest seasonal changes of climate.

The steady progress towards gymnosperms (plants whose seeds are not enclosed in an ovary) continued through the vanishing Cordaitales of the Carboniferous to complete development in the European Limestone Period. Chief among the conifers was the genus *Walchia*. The first cycads also appeared, forming a sort of mid-way stage between ferns and palms. They are represented today by the well-known tropical sago-palm. Furthermore, the class of Gingkoales is represented, of which only one species still exists today, the *Gingko* tree, which is much admired as a park ornament. *Gingko* and its relatives first appear in the late Permian, and the distinctive fan-shaped foliage is often abundant in strata of Mesozoic age.

In the animal world, too, a considerable change took place. The trilobites now vanished completely from the scene, an age-old, outworn, superseded class. Important marine lime deposits testify to a further flourishing of the one-celled Fusulinae. But with the end of the Permian their powers of

survival ebbed too. Conspicuous among the Permian brachiopods were relatives of the important Carboniferous genus
Productus, which lived together in great colonies like corals
and thus actually formed reefs. The tetracorals diminished
and were finally replaced in the subsequent Triassic Period
by the hexacorals. Among the cephalopods the predatory
ammonites, gradually superseding the already increasingly

19. *Branchiosaurus*, an amphibian from the Permian
(according to Henning)

obsolescent goniatites from the long-ago Carboniferous,
became widely disseminated. There will be much more to say
about the former. Bivalves and gastropods appeared in an ever-
increasing number of new forms. Among the crustaceans,
too, there was a great dying out of the old in favour of more
modern forms. Development of the fishes proceeded comparatively steadily. It appears as if the sharks became somewhat
scarcer.

An important step forwards was made by the insects. The climatic conditions, which were certainly most unfavourable compared to those of the Carboniferous, led to the introduction of a pupation stage in which the not yet fully developed young insect could exist for a considerable time without external nourishment. At least, it must be assumed that environmental influences played a large part in this development. At the same time, the tendency to grow to a gigantic size diminished.

The course of evolution of the land vertebrates led steeply upwards. Among the amphibians the Stegocephalia were represented by several orders, which, ranging from the crocodile type to the snake-like, displayed a great capacity for variation. Stegocephalians are also called labyrinthodonts (from the labyrinth-like appearance of their furrowed teeth, which in cross-section resembled those of the crossopterygians). *Archegosaurus*, a crocodile-like creature in shape and length (about 4.5 feet), and also the branchiosaurs, tiny animals which seem to be young forms of some other group, are particularly well known.

The original slithering method of progress must have developed—probably as a result of the necessity for quicker movement to cover the greater distances between water-patches—into a walk which would not, however, have resembled the elegant, gliding movements of many reptiles. The English naturalist Thomas Huxley (1825-1895) expressed this very vividly by stating that with their fat stomachs and short legs these creatures must have stumped forwards like Sir John Falstaff.

Among the reptiles the famous ancestral group, the Cotylosauria, was flourishing and important Permian discoveries have been made in Brazil, Texas, Russia and South Africa. The variations in reptile forms were great and somewhat suggestive of the experimental shapes of saurians during the Earth's middle ages. Nine-foot-long crocodile- or lizard-types are not rare. *Eunotosaurus*, with its widely projecting ribs, already carries a suggestion of the tortoise and can be regarded as its ancestor. Teeth reveal that their diets were extremely varied. Some types were herbivorous. Others lived on hard-shelled animals. Others again, like *Labidosaurus*, were obviously predatory lizard-like animals. As well as straddle limbs, one finds mole-like digging feet.

Mesosaurus, a Permian reptile from Brazil and South Africa, is particularly interesting. It is the oldest known case of a land animal reverting completely to the water, its paws becoming paddle-shaped and its diet limited to fish. Later, cases of this sort occur frequently.

Even more interesting, however, is the reptile world of South Africa. The Karroo formation in the Tableland of the

20. *Edaphosaurus*. A 9-foot-long reptile from the Permian, discovered in Texas

Cape, an immense stratified mass of marl and continental sandstone of a height between 2,000 and 3,000 feet, has preserved in it a whole series of Permian reptiles placed in the order Therapsida. These interesting creatures already show many features characteristic of the mammals (a group which was still to evolve). In particular this future trend was revealed in their skull and tooth structure. Thus these therapsids already had teeth divided into incisors, canine and molar teeth. The structure of the pelvis is very important, for it suggests that these reptiles may have given up laying eggs and, instead, brought forth living young into the world.

This means that one of the most important steps forward in the whole history of the animal world had taken place. Remarkable and very enlightening is the fact that this happened in Permian Gondwanaland with its extremely unfavourable climatic Ice Age conditions. Just as the insects in rearing their young "discovered" the protective pupation stage, so the reptiles of that harsh region would also have had to attempt something to ameliorate the lot of their brood. Hitherto they had generally laid their eggs in hot sand and left the final hatching to the all-beneficent mother-Sun. But this amenity ceased when the Ice Age radically altered the climate, and undoubtedly for a very long time something approaching mass extinction took place until Nature lit upon the solution of ensuring, by the means of direct birth of living young, the continued survival of the species. From this emerges the fact that development in a progressive sense takes place faster in a period of menace and danger than in one of idyllic serenity. This is even more obviously apparent when we come to the development of man. For pre-man made a timid, tentative appearance in the Tertiary warm period over 20,000,000 years ago, and thereafter made negligible progress; then during the Pleistocene Ice Age which lasted a mere half million years he rapidly achieved his present-day maturity. Darwin's "Survival of the Fittest" is indeed one of the most penetrating concepts of biological cause and effect.

So much for a brief survey of the Permian Period which, forming the conclusion of the Earth's antiquity, was the forerunner of vital and decisive developments to come.

CHAPTER ELEVEN

New Red Sandstone, Muschelkalk and Keuper

THE Middle Age of the Earth (*Mesozoic*) begins with the Triassic Period. It lasted 45 million years. The chief subdivisions are, from bottom to top: New Red Sandstone (Bunter), Muschelkalk and Keuper—this three-fold division giving the period its name. Its geographical map displays, so far as we know, the greatest agglomeration of land-masses in the whole of Earth's history. During the New Red Sandstone Era Gondwanaland once more expanded vastly. Only the Tierra del Fuego tip of South America seems to have remained isolated. As to the possible linking of the present continental portion of Antarctica with Gondwanaland, unfortunately far too little is known today to enable us to make any definite pronouncement. The Tethys Sea formed two constricted basins, one in the Atlantic and a second in Europe-Asia. Solid land-bridges connected Gondwana with the northern land block. These probably crossed the regions of the central American Antilles, West Africa and Indo-China. North Asia and Alaskan America were separated by a broad arm of the sea at the latitude of Sakhalin. Europe, in the Tethys region, presented a predominantly insular aspect. Thus it would have been possible to make a trip round the world dry-shod, from North America, via Northern Europe, Central Asia, the East Indies, Australia, and thence to Africa and Brazil and back again to North America. But this arrangement of land and water areas must not mislead us, for the actual aggregate proportion of land to sea must have been roughly the same as it is today.

Tectonically the whole Triassic Period was comparatively peaceful. No noteworthy cases of mountain-forming are known. Even deep eruptions and vulcanism have left behind only very slight traces. The folding-wave of the Carboniferous-Permian had long since come to a standstill. Following on the cyclic alternation of erosion and re-folding, there came now the sequence of erosion and sedimentation. In the New Red Sandstone the eponymous brown, red and white sandstones were the first deposits, as well as clay, marl and chalk sandstone marbled with coloured veins. The Island of Heligoland is an outstanding example of the stratifications of that time. The Muschelkalk Era produced organogenic limestone banks (lamellibranchs, Echinodermata, algae), marl, and dolomite chalk. The Keuper Era contributed, *inter alia*, schistous clay and quartz sandstone.

During the Muschelkalk and Keuper times, large deposits of gypsum and rock-salt were once more laid down. So, as far as climate and geography went, everything must have much resembled the Permian. The temporary expansion of the Tethys Sea produced the Muschelkalk Sea which, like the Permian Limestone Sea, evaporated rapidly and left behind salt deposits. The rust-red coloration of the New Red Sandstone sediments also suggests the characteristics of a desert.

This desert-like nature of the Triassic Earth was not exactly favourable to the spread of vegetation. Although here and there luxuriant forests did definitely appear, in every case they were predominantly of the oasis type. Local areas of vegetation were the rule. The banks of rivers presumably supported gallery forests, the shores of the shallow seas and swamps would have been covered with thickets of cryptogams which, further inland, would give way to light clumps of conifers. The whole floral scene was composed of cycads, tree-ferns, and conifers as well as horse-tails, bushy ferns and Lycopods. Represented among the conifers were the araucarias (up to 180 feet in height in the Trias of Arizona), *Taxus* and *Gingko*. At the end of the Keuper Era came the first pines. After the cycads arose the Bennetitales from which, possibly much later, the first flowering plants developed. Adapting themselves to the dry ground, there also emerged plant forms very much resembling cacti. Thus life developed. But the total impression of the period gives the feeling that the overwhelming dryness of that land-building era made things very hard for all vegetation. In the sea it was once again the lime-depositing algae which built up tremendous reefs, particularly in the island-area which subsequently became the Alpine region.

The Triassic marine fauna was differentiated from that of the Permian by a spate of entirely new species, so that the distinction of Palaeozoic-Mesozoic is justified by this alone, although there are scientists who would regard the Permian and Triassic as one period.

The trilobites and tetracorals, as well as the majority of primitive crustaceans, had already died out. The brachiopods, formerly so widespread, were now very rapidly on the wane, as were also the sea-lilies (crinoids) among the echinoderms. In their place the hexacorals together with the lime-depositing algae were now building enormous reefs in wide stretches of the open seas. In the Pacific regions of Canada down to California, as well as throughout the whole of the Tethys Sea, their fossilised traces are to be found in immense deposits. Tourists and climbers in the present-day Dolomites are walking over former ocean deposits from the Triassic Period which subsequently were pushed up to form mountains. More and more lamellibranchs appear in quantities, rich in variety and beautiful in form. Indeed, the sediment of the Muschelkalk gave its name to the middle part of the Triassic. Crustaceans appear in modern shapes, the predecessors of lobsters and crayfish. Among echinoderms the sea-urchins developed entirely new families, from which the present-day types have ultimately evolved.

A peculiar happening occurred among the ammonites. (These belonged to the Cephalopoda, as do our present-day squids, which are the most highly developed animals among the molluscs; a considerable degree of intelligence, even, is ascribed to the squid and its senses are excellently organised.) At first during the Triassic, the ammonites evolved in a rich variety of forms. The gas-filled chambers of their snail-like housing provided an efficient protection for their soft bodies and allowed them to become proficient swimmers. To judge from their wide dissemination (they are thus of outstanding value as zone fossils), they must, by their aggressive and predatory habits, have largely dominated life in the seas. Nevertheless, towards the end of the Triassic, they suffered a strange and totally inexplicable mass extinction. Only one family, the Monophyllitidae, survived and became the ancestors of new forms of ammonites that flourished in the following Jurassic Period. The circumstances causing this mysterious waning and waxing are completely unknown.

Closely connected with the ammonites, but probably even more closely related to the squids, are the belemnites. They had, like the squids subsequently, already dispensed with external housing and had acquired a sort of "cuttle-bone" as an internal framework, which, through increasing accretion of lime, extended backwards in a straight, pointed structure. Since in the great majority of cases only the internal skeleton became fossilised and survived as fossils, they featured in popular superstition for many centuries. Long before it was discovered what they really were they were called thunderbolts, finger-stones and devil's fingers. It was assumed that they were the products of thunder and lightning, and magical powers were ascribed to them. In the Triassic the cephalopods still had six tentacles, i.e. prehensile limbs attached to the head. The eight-tentacled type only arrived later with the octopus. Several lucky finds have brought to light samples of their skin pigment, which proves that they also had the property of being able to discharge "ink" and thus camouflage themselves in clouds of dark liquid. They, too, were expert and rapacious predators. Apart from them, sharks and rays, as well as bony fish resembling pike, dominated the marine world. Another familiar acquaintance of ours, the Australian lung-fish, *Ceratodus,* now reached its first full development.

The amphibian world was still represented by the Stegocephalia. A particularly enormous specimen was *Mastodonsaurus,* which had an overall length of 9 feet, the head alone being 3 feet long. Their fossilised remains are numerous. In South Germany, South Africa and North America quantities of them have been found within very small, often marshy, areas. At first sight these would appear to have been accidental accumulations of dead bodies; but in such restricted spaces it is far more probable that mass deaths occurred from some cause or other. What actually happened can only be surmised. The Stegocephalia were always clumsy beasts. Their breast and stomach armour, as well as their short legs, suggest that they were never as mobile as conditions of life on dry land really required. Perhaps they returned again and again to the water to which they were so accustomed, until the extensive emergence of land, the drying out of the Triassic oceans and inland seas, finally proved their doom. Indeed, the last fossils of their race were found in the so-called "Letten-kohle", former swamp-forests of the Keuper. Once again a primordial animal type had vanished from the face of the Earth.

21. *Mastodonsaurus* of the Triassic Period

Among the reptiles, the first turtles appeared. To begin with, they were genuine land animals, equipped with a full complement of teeth and entirely adapted to life on the steppe-like dry-regions which, indeed, were virtually deserts. Only very much later did they develop types which took to the water and became—as they are today—open-sea dwellers who only come on land to lay their eggs.

There was considerable diversity and novelty among the other reptiles. The great age of the saurians was dawning. The cotylosaurs, their original ancestors, had vanished. In their place the world began to swarm with grotesque and fantastic creatures, and it must be borne in mind that as yet we only know a fraction of that vanished animal world. Innumerable types may still lie undiscovered in the rocks. Many, possibly, never became fossils at all. From both the Permian and the Triassic Periods numerous footprints survive which only in a few cases can be identified with known primeval animals. In this context *Cheirotherium* (literally "hand animal") is particularly celebrated, being known only from its footprints. On the basis of the length of its stride, the shape of its feet and the depth of the impressions, the palaeontologist Soergel made an attempt to reconstruct it. His extremely interesting work has caused much controversy, but it is to be hoped that one day a lucky discovery of fossil remains will provide the same confirmation as was given to Cuvier's brilliant reconstruction of *Palaeotherium*.

Two animal characteristics are particularly representative of the Triassic: first, the raising of the body erect to walk on two legs; and second, a tendency towards adaptation to life in the water. It is quite certain that all reptiles first developed on land, probably in arid, climatically unfavourable regions which greatly aggravated the struggle for existence. In such circumstances all possible bodily postures and corresponding means of controlling them must have been tried out. Included among these was the upright carriage of the body for the purpose of a more extensive view over the terrain and an early sight of prey or enemies. This erect posture was certainly associated with the transition to rapid movement.

An extremely interesting reptile of the Triassic Period was *Plateosaurus,* an animal nearly 18 feet long, of which nearly forty well-preserved skeletons were discovered for the first time (between 1909 and 1914) in a clay pit of the Upper Triassic near Halberstadt, Germany. For discoveries such as this the scientific world is very frequently indebted to the intelligence of quarry workers. In the case of the Halberstadt deposit, it is almost certain that many fossil skeletons must already have been lost during the excavation of the layers of clay, before a worker reported his suspicions of the presence of "antediluvian" animals, thus bringing geologists and palaeontologists hurrying to the spot.

Plateosaurus was already a genuine dinosaur, one of those "monsters" which later achieved such an extraordinary culmination. These creatures must have been at least 9 feet tall, and their front feet were already capable of gripping. Probably they were herbivorous.

As in the case of *Mastodonsaurus,* their mass graves within comparatively restricted areas at first suggest that we are concerned with a heap of animal bodies swept together by running water. But against this is their excellent state of preservation and the fact that they were embedded in what was formerly red clay dust. Further discoveries subsequent to 1911, in the region of Trossingen in Swabia, caused F. von Huene to visualise the Keuper landscape in that particular area and thus produce a picture which suggested a possible reason for the extinction of these creatures.

As a result of geological finds he reconstructed, notionally, in that part of Germany an extensive desert area beyond which extended an inland sea. Across this desert stretched a regular migratory track made by the plateosaurs—a track permanently in use, in order to enable the beasts—perhaps annually—to leave their normal habitats that were drying out and seek the richly vegetated shores of the inland sea. This very exhausting communal march would have proved too much for the weaker creatures. Yet all must have gone well until they reached that "death-trap" in Trossingen. Their doom here was a quagmire of partly dried clay which stuck to the feet of the saurians, inhibited their further progress and finally brought about the collapse of the weakest. The fine desiccated dust of the clay buried them and led to their conservation. This happened for many years on end, which explains why many skeletons lie vertically separated six feet or more apart. Von Huene was certainly right, and he thereby provided an excellent example of the intuitive imagination required of a palaeontological investigator if he is to achieve any measure of success.

Among the bipeds, the Pseudosuchia appeared—agile, generally small lizard-like creatures from which, it may be assumed, the whole range of dinosaurs, crocodiles and birds subsequently developed. *Ornithosuchus,* whose skulls and skeletons have been found in the Triassic in Scotland, had skull—and skeletal—structures so greatly resembling the primal birds that they were probably near to the actual

ancestors of the birds. It is possible that this particular deviation of the reptiles, as in the case of the therapsid ancestors
of the mammals, began in the Permian Period. But actual
proof of this is still lacking.

Among the quadrupeds the Rhyncocephalia, a reptilian
order from the Triassic, were very widespread. In appearance

22. *Plateosaurus* (according to Abel)

they resembled a cross between lizard and crocodile. This
order of reptiles has left no fossil traces after the Jurassic, and
yet we have here a story which parallels that of the coelacanth.
About 1830 there was discovered, in rock-caves near certain
beaches in New Zealand, a reptile about 2 feet long which,
for a considerable time, proved difficult to fit into the systematic scheme (it is called the tuatara or *Sphenodon*). Today it
is known that this is a very primitive animal with a third

pineal eye on the top of its skull, and is in fact the only surviving member of the Triassic and Jurassic Rhyncocephalia, the rest of which died out some 140 million years ago. Its life-span in an undisturbed habitat is astonishing. So far as is known this survivor from primeval times can live to be at least one hundred years old.

Very like small crocodiles were the Aetosaurs, of which some 24 specimens were recovered from a Keuper deposit near Stuttgart. Some of these animals were 30 inches long, and had died simultaneously but in such confusion that a

23. The New Zealand tuatara, a contemporary descendant of the Rhyncocephalia

common disaster must have occurred, perhaps an earth-slide which buried them all together. They were armoured like crocodiles, but had triangular skulls with large eyes and lateral nostrils, which definitely suggested bird-features. They certainly resemble the common ancestors of the dinosaurs and the crocodiles, but are not now regarded as lying in the direct line of descent. The same can be said of *Belodon,* a creature only outwardly, and not in an evolutionary way, akin to the crocodiles.

Another characteristic animal of the Triassic, of very extraordinary form, is *Tanystropheus.* Its general appearance was that of a snake, up to 18 feet in overall length with lizard-like legs. For such an animal the head was tiny, only about 1 foot long. In contrast the neck and tail were enormously long —the neck as a result of the unusual length of the backbone. It is possible that *Tanystropheus* was a water reptile, catching its prey by snake-like dartings of its neck. More probably, however, this predatory animal simply caught fish from the bank by plunging its head into the water.

Genuine water reptiles were now in existence. The fact that reptiles originally destined for life on land returned wholly to the water need not be regarded as a retrogression. The versatile and flourishing vertebrates simply conquered the water as another element to live in. At first there were two groups belonging to the Triassic only and disappearing at its end, represented by *Nothosaurus* and *Placodus*. Both belong to the order Sauropterygia. *Nothosaurus* is known in Europe as well as in North America (Wyoming). It must have been a huge beast, whose crocodile-like head alone, poised at the end of a long neck, measured 3 feet. Its tail was correspondingly short and cannot have contributed in even the slightest degree to its serpentine forward movement. In fact, this motion was produced by four feet shaped like paddles. It is clear that the nothosaur had its hunting-grounds along the river banks.

Placodus, on the contrary, was a reptile that dwelt on the bed of the sea. Judging from its teeth, it must have lived on hard-shelled creatures, especially clams, which it tore from their anchorage and crunched up. It possessed a strong belly armour composed of ribs which, at the sides, turned up at right angles, giving it a strange unfamiliar appearance for the animal world. It seems to have survived somewhat longer than *Nothosaurus,* but after the Triassic it soon vanished.

True oceanic reptiles now appeared in the form of the well-known and audaciously shaped plesiosaurs. For the last hundred years their fossils have been familiar from well-preserved discoveries and they have been reconstructed with almost complete accuracy. Apart from variations in their size, chiefly as regards the length of their necks, their numerous species and families were all uniformly constructed. The body was circular like a tortoise, the tail short, the reptilian legs transformed into powerful paddles, and the neck generally long and snake-like. This whole structure was crowned with a tiny head (except in the short-necked plesiosaurs which had a large head), the snout being very liberally equipped with pointed, backward-sloping, reptilian teeth. All in all, it was a fierce, aggressive primeval creature which was able to survive for 170 million years.

The best known of all prehistoric lizards are undoubtedly the ichthyosaurs (fish-lizards). Their fossils have been known for somewhat longer than those of the plesiosaurs. But that was not what made them so celebrated: their fame is due to the almost inexhaustible numbers of their skeletons that were

24. *Tanystropheus* from the Muschelkalk (according to Peyer)

found in the Lias schist of the Jurassic. They were discovered, and brought to the light in which they had previously basked, in all conceivable states and conditions of preservation, from small fragments to complete skeletons, some even with remains of skin, so that today there is scarcely a museum in the world, or even a private collection, that is not richly endowed with their remains. The brisk trade in fossilised ichthyosaurs provided ample pocket-money for quarry-workers who gradually became on the look-out for such "beasties". The famous geologist Oskar Fraas asserted with humour and truth that no horse-coper had ever haggled so keenly and persuasively as the purveyors of saurians.

The ichthyosaurs varied enormously in appearance, their

bodies ranging from torpedo- to spindle-shaped. In general, they resembled the dolphins, although of course they were not even remotely related to these mammals; it was just that in the ichthyosaurs Nature tried out a sleek swimming shape, which has successfully survived in other animals. And like the dolphins they had scarcely any neck at all. Their pointed snout was equipped with as many as 200 teeth. From the evidence of later toothless forms it seems that the diet of these animals at some time had changed from fish to squids. Their eyes were surrounded by adjustable rings of bone which functioned like the aperture of a camera and probably served as a form of protection against the pressure of the water. The ribs, resembling fish-bone, were extremely supple and enabled these lung-breathers to dive under water with considerable reserves of air. The limbs were transformed into powerful fins. The end of the lizard-tail was now curved downwards and supported the powerful bifurcated tail-fins. The skin was no longer in the form of reptilian scales and had become completely smooth. All this adds up to the picture of an animal completely adapted to life in the sea. The ichthyosaurs were viviparous—an improvement that Nature had already discovered in the Permian—and no longer went on land to give birth. In this context, one sensational fossil discovery has been found: a mother animal that not only had within her well-developed embryos, but was overwhelmed by death in the very act of giving birth. The unnecessary objection that has been raised—that these so-called embryos were in fact young animals that had been eaten and were still in the stomach—is completely untenable since no bite-wounds are visible and the size of the fully developed embryos is roughly the same in every case. The length of an ichthyosaur's body varied considerably. Whereas those found in the Jura Mountains averaged from 4 to 6 feet, a 36-feet-long example has been discovered in the Triassic in Spitzbergen. Other areas of the world, too, have yielded up similarly huge fossils—as well as the smaller varieties. From this it is clear that the ichthyosaurs were cosmopolitan. They died out only towards the end of the Cretaceous Period. Since their later forms developed uncommonly large eyes and an extension of the neural spine, they may, with luck, reappear one day like the

coelacanths; for both these characteristics suggest that they
became deep-sea dwellers and in their hunt for food
(cephalopods) frequented, more and more, the inaccessible
depths of the oceans which the squids usually inhabit. But
that is pure speculation, and there is no actual proof for it.
(A contemporary footnote: it has been suggested that the
Loch Ness "Monster"—if it exists at all—is actually an
ichthyosaur!)

From the days of the Permian we are already familiar with
the huge and very varied forms of the Therapsida among
which certain lineages first displayed mammalian characteristics. How far along this road did Nature progress during
the 45 million years of the Triassic Period? Certainly not as
far as was believed until quite recently. In the Keuper layer
in South Africa were discovered fragments of skulls, and
above all teeth, belonging to small animals which were
assigned to the genus *Tritylodon,* and which, on the evidence
of their mammal-type molar teeth, would have to be reckoned
as the oldest genuine mammals. But when the corresponding
lower jaws were discovered and proved to be reptilian as well
as mammalian in nature, this classification seemed by no
means so certain. Palaeontologists have therefore created
the name "Ictidosauria" to contain this hitherto unknown
group of animals. However, it is quite certain that it was from
their family, and their family only, that the genuine mammals
developed. The earliest indisputable representatives of the
mammals—and this must be stressed—can only be dated
back to the Jurassic Period. That is not to say that they did
not exist earlier. It is just that there are vast hiatuses in
our geological knowledge which have not yet been filled
in.

Obviously, the way from reptile to mammal must have led
through a multiplicity of stages still completely unknown to
us; and this, of course, was also true of the development of
other animal species and classes. In the case of the mammals,
it was not only the fact of their being viviparous that distinguished them from other animals, for this stage of development was achieved by many reptiles (though without a true
womb). Two other factors are more important: first, the
suckling from the mother's milk-glands of helpless young

creatures incapable of feeding themselves; and second, the acquisition of a definite, constant blood-temperature which could be maintained despite unfavourable climatic conditions. All reptiles are cold-blooded, or, rather, fluctuatingly warm-blooded; the temperature of their blood being to a very large extent determined by the external temperature which regulates their activity and vitality. Now the ictidosaurs were little animals which partly fell victims to the huge predators among the saurians. And what does a small, helpless, persecuted creature do—and has always done? It creeps away and hides itself, out of fright and out of the instinct of self-preservation. During the daytime it dares not emerge. Only under the cover of night, when its enemies are sleeping, does it creep out in nocturnal search of food. Now night, always and everywhere, is colder than day. The difference in temperature is particularly acute in steppe and desert areas. Cold makes the reptiles, with their fluctuating body heat, lethargic; it paralyses them. Perhaps these small animals owed their survival to their having developed a constant blood-temperature and ultimately, as well, a protective hairy covering in place of the reptilian scales. That was the most important step in higher evolution, a step which was also achieved—over roughly the same period—by the birds. Simultaneously (but only much later did it become of paramount importance), a new and so far almost entirely negligible weapon began to develop: the brain. The gigantic saurians, with their teeth, spines, armour-plating and physical strength, had scarcely any need of a brain. Even in the largest of them, their brain-pans were absurdly small. But in the case of the defenceless primal mammals the skull and brain-pan began to enlarge and proved to be the conclusive, dominating factor in their existence.

Thus, in the Triassic (and almost certainly even further back) are to be found the origins of all the higher vertebrates which, in due course, completed the picture of the living world as we know it today.

CHAPTER TWELVE

The Jurassic and Cretaceous Periods

HITHERTO the main deposits and the times in the Earth's history during which they were formed have been individually treated according to the geological scheme which, naturally, is not purely arbitrary but is arranged strictly according to scientific data. But this history is an incessant flow into which we have inserted often artificial boundaries. These "boundaries" must in reality have extended over immense periods of time; we would have to fall back on the "catastrophic" theory of Cuvier, if we really wished to believe that one epoch was divided from another by a hair's-breadth. So it is almost a matter of opinion whether those periods following the Triassic—the Jurassic and the Cretaceous—should be regarded as one and the same or separate, according to what fits in best with the systematic scheme. Naturally, from the scientific viewpoint there are reasons enough for distinguishing the Jurassic from the Cretaceous. The Jurassic formations are older, and the Cretaceous younger, their fossil beds separate. That is incontrovertible. But the biological scene, the great world of reptiles, is common to the two, so that it is no scientific sacrilege to survey both as one.

The Jurassic and Cretaceous together covered a time-span of altogether 110 million years; of these 45 million belonged to the Jurassic Period, and the remaining 65 million to the Cretaceous.

The Jurassic Period was named by Alexander von Humboldt (1769-1859) after the Jura mountains. The sedimentary rocks formed during this period are probably more varied than in any other geological period, and the rapid alternations of clays, limestones and sandstones often have marked effects on the scenery. The lowermost beds in Britain are the black shales of the Lias, while massive oolitic limestones are characteristic of the Upper Jurassic. The oolitic structure of these rocks, where the calcium carbonate is formed into minute spheres (as in the Portland Stone used for facing buildings in London), most likely resulted from chemical precipitation in evaporating shallow seas. A similar indication of the existence of such shallow seas is provided by the numerous fossil coral reefs, as well as by the sandy sediments which were certainly not deep-sea deposits. It is, however, impossible to generalise about conditions during the Jurassic, since they varied so remarkably at different times and in different areas.

The name Cretaceous is certain to mislead anyone into thinking that chalk-building was the predominant geological feature of those 65 million years. But once again must be repeated what has already been said before: names are names and nothing more. For the fact is that the animal chalk deposits of that time are no more than a mere episode in the Upper Cretaceous Period. The nomenclature originates from England, whose tall chalk cliffs were laid down during this period. The main geological division is into Lower and Upper Cretaceous, with further sub-divisions which here need only be mentioned in certain instances.

The last great transgression—flooding of extensive land areas by the seas—had occurred in the already far-off Silurian Period. After that came the waves of Caledonian and Variscan mountain foldings which welded together gigantic land-masses and drove back the ocean. Land building probably reached its high-point during the New Red Sandstone Age of the Lower Triassic Period. Now once again the time had come for the unleashing of that mighty cyclic phenomenon which runs through the whole of Earth's history. The geosynclines, the deep marine hollows, were filled up with sedimentary rocks. The sea-level rose correspondingly. The greatest transgression since the Silurian Period, reaching its climax in the Cenomanian—the first sub-division of the Upper Cretaceous—overwhelmed the land-blocks. Central and Southern Europe became an archipelago. The heavily weighted geosynclines finally sank. The Earth's crust started to move. Even the Gondwanaland continent, which had remained firm almost from the beginning of time, finally broke into pieces and the Indian Ocean was formed. Australia was isolated and has remained so to this day. The whole of the region of the Urals was submerged. The primal continent of Northern Europe escaped inundation, but joined up yet again with both Laurentia and Angara-Siberia. Where today the Alps, the Caucasus and the Himalayas tower towards the sky, the Tethys Ocean stretched. Intensified irruptions and vulcanism were continually changing the face of the land. The basaltic extrusive plateau of Western India arose during the Cretaceous. Naturally, a fresh wave of mountain-building was taking place. It had already started in America during the Jurassic and was to continue in numerous separate phases for more than 100 million years, lasting into the following Tertiary Period. Its climax was, indeed, in the Tertiary, so that when we reach that point we shall then revert again to this "Alpine" folding.

The climate during the Jurassic must on the whole have been almost uniformly sub-tropical. But the onset of the Cenomanian inundations apparently caused it to become more regionalised and differentiated. Perhaps, also, the isostatic movements of the Earth's crust may have brought about an increased tilt of the axis, thus making the climatic zones more noticeable. The retreat of the corals southwards and the evidence of the annual rings in trees in northern regions support this assumption. The Arctic, certainly, was ice-free.

The vegetable world of the Jurassic presents us, rather unexpectedly, with some problems. Until recently it seemed that the flora—naturally enough—derived from that of the Triassic, giving fresh impetus to new species and orders of its gymnosperms, and spreading further and further over the surface of the land. Tree-ferns, horse-tails, lycopods, cycads were still in evidence and occupied the moist regions; whereas the gymnosperms, such as conifers and gingkos, conquered the drier areas. They did all this on a vast scale, for the Jurassic Period produced the most even distribution of vegetation in the whole of Earth's history. It would be no exaggeration to speak of the world-domination of the gymnosperms. That new forms appeared—such as junipers, cypresses and yews—was part of their natural process of evolution. But recently a question that has been more and more frequently asked is: where are the angiosperms, the flowering plants? The Jurassic Period lasted 45 million years. The oldest traces of the existence of angiosperms so far discovered are in the Lower Cretaceous of Texas and New Zealand. And only at the end of the Upper Cretaceous do we know that there appeared in Europe, with quite amazing spontaneity, trees with leaves (oak, poplar, beech, palm, birch, willow, ivy, maple, etc.). The first flowers—magnolias, water-lilies—date from this period also. Their place of origin seems to have been in America. The favourable circumstances that enabled them to proliferate into so many types, and to spread so rapidly, are unknown. But there is possibly some mistake here, and their apparently "spontaneous" appearance may on the contrary have actually been spread over a very long period of development, as was formerly always considered to be the case. Indeed, the voices of experts are being raised increasingly in favour of a greater age for the angiosperms. Studies of pollen, for instance, seem to indicate that angiosperms must have existed at least as far back as the Jurassic and possibly at an even earlier point in time. Very curious and possibly of great importance is the impression of a leaf found in the Lias at Bamberg (Germany) in 1955. Expert investigation confirmed that this little, $1\frac{1}{2}$-inch-long leaf came from a dicotyledonous angiosperm, and from all that we know it is improbable that it was the very first specimen of an angiosperm. A long line of evolution must certainly extend far back, well into the Triassic or even into the Permian. But we still do not know for sure. Further discoveries alone can be decisive, and these, as a result of unfavourable circumstances in the older strata, have not yet been made. With this we conclude our description of the flora of the Cretaceous, which, towards the end of the Mesozoic, already bore thoroughly modern features. It can be taken as quite certain that the ascendance of the angiosperms was of enormous importance to the further development of birds, mammals and insects.

Life in the oceans during the Jurassic-Cretaceous Periods was of an almost inconceivable richness and variety. The hexacorals were now building their reefs extensively in the warm-water regions of the Tethys. The seas in higher latitudes must gradually have grown cooler. Sponges were abundant and left behind high submarine rocks. The sea-urchins proliferated; they also transformed their shells from five-pointed structures to ones showing bilateral symmetry. The brachiopods, on the other hand, continued to dwindle. In their place the lamellibranchs developed in a great variety of new types. Particularly striking were the oyster-like Rudistes of the Cretaceous. These sedentary forms grew to an enormous size (up to 6 feet) and lived with their lower valves cemented on to rocks and other shells in the reef. These lower valves were roughly in the shape of a chalice or tulip on to which the upper shell could close like a lid, and were immensely thickened with layers of calcium carbonate.

The gastropods also abounded in a great number of varieties; and the world of smaller creatures, too, once more increased and flourished intensively during the Cretaceous. This is very evident in the unicellular Foraminifera. The well-known genus Globigerina first appeared in the Cretaceous, and is still abundant in our present-day oceans, where its accumulated deposits (the Globigerina-ooze) covers about one quarter of the total surface area of the earth.

The ammonites and belemnites proliferated extravagantly in a multiplicity of forms, reached a brilliant climax—and then vanished! These highly organised and dangerous predators must have tried out every possible practicable variation of shell-housing. An imaginative artist of the present day would be hard put to it to devise such involved and decorative shells as these molluscs produced. In addition to the normal "snail-shell", there were others with open whorls, spindle-shaped twists, necks like sea-horses, giant forms (over 6 feet), as well as a hundred intermediate sizes, ridged, smooth, spiked, pitted, an endless wealth of every imaginable variety. It is difficult to say what the biological value could have been of so many of these remarkable ornamentations. The strange fact remains that the whole group of ammonites reached an astounding climax in numbers of individuals and in complexity of form, and then suddenly died out for no obvious reason. In arriving at any conclusion as to what may have been the causes of the extinction of such a group many factors have always to be taken into account. Among these, of course, are the decrease in evolutionary vigour of that group (which seems to have played an important part in the disappearance of the ammonites), superior enemies, difficulties in obtaining food, restriction of environment leading to forcible specialisation, and threats to the survival of progeny. Among possible enemies it is conceivable that the ichthyosaurs, which were now coming powerfully into their own, played such havoc

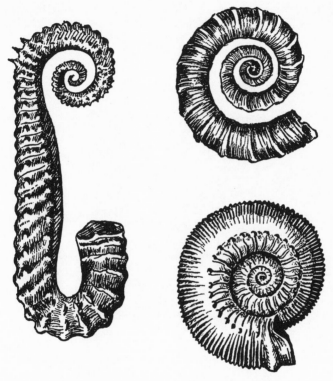

25. Different forms of ammonite shells

that they reduced this particular branch of the cephalopod population to a point where it was unable to survive.

But the highly organised cephalopods as a whole did not suffer extermination; indeed, they have continued to exist right up to the present day. Even in the Jurassic there existed real "naked" squids which had transferred their bony structure inwards. In their case, too, one of the next evolutionary stages to be aimed at was an immense increase in size.

In every century there have been frequent reports from sailors and fishermen of terrifying encounters and deadly struggles with "kraken". Even though many of these may be no more than seamen's yarns, the existence in the ocean of giant squids with tentacles 40 to 50 feet long has been well established. Creatures such as this, or even larger, developed during the Cretaceous; at that time there were at least 8,000 species, and today about 500 are known.

26. Old French drawing of an encounter (imaginary) between a giant squid and a ship

Among the fish, during the Cretaceous, the last step was taken in developing the bony skeleton which predominates today. The ganoids diminished rapidly and died out except for a few forms that still survive.

The vast insect kingdom was now almost completed. Beetles and dragon-flies, Hymenoptera (primitive bees, wasps and ants) and flies, all were in evidence during the Jurassic. The fine-grained limestones of Solnhofen have preserved the most delicate insects' wings in a state of almost living beauty. Most significant, also, is the first appearance of butterflies in the Jurassic, for butterflies are creatures which need flowers for their existence. If one likes, one can deduce from this an indirect proof for the Jurassic existence of angiosperms. But it is tenable that conifers alone would have been quite sufficient to supply all the needs of butterflies at that time. However, it can be taken as quite certain that the great development of such insects during the Tertiary coincided with the abundant angiosperm flora of the period. As a general rule, it seems that the evolution of flowers and the evolution of their pollinating insects have gone hand-in-hand. Only the most highly developed stages of bees and ants were missing during the Mesozoic.

CHAPTER THIRTEEN

The Empire of the Reptiles

T H E reptile lords of the seas, the ichthyosaurs and plesiosaurs, have already been mentioned. Some of the richest and most perfect deposits of ichthyosaurs were discovered at Holz-maden and various other places in the Jura Mountains. Here again a mass extermination evidently occurred in a com-paratively limited area, a happening that always requires an explanation. It is known for certain that at that time the Tethys Sea had a long, curving arm that roughly followed a line across South Germany. This Jurassic Sea was a shallow stretch of water with, undoubtedly, numerous lagoons cut off from the open sea by coral reefs, and therefore only accessible over narrow, low "necks" such as are found today round the lagoons of South Sea atolls. The floors of these areas of virtually standing water were presumably covered by a clayey layer of rotting slime impregnated with sulphuretted hydrogen, as is evidenced by the oil-bearing Posidonian shales from Holzmaden containing the characteristic fossil *Posidonia*. This—as in certain areas of the Black Sea today and in the graptolite ocean of the Silurian Period—would have been a zone absolutely inimical to life. The ichthyosaurs, greedily pursuing their prey or in search of fresh hunting grounds, possibly swam into the trap, found themselves in this poison-ous region and died. They then sank down into the slimy clay which offered the very best chances for their enduring pre-servation as fossils. That, at any rate, is how it *may* have happened. But whatever the cause, the result was that the "death-trap of Holzmaden" became, 150 million years later, a happy hunting ground for palaeontologists.

On the subject of the plesiosaurs, it only remains to add that in *Elasmosaurus* they produced a reptile 45 feet long (Upper Cretaceous in Kansas), 21 feet alone being taken up by the snake-like neck which—a record in the animal world—was composed of 76 vertebrae. This must have made its head immensely mobile and much facilitated attacks on prey by means of rapid striking from the neck. With the disappearance of the plesiosaurs at the end of the Cretaceous, the Sauropterygia came to an end, as also did the ichthyosaurs. This dramatic epitaph—" died out at the end of the Cretaceous " —can be applied to almost all forms of reptiles so far mentioned; for not one of those almost legendary monsters survived to see the dawn of the mammals in the Tertiary Period.

Another fiercer predator from the late Cretaceous Period was the mosasaur, which looked like a giant lizard with paddles instead of legs. The first example, discovered in the Cretace-

27. *Mosasaurus* from the Cretaceous

ous strata in Maastricht in the Netherlands, was one of the oldest fossil finds to attract widespread attention. It also aroused a great deal of scholastic argument which was not without unintentional humour.

In the year 1780 the garrison physician of Maastricht, Dr. Hoffman, extracted with considerable difficulty from a quarry in the Petersberg a lizard's head more than 3 feet long and equipped with teeth. Now this quarry was the property of a certain Canon Godin, who entered upon what was probably the first law suit in the history of the world concerning a fossil. And he won possession of the treasure. Up to 1795 he was able to enjoy his unique possession. Then the troops of the French " army of liberation " under Freicine approached and began bombarding the fortress of Maastricht. Evidently

Godin was more concerned for his fossil than for his life, as his greatest anxiety was to find a secure hiding place for his block of limestone containing the monster. However, Freicine had already been sent instructions from Paris to safeguard the worthy canon's house in order that no harm should befall the antediluvian inhabitant whose fame had already spread far and wide. Cuvier was bent upon having it. Freicine adhered strictly to his instructions, and no harm befell Godin or his house. But the fossil by this time had disappeared, the Canon naturally not having the slightest idea where it could have gone. Freicine must have been a man of parts, because

28. Komodo dragon (Varanidae)

instead of intimidating Godin with fearful threats, he simply offered a reward of 600 bottles of wine to whoever of his soldiers should discover the treasure. The bribe worked; and the very morning after the surrender of Maastricht twelve soldiers bore the limestone slab in triumph into their camp. It subsequently reached Paris and Cuvier, who at once, with his customary brilliance, recognised an extinct reptile which must have been related to the Varanidae, a family of lizards (Monitors) which includes the Komodo dragon, *Varanus komodoensis.*

This relationship has never been disputed. The mosasaur and present-day Varanidae must both have descended from a common ancestor. They were deviations from the ordinary lizards, who took to the sea but the former became extinct at the end of the Cretaceous, together with so many other marine reptiles. The Varanidae of Asia and South Africa have long been known, but it was only in 1912 that the giant Komodo dragon, measuring up to 9 feet in length, was discovered on the island of Sunda. An encounter with one of these beasts in the depths of the jungle must indeed have been a really primeval experience.

After the historic discovery at Maastricht, numerous identical or similar discoveries were made in Cretaceous deposits of many countries: in New Zealand, in widely varied places in Africa, the East Indies, and, above all, in North America, which proved as fruitful for reptiles of the Cretaceous Period as did the Jura Mountains for their eponymous fossils. In the Belgian Hennegau area, a complete skeleton was discovered measuring over 30 feet in length, and an American palaeontologist reconstructed from Cretaceous fragments discovered in Kansas a monster that may have been even longer.

To judge from their teeth, they were terrifying predators who, because of a special articulation in their jaws, were able to swallow, even sideways, large animals whole, just as our present-day snakes are able to do, though for different anatomical reasons. Their progress through water was achieved by sinuous movement, aided by small, still very lizard-like paddle-feet. In contrast to the ichthyosaurs they were not smooth-skinned but covered with scales; yet, like the ichthyosaurs, their young were born alive in the sea. Some types, too, resembling the late ichthyosaurs, had domed instead of pointed crowns to their teeth, which plainly indicated concentration on a diet of hard-shelled creatures. A striking thing about the remains of these animals is the number of bite-wounds on the skeletons, which appear in the form of more or less healed fractures in all parts of the body. Since the mosasaurs appear to have lived socially in colonies there must have occurred battles between them and other marine giants, although there is the possibility—a very real one—of mating fights. But with these creatures, too, there was the routine climax: extinction at the end of the

Cretaceous. (Present-day fiction, it may be noted, claims *Mosasaurus* as the classical ancestor of the good old sea-serpent!)

Among the reptiles which returned to the sea during the Cretaceous Period were the turtles, which we have already encountered as fully developed, mainly toothed land animals in the Triassic. The difference between life in the sea and on land led to considerable changes in their upper and lower shells. And these creatures, too, followed the trend towards giantism. In the fossil-rich Upper Cretaceous beds

29. Skeleton of a giant turtle, *Archelon*, from the Upper Cretaceous in Kansas (Scale 1 : 40)

in Kansas an example of the genus *Archelon* was found—minus a hind leg that had perhaps been bitten off—measuring 10 feet in length. The three-feet long head of another specimen must have belonged to a monster at least 15 feet from head to tail. Here, for once, we need not use the epithet "extinct" because, although the number of varieties of turtles has vastly decreased since the Cretaceous (only a few marine types survive), these reptiles have shown marvellous powers of survival. To the question: "Why the turtles in particular?" there is no answer, for they must have had innumerable hungry, powerful enemies in the Cretaceous seas. Moreover, they were not particularly well adapted to defend themselves, although several species were equipped with sharp teeth. But Nature had taken other steps and armed them with three indirect weapons: the capacity to exist for a long time without feeding and without suffering any ill effects therefrom; enormous fertility; and the ability to live to over 100 years of age. And in their case the laying of eggs on land was an advantage. Altogether, these characteristics sufficed to get them round the critical bend! Whether the greatest enemy of animal life—Man—will now exterminate them, time alone will tell. But what are a mere 1,000 years in the life of a group of animals that carry some 250 million years on their horny backs? One hopes that it will be some aeons yet before turtle soup has to be struck off the menus in our more expensive restaurants.

The ancestors of present-day crocodiles are known from the Triassic-Jurassic boundary, and are represented by such genera as *Protosuchus*, a small and heavily-armoured reptile. One Jurassic line developed into the geosaurs, a marine group with a powerful tail which—like that of the ichthyosaur—bore a vertical fin supported by the end vertebrae of the tail. The hind legs, too, which, in contrast to the extremely stunted forelegs, were powerfully developed, must also have worked as paddles. But in this case the attempt of these creatures to adapt themselves to the open sea obviously failed. They barely survived the Jurassic-Cretaceous. Once again, one can only guess at the reason for their rapid disappearance. Perhaps these beasts were simply too unwieldy and succumbed to superior numbers of more agile aquatic enemies. The true, surviving crocodiles from the Cretaceous avoided repeating that dangerous experiment and remained land and freshwater animals. A solitary exception seems to be the gigantic estuarine crocodile (*Crocodilus porosus*) of the East Asian and Australian islands, which may often be encountered well out at sea. Here further observation is necessary to decide whether this is truly a second attempt by crocodiles to conquer the ocean.

Returning again to land, we find that the most extraordinary creatures have by now established themselves. Whatever the terrain—desert or forest, swamps or steppes, uplands or brackish inlets—the denizens turn out to be monsters of terrifying aspect whom one would certainly never believe to be all entirely harmless. These prehistoric creatures were given the collective name of dinosaurs (which roughly means "terror lizards"). During the last century they have emerged from their rocky tombs and now, like ghostly monsters, occupy a space in most natural history museums. Although it is certain that only a very small fraction of the then existing saurian world became fossilised and subsequently discovered, as a class they were so varied in their types and were indi-

30. Reconstruction of *Iguanodon*

vidually so numerous that it is possible, to a very large extent, to reconstruct exactly their appearance and way of life. And here systematic biology comes into its own. Today a distinction is made between two major groups: the Saurischia and the Ornithischia. To the former belong the carnivorous theropods and the enormous sauropods, whilst the latter includes a number of herbivorous creatures, none of which, however, attained the size of the largest sauropods.

Among the Ornithischia, or bird-lipped dinosaurs, *Iguanodon* is certainly the best known. In 1878, Belgian miners at

Bernissart, driving a gallery through Lower Cretaceous Wealden clay 700 feet below the surface, came across fossilised remains. Fortunately, by this time so many reports had been coming from all over the world that the authorities were intelligent enough to halt immediately all further work on the seam and to call in the geologists, who very laboriously succeeded in bringing to the surface a veritable treasure of fossils which, in view of their fragile condition, were transported to the Natural Science Museum in Brussels still embedded in slabs of their mineral surroundings. Here, it emerged, were the collective remains of 29 iguanodons. Traces of these animals had been discovered in Kent about fifty years before by an Englishman called Mantell, who had given them their name. However, Mantell's finds were limited to teeth and fragmentary bones, and it had never proved possible to run these mysterious primeval monsters to earth. Now the time had come when several compete skeletons could be reconstructed. And they still stand before us today: gigantic, bow-legged monsters measuring 30 feet from head to tail. Their claws were prehensile, the thumbs ending in a strong, defensive prong. The palaeontologist Dollo established from anatomical discoveries that the animal's enormous tail must have been rigid and immobile and therefore useless as a support or in defence. Subsequently, numerous iguanodon footprints were discovered, and they all confirmed Professor Dollo's opinion, for there was never a trace of a dragging tail. Probably the tail merely acted as a counterbalance to the massive body. The teeth of these animals (there were several types) showed that the iguanodons were undoubtedly herbivorous, grazing on the shoots of coniferous growths.

The Bernissart coal-mine proved to be a real fossil graveyard, for, in addition to the iguanodons, it yielded up fossilised remains of turtles, crocodiles, and over 2,000 fish, not to mention plants.

Closely resembling the iguanodons were the duck-billed dinosaurs from the Upper Cretaceous of North America (Wyoming and Canada). Here, too, wonderful skeletal remains were discovered. Even exact impressions of skin were found in sandstone which had hardened subsequently. The trachodonts such as the *Edmontosaurus* were aquatic creatures, as is shown by their webbed extremities. Their skulls have helmet-like protuberances, and the shape of their snouts resembles a duck's bill. Their body length was about 24-30 feet, about the same as the iguanodon's. A relative of *Edmontosaurus* was *Parasaurolophus*, an animal from the Upper Cretaceous in Alberta, which had on its head strange hollow bones which curved back like horns. As these were directly connected with the nose, the palaeontologist Abel deduced that this probably gave them a highly developed sense of smell which, in the case of the males, helped them to seek out their females at mating time. The main function of these protuberances, however, was probably to aid the animal in breathing when feeding in shallow water.

The most striking members of the group of ornithischian dinosaurs were the stegosaurs and ceratopsians.

The richest finds of stegosaurs come from the strata of the Upper Jurassic in Colorado and Wyoming. They were absolutely grotesque creatures, with armour-plating that would have been considered excessive on a knight of the Middle Ages. These monstrous quadrupeds, up to 30 feet in length, carried on their backs a double row of vertical, horny, triangular-shaped plates which ran from a very tiny head, along the neck and back, to the middle of the tail. The end of the tail was equipped with pairs of huge spines. It can be assumed that the sides of the body, too, had similar spinal excrescences. It is difficult to imagine what predators of that period could have successfully attacked such a heavily defended animal. Not much can be said about the mobility of this dinosaur. One can only assume that its muscular development kept pace with its weight and at least produced a steady, if not particularly rapid, gait. The stegosaurs must, *ex hypothesi*, have been able to move over considerable areas in order to exist, for they were mainly desert dwellers whose chief form of nourishment was succulent plants, i.e. cacti which store water in their stems. But plants such as these do not grow thickly, being generally widely dispersed. The brain of the stegosaur was minute, and the sacral enlargement of the spinal nerve cord was at least ten times as large in volume; so there could have been no question of real intelligence in these creatures. Reflex reactions, brute force and protection through armour-plating were sufficient to keep such animals alive in the world of their day.

Another branch of the Ornithischia is represented by the Ceratopsia. They are known mainly from the Cretaceous Period in North America and Mongolia. At first glance many of their reconstructions resemble out-sized rhinoceroses with whom, of course, they have no evolutionary relationship. Rhinoceroses are mammals and the Ceratopsia are reptiles. Their best known representative is *Triceratops* (three-horned), a ponderous, heavily-armoured giant about 24 feet in length. Most striking in its appearance was a gigantic neck-shield

31. *Stegosaurus* (up to 27 feet long)

which encircled the head rather like an upright collar or ruff. Two long, pointed horns projected above the eyes, and a third, short horn over the nose. The body itself seems not to have been armoured, merely clad in a thick skin. In the case of another animal of this type, the *Styracosaurus*, the nose horn was more prominently formed, and from the ridge of the neck-shield protruded enormous spines. All the Ceratopsia were herbivorous upland animals, which probably lived in large herdlike groups, grazing in a manner much like that of present-day cattle.

One of the most primitive of the ceratopsians is *Protoceratops*. In 1924 an expedition from the American Museum of

Natural History in New York made a sensational discovery in the Upper Cretaceous in Mongolia. They dug up a clutch of 13 eggs of these dinosaurs, in some of which there were embryonic remains. Naturally, following this the whole area was scoured, with the result that, quite near by, a complete herd of about 70 protoceratops was unearthed. They must have been overwhelmed by a sandstorm, of such violence as can only occur in those desert regions, and simply perished. From the well-preserved skeletons it proved possible to reconstruct animals that were certainly considerably smaller than e.g. *Triceratops*, but which carried neck-shields like all other members of their family.

The question of where geographically, and on what dietetically, these early land-dwellers lived is naturally open to some argument. Tooth-formations generally offer a good clue to the answers. Most helpful are comparisons with similar types of animals still living today. This is possible even in the case of the Ornithischia, for the present-day animal world includes the girdled lizard (Zonuridae) of Africa and Madagascar, the moloch of Australia, and the horned toad of North America, which ordinarily live in dry desert and steppe country. From these it is logical and permissible to draw conclusions about the way of life of their remote ancestors.

Other armoured dinosaurs from the Cretaceous were *Palaeoscincus*, protected by a horn-plated back and lateral spines, and its close relative *Scolosaurus*. Both had a tortoise-like armour shell into which the tiny, equally tortoise-like head could probably be withdrawn for protection. The short, thick tail was a spine-studded weapon. These creatures, too, must have been desert-dwellers rather than aquatic animals.

Only the duck-bills among the Ornithischia remained bipedal, the other groups such as the ceratopsians and armoured dinosaurs becoming secondarily quadrupedal. Abel assumes that in their earliest form they ran on two feet and it was only the weight of their increasing head- and neck-armour that forced them down to a four-footed mode of progression. "Assumptions" such as these are not always pure guesses, but are usually based on precise anatomical investigations and comparisons, the results of which lead to certain conclusions.

This must be emphasised in order to dispel any idea that palaeontologists may suffer from an excess of imagination, though there is no doubt that imagination can be a valuable aid in research.

The other order of dinosaurs, the Saurischia, produced in the Sauropoda the mightiest land animals that have ever existed. Although their fossil remains have been known in different places for a considerable time, the great spate of discoveries only began in 1878, the very year when the iguanodons emerged from the mines of Bernissart. One monster after another was discovered and presented in reconstruction to an astonished world. Quickly *Titanosaurus, Brontosaurus,*

32. *Scolosaurus* from the Upper Cretaceous in Canada (up to 15 feet in length)

Diplodocus, Brachiosaurus, appeared as examples of fantastic creatures from another world. Today it is known that they in fact flourished all over the Earth. Numerous finds in Europe, East Africa, China, Australia, East India, North and South America all reveal basically similar forms. Huge, round bodies were supported by stout elephantine legs. The long necks carried a tiny horse-like head. The tails were long and powerful. The variations between genera were not on the whole very great. The neck of *Diplodocus* was somewhat longer and slimmer than that of *Brontosaurus.* With some of them, the hind legs bore the main weight of their gigantic bodies, but in the case of *Brachiosaurus* it was probably the front legs. The body length varied somewhat, but was generally between the limits of 70-90 feet. The weight of *Diplodocus* must have been about 40 tons.

It is difficult to conceive of these clumsy, colossal mountains of flesh as being mobile land animals, moving about with the agility of elephants. Yet this was the first view held of them. The name *Brontosaurus*, for example, means "thunder lizard", a semi-poetic description based on the myths of the Sioux Indians in whose hunting grounds the fossils were found. Today, however, it is believed that these creatures were semi-aquatic, living about lakes and rivers, the water enabling them to move with less difficulty. This does not exclude the possibility of their taking to the land at intervals, particularly for the purpose of laying eggs. To judge from their teeth, they were not predatory. Certainly they were extremely unintelligent (their brains were absurdly small), and they ate practically everything they found in front of their snouts, chiefly plants. All in all, they present a picture of a stolid, lumbering group of animals, of incredible stupidity, which, in their utterly vegetative existence, were already marked out as one of Nature's failures. But they survived on Earth for 100 million years!

Up to this point only the herbivorous dinosaurs of the order Saurischia have been mentioned. However, there is another group of saurischian dinosaurs called the therapods, which were predators living on the flesh of other animals. These carnivorous dinosaurs were two-footed animals and were represented from Triassic times onward by a variety of small, medium and large forms. The largest of the therapods was *Tyrannosaurus*, which appeared in the Cretaceous Period, 40 feet long from the tip of its snout to the end of its tail, and with a terrifying array of teeth. A head of this monster, *Tyrannosaurus rex*, discovered in the Upper Cretaceous of Montana, measured 4 feet in length. Various tracks undoubtedly left by these beasts have been found in coal seams in Utah and Colorado, and show a stride of about 11 feet. Their forelegs had dwindled away to almost nothing, being tiny, superfluous appendages, of no practical use.

Much has been discovered about these creatures, who were undoubtedly the greatest land predators in all of Earth's history. Earlier reports and descriptions always portrayed tyrannosaurs furiously attacking and devouring their ponderous prey such as a brontosaur or a diplodocus. This may, indeed, have been a truthful picture, since the predators, like their victims, lived in swampy regions which offered them the best hunting. The palaeontologist Abel, however, propounded a contrary view: that the tyrannosaurs and similar predatory dinosaurs were carrion-feeders. That, too, of course, is possible. But it would be strange if, out of the whole world of monsters, the dinosaurs alone lived together in amity and never fell victims to the "eat or be eaten" law which had existed since life began. However, that is no valid objection. Far more telling is the fact that today scavenging animals are predominantly shy night-creatures (like hyenas) or birds (like vultures) whose keen eyesight enables them easily to scan large areas of territory. That the "cold-blooded" saurian, even with its strength and armament, would be capable of making nightly forays is improbable. And great bodily agility which is essential for hunting out carrion over a wide territory is a quality that, by its absence, directly contradicts Abel's theory. So there remains the plausible picture of monstrous predators attacking, rending and devouring their prey wherever and whenever they came across it.

The tyrannosaur is known only from the Upper Cretaceous. It was about the last of its predatory race, for they all died out by the end of the Cretaceous. Somewhat older is its predecessor, *Antrodemus,* from the Upper Jurassic, which was, however, considerably smaller, as was the European *Megalosaurus,* and *Gorgosaurus* from the Upper Cretaceous in Canada.

The very idea of a dinosaur always suggests a terrifying, gigantic monster. In general this is true, as we have already seen. A brachiosaur which towered to a height of 90 feet and could easily have looked in at the fourth-floor window of a block of apartments, or a teeth-gnashing tyrannosaur as tall as a tree, were indeed like creatures out of a nightmare. But beside these saurian Goliaths there were also the Davids. From the Jurassic in Bavaria we know of *Compsognathus,* an exceptionally tiny predator, perhaps the size of a cat, which must have moved very rapidly on two legs. Similar was *Ornitholestes,* a little animal of tremendous agility. These fed on small beasts, as was revealed by the stomach-contents of *Compsognathus,* or else were egg-thieves as is indicated by the name of *Oviraptor,* which was found, together with *Proto-ceratops,* in Mongolia.

Although the foregoing may suggest an abundant variety of types, those that have been mentioned represent a mere sampling of the most typical and best known. Numerous scattered fossil remains are still awaiting reconstruction and systematic arrangement. At any moment a fresh lucky discovery may bring to light a new, unknown saurian embedded in the rocks. But quite apart from this possibility, what we know today fully suffices to produce a complete biological

33. *Compsognathus,* a cat-sized predatory saurian from the Jurassic (according to Heilman)

picture of the Jurassic-Cretaceous and to confirm that this was the kingdom of the reptiles. And, indeed, it was so in the fullest sense, for the air, which hitherto had only been accessible to flying insects in a very restricted degree, was for a long period dominated by the reptiles.

This almost unbelievable fact took a long time to gain acceptance. As early as 1784 there was discovered in the Jurassic formation at Eichstätt in Bavaria a fossilised animal that could not be " placed " in any category. It was thought to be a sea beast or an aquatic bird, until Cuvier, with his incomparable ability, identified it as a flying reptile and named it *Pterodactylus.* At first not even he was believed; then the discovery of further specimens, some very well pre-

19. Saurians of the Mesozoic seas. (*Above*) *Plesiosaurus* and *Ichthyosaurus*. (*Below*) The predatory lizard, *Tylosaurus,* and in the air the huge flying reptile, *Pteranodon*.
Chicago Natural History Museum.

20. **Dinosaurs of the Cretaceous.** (*Above*) *Edmontosaurus* (right), *Palaeoscincus* (middle foreground), *Struthiomimus* (middle background), *Corythosaurus* (front left), and *Parasaurolophus* (left back). (*Below*) *Tyrannosaurus* (right) and *Triceratops* (left). *Chicago Natural History Museum.*

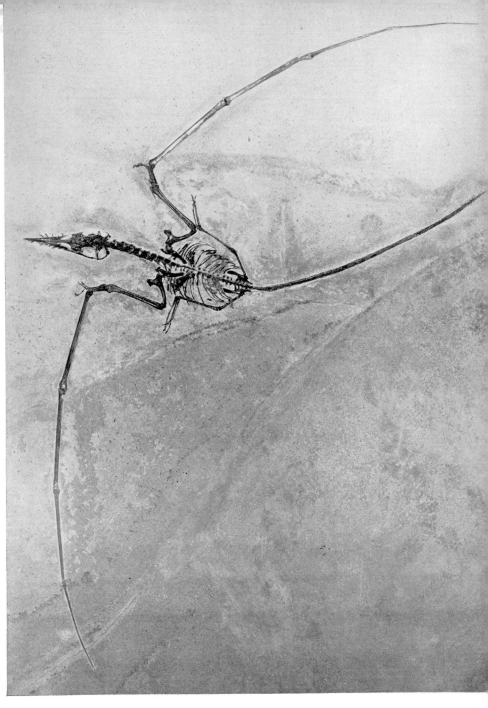

21. *Rhamphorhynchus*, from the Upper Jurassic of Solnhofen. *Natur-Museum Senckenberg, Frankfurt-am-Main.*

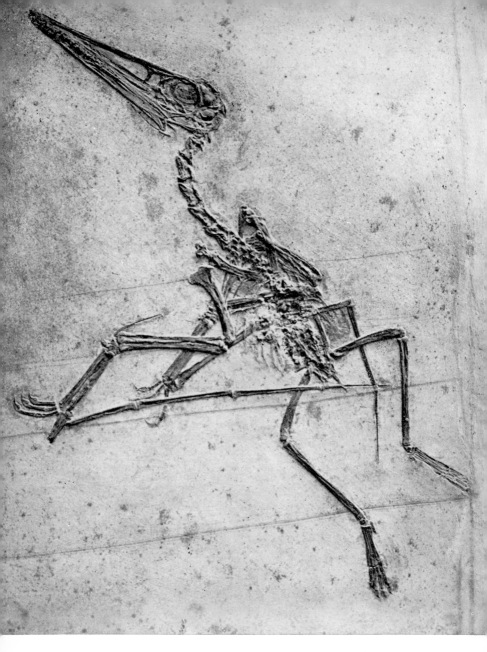

22. Pterosaur from the Upper Jurassic of Solnhofen.
Natur-Museum Senckenberg, Frankfurt-am-Main.

23. Life-size reproduction of a brontosaur.

24. Swamp landscape in the Everglades of Florida, a scene resembling the primaeval brown coal forests.

served, no longer left any doubt as to the prehistoric existence
of flying reptiles. With this group of vertebrates Nature had
now tried out every possible variation on ways of life.

It is easy to follow how, slowly and gradually, this invasion
of the air took place. The early pterosaurs were still very small,
clumsy flappers. The fourth fingers on each hand were
enormously prolonged, and the broad membranous wings

34. *Ornitholestes*, a small predatory saurian (according to
Osborn and Knight)

were stretched between them and the thighs of the hind legs.
The first three fingers had claws, the fifth was completely
stunted. The projecting three fingers were probably used to
grip when climbing about in the branches of trees. The teeth
included fangs which suggests that the pterosaurs may have
hunted small fish, a pursuit that would have required relatively accomplished flying. Their position of rest may have
resembled that of the bats, with their claws grasping a branch
and the body hanging head downwards.

The pterosaurs are represented by Jurassic forms such as *Rhamphorhynchus,* which still had a long sinewy tail, equipped at the end with a projecting membranous "sail" which could be used for the purpose of steering during flight. *Rhamphorhynchus* had a body the size of a dove and wings more than three feet across.

Pterodactylus, although smaller than *Rhamphorhynchus,* was a more advanced type with its tail reduced to a stub and its dentition beginning to disappear. Later forms had a horny beak instead of teeth.

The next forward step in the evolution of these saurians was possibly the growth of a hair covering and perhaps even— which would have been an immense step forward—a constant blood temperature, such as only birds and mammals possess today. Their brains, too, developed a greater, almost bird-like intelligence.

The giant among the pterosaurs—this being the general name given to flying reptiles from the Jurassic-Cretaceous— appeared during the Upper Cretaceous in the form of the *Pteranodon.* In Kansas, numerous fossilised remains have been found which suggest a gliding flier about the size of a man, with a wing-span of up to 24 feet. It thus considerably exceeded the wing-span of any bird living today. As in the case of the closely related pterodactyl, the tail of *Pteranodon* was almost entirely lacking. For the purpose of steering, a narrow bony excrescence, arising from the head and extending backwards in the same plane as the long pointed beak, must have been of great assistance. In contrast to its relatives in the Jurassic, who hunted near the shore, this animal would have been able to cover considerable distances over the open sea, living on fish and soft-bodied animals. To judge from its anatomic structure, its flying cannot have been achieved by actual flapping of the wings. The breast-bone was too weakly developed for this. But it was an accomplished and even elegant glider, with keen eyesight, a constant blood temperature and brains superior to those of other saurians. Yet these really excellently equipped reptiles died out too at the end of the Cretaceous.

In addition to the three genera just mentioned, there were also a number of other forms which have been found

in widely separated parts of the world. However, among the
pterosaurs there was nothing like the variety which prevailed
in the world of the land reptiles, or so we must assume from
their generally scanty fossil remains, the rich Jurassic and
Cretaceous layers in South Germany and North America
being quite exceptional cases. Discoveries elsewhere have been
very sparse, so it is by no means certain that these creatures

35. *Pteranodon*, the largest and most skilful flier among the
pterosaurs

were distributed all over the world. On the other hand, it
may be that the delicate, hollow bones of the flying saurians
were particularly susceptible to decay.

This bold attempt by Nature to conquer the air through
her favoured reptiles, in whom bird-like characteristics were
apparent not only in their powers of flight, might seem to
suggest that the true birds developed from them. But this was
not the case. The birds certainly evolved from the reptiles,
just as did the mammals, but not from the pterosaurs, which
must be regarded as a distinct line of development on their

own. The origin of the birds, the point of their branching off from the line of descent of the reptiles, must lie much further back, at least in the Triassic Period. So a common ancestry of dinosaurs and birds is probable.

We know next to nothing about the path followed by the reptile-bird line of descent during the 50 or so million years from the Triassic to the Jurassic. In this respect the fossil treasure of the Earth has failed us. It was only in the Upper Jurassic that the first true archetypal birds were discovered. The excitement this caused was tremendous, and it precipitated one of the bitterest arguments ever to arise over fossils.

In the year 1861 the quarries near Solnhofen yielded up an animal about the size of a crow, which had actually been feathered. The local Solnhofen doctor, one Häberlein, immediately realised the sensational importance of the find and acquired it. Shrewdly he spread the news about and offered the fossil for sale to the scientific world—at an immense, but wholly justifiable, price! He guarded his treasure so closely that he forbade any photographs or drawings of it. But he found no buyer in Germany. Since the head of the animal was at first thought to be missing and it was also in other respects defective, there was a great deal of critical talk, including the mention of the word "fake". But the British Museum, which had at least examined the object, put its trust in the fossil El Dorado of the Jura Mountains and acquired the disputed treasure in the face of all the conflicting opinions of the pundits. The amount paid was £600 (14,000 gold marks), a huge sum considering the value of money in those days. The British naturalist Sir Richard Owen quickly dispelled all doubts and confirmed that this was indeed a fossil with partly avian, partly saurian characteristics. So it joined the sum of scientific knowledge under the name of *Archaeopteryx*.

But this was not the end of the case of the "early bird". In 1877, in the Blumenberg near Eichstätt, a second specimen was discovered. Häberlein was once more quickly on the spot and bought it from the owner of the quarry. This second example was considerably better preserved than the first, and the head, being present, revealed a toothed beak. So up went the purchase price to 36,000 marks. Once again there followed a wearisome bargaining conducted by the shrewd doctor, who eventually came down to 26,000 marks but was still unable to dispose of his treasure in Germany. It almost looked as if some other country would succeed in securing the prize, when Werner von Siemens decided to pay 20,000 marks and saved the fossil for Germany. A little later the Prussian State Museum bought it for the same sum and it was given to the Berlin Natural History Museum.

This second flying beast was at first named *Archaeornis*, but it is now considered to belong to the same genus as the first, *Archaeopteryx*.

Although these two specimens must surely have been the most expensive fossils ever found by man, their actual contribution to science, in lending powerful support to the evolutionary theory, is indeed immense. They are animals representing the stage of development midway between reptile and bird. Both specimens have reptilian characteristics in the toothed beak, the freely movable rump- and tail-vertebrae, and the three-clawed, lizard fingers projecting from the wings: the primitive bird is evidenced in the beak itself, the plumage, and the ability to fly. So we have here transitional forms which could hardly be more revealing. Their flying skill cannot have been very great; at that stage they were still "learning".

The further stages on the road to the true birds are, so far, unknown for lack of relevant fossils. Throughout almost 70,000,000 years of the Cretaceous, we have, in this respect, virtually no information at all. Indeed it is not until the highly productive Upper Cretaceous in Kansas that we have definite knowledge of two true water fowl. These are *Hesperornis*, a swimming bird with extremely stunted wings which rendered it wholly incapable of flight, and *Ichthyornis*, which must certainly have been a good flier. Both forms still had toothed beaks.

Evidently the great development in the bird world, as in the world of mammals, first occurred in the following Tertiary Period, so that we shall have to take up the subject again then.

We have now covered the extremely colourful, adventurous, and undoubtedly monstrous world of the Jurassic and

36. Limestone slab containing specimen of *Archaeornis* from Eichstätt

Cretaceous Periods. The Mesozoic Era—the Earth's Middle Age—is over, and we are standing on the brink of the Modern Era in geology. Once again it must be emphasised that there are scarcely any clear-cut distinctions between individual eras or epochs. However, between the Cretaceous and the Tertiary there took place a tremendous biological event which characterised the beginning of the Modern Era and which does justify placing a caesura here: the saurians died out.

It must be understood that not all saurian forms became extinct, for lizards, crocodiles, snakes and tortoises still exist today as their direct descendants. What happened was that the groups dominating the Earth—the sea reptiles, the dinosaurs and the flying reptiles—vanished from the scene, not one of them surviving the end of the Cretaceous. In addition, certain other flourishing groups, such as the ammonites and the belemnites, also became extinct at this critical time.

The consequences of this biological change are abundantly clear. Vast living spaces were left uninhabited as a result of the disappearance of the saurians, and almost immediately the rise and spread of the mammals and birds began. Such a complete " changing of the guard " is unique in the history of the world and raises whole complexes of questions on the subject of evolutionary history. From the conditions prevailing, one thing must be accepted as a fact: the saurians had first to disappear, before the mammals could flourish. We have already established the earliest origins of the mammals with the therapsids of the Permian. From the Upper Triassic there are some very limited fossil remains (teeth, fragments of jaws, little pieces of skeletons) which evidently belonged to true mammals. In the Jurassic and Cretaceous, too, there are quite a few instances of remains of small animals which must certainly have been mammals. This means, therefore, that this highest class of animal was in existence for at least 120,000,000 years, up to the beginning of the Tertiary, without, over that enormous period of time, succeeding in making the smallest advance along its own evolutionary line. And one must remember that subsequently, in half that time, the mammals managed to develop from primitive, marsupial-like animals into men. This initially slow development can only be attributed to the saurians, whose strength and prevalence nipped in the bud any flowering of larger and more highly organised mammal forms. Helpless and humbled, hunted and literally down-trodden, these later lords of the earth crept away into every available escape nook and scarcely ever grew larger than a field-mouse—and when they did, it immediately proved their doom. Even widespread dispersion was made difficult by the fact that their environment was dominated by giants, one reason for the scantiness of surviving remains of their puny forms. And so the dying out of the saurians was a biological stroke of luck; for had the saurians completed their work and entirely destroyed the mammals, mankind would never have existed.

What caused this general decline of the saurians which finally led to their extinction?

This has always been, and still remains today, a riddle never wholly satisfactorily solved. The death of a species, the complete extinction of a class of animal or plant, is something that has often been known to happen in the past. Whether it was a matter of trilobites, graptolites, eurypterids, stegocephalia and Rudistes, or whole families of primitive rockbuilding corals, or trees such as *Sigillaria* and *Lepidodendron* from the Carboniferous, there was nothing unnatural or inexplicable in their vanishing from the face of the Earth after a long existence. They appeared always at a time of favourable physical environment to which they could respond. In every case an undeveloped youthful stage was followed by maturity when they were at their biological prime, then a period of ageing, and finally senility. This life-cycle is so familiar to us from individual examples, so much a part of the world of nature, that we can easily envisage its applying to the growth and death of whole groups of organisms. Every species in its development reaches only one climax, which is achieved by using all its inherent possibilities for development in the struggle for survival. Beyond this point, as the result of the exhaustion of inner potentialities, there is no possibility of further progress, the only further developments being purposeless aberrations which cannot possibly survive. The best example of this has been seen in the weird and useless shapes assumed by the ammonites. In every case, over lengthy periods of time, the physical and biological environment alters and makes fresh demands which, after reaching and exceeding certain limits, can no longer be satisfied. Suddenly there are better swimmers or runners, swifter and more agile enemies, who previously were lacking. Stronger animals will devour all the vegetation on which the weaker feed, or a change in climate effects a change in the vegetation which hitherto had provided sustenance. Predatory animals destroy the young of others, thereby imperilling the future generations.

There are many other possibilities of this kind which can satisfactorily explain the extinction of species no longer capable of further development. But what took place at the end of the Cretaceous far exceeded anything we can imagine. It was not a matter of the disappearance of a genus or species, or even of a whole family, but of an entire *race* of reptiles, distributed perhaps over the whole world, on the land, in the sea and in the air. If it were only *Brachiosaurus* that had died out, or just *Brontosaurus,* there would have been scarcely any cause for wonder. Such huge mobile mountains of flesh, with their tiny, inefficient brains, were a specialised form of life with very restricted possibilities for survival. A change in the flora on which they fed, or an increase in carnivorous enemies, would alone have sufficed seriously to threaten their existence. But an individual instance such as this could have had no effect upon the whole Mesozoic saurian world whose undisputed *Lebensraum* was the whole Earth. A failure of vegetation can only have occurred locally. And everywhere the plant world had been vastly enriched by the angiosperms. The dinosaurs could always have found their food. In the seas, the ichthyosaurs and particularly the mosasaurs were redoubtable enemies of the powerful sharks. And it is quite inexplicable why the beautifully developed and, moreover, intelligent *Pteranodon* is not today still soaring over the oceans of the world. There must, therefore, have been quite exceptional circumstances which, at a definite point in time, spelled the doom of the saurian world.

Conditions in their physical environment could scarcely have proved decisive, for the Palaeocene (the oldest part of the Tertiary Period) did not differ so greatly from the preceding Cretaceous. Even local geological upheavals, such as the Alpine mountain building which may have led to the drying out of swampy regions, could not have been a vital, all-explanatory factor. On land there were very few enemies—in fact, there were only the predatory saurians. And could *these* have so decimated the herbivorous saurians, that eventually they too died out one day for want of meat? Experience in the world of mammals has shown that no beast of prey has ever brought about the extermination of its victims. *Pteranodon,* moreover, had, among the scanty bird-life over all the wide oceans, not an enemy to fear.

There remains to be considered the threat to progeny from egg-eaters, an always debatable point which must be taken into very serious account. It is known for a fact that these egg-eaters existed among the smaller saurians (*Oviraptor,* for example). But to have menaced the existence of the dinosaurs, they must have been overwhelming in their numbers, which is not confirmed by fossil finds.

Professor Beurlen has considered the possibility of intrinsic causes. Every increase of size in a species, such as is typical of most saurians, necessitates a longer period of growth and a later onset of sexual maturity. As a result the intervals between generations naturally grow longer. At the same time, such animals usually bring fewer young into the world, which means a decrease in the total number of the species. Late maturing also brings about a weaker development of the sexual glands and a degeneration of the other ductless glands whose hormone secretion is partly regulated by the activity of the sexual glands. This results in bodily over-development which commonly leads to degeneration of the species.

A final possibility is the appearance on the scene of enemies who so far have apparently played no part in the world—the bacteria and viruses.

To what extent diseases existed in prehistoric times is not known. Until recently it was doubted that cold-blooded animals are susceptible to infectious diseases. However, in the past two decades investigations have revealed that death from infections occurs among large numbers of present-day reptiles. Hence the possibility exists that disease might have attacked the saurians. The world of bacteria may perhaps have come into existence in the far distant past, and up to the present day the dreaded prevalence of these microscopic creatures has not diminished. Indeed, they are still the most dangerous adversaries of higher forms of life, more frequently destroying us than we them. Their vitality is astonishing, and their capacity to become resistant to the most modern drugs, really alarming. What, therefore, if they had first " discovered " during the Cretaceous Period how to live as parasites in the bodies of the reptiles? Such an assault upon higher forms of life which lacked the necessary antibodies in their blood, would have been overwhelming and could certainly have been the cause of universal and almost simultaneous extinction. Admittedly, it is not known exactly what was the length of the period covering the final disappearance of the saurians. If there were a number of gradually accumulating causes, it might have been millions of years. But it equally might have been a mere few hundred years, if the desperate scourge of disease had swept the world. Over this subject hangs the darkness of a biological mystery that has yet to be dispelled by the light of science.

After the Carboniferous the world of the saurians is undoubtedly, to non-geologists, the most " popular " period in Earth's history. Among laymen, the age-old and widespread belief in the existence of " dragons " suddenly enjoyed a substantial renaissance as a result of the rapid accumulation of fossil treasures in museums. Even the most gruesome tales of griffins and fabulous monsters of antiquity seemed to be confirmed, at least partly, thus justifying all past suspicions. There followed rapid " explanations ": that the origins of these legends were based upon encounters between prehistoric men and saurians. But that, of course, is entirely out of the question. Man and dinosaur never came face to face. Even random discoveries of fossil skeletons, which early man may easily have made, could never have sufficed to stimulate mental reconstruction of such dragons. For that, anatomical knowledge and techniques, such as not even the Middle Ages possessed, were required.

But how, in fact, are 'the numerous dragon legends that exist among peoples of all nations to be explained? Is Siegfried's battle with the dragon entirely fictitious, nothing more than the product of a poet's imagination? Apparently the answer is yes. For among the thousands of cave drawings of Ice Age man, who lived long before the period when these legends first arose, there appear only animals that are well known to palaeontologists and not a single beast even remotely resembling a surviving dinosaur.

Cave art emerged in the areas bordering the glaciers which for a long time covered most of North and Central Europe.

In spite of lengthy and quite warm intervals, Europe was not an area that held much attraction for cold-blooded animals like the saurians. On the other hand, is it not possible that, in areas more climatically favourable, the last of the saurians may still be surviving up to this day—for instance in Central Africa, in the jungles and swamps of the Congo or Angola?

Since the beginning of this century there have been quite a number of reports suggesting just this, many embellished with every kind of lurid detail. Mighty animals such as rhinoceroses, hippopotamuses, and even elephants are said to have been attacked, mutilated and mangled. Vegetation at the scene of such battles was devastated as if a battle of Titans had taken place. Gigantic footprints and tracks suggested the presence of some enormous creature. Natives who chanced to be present at such encounters and bolted in panic, spoke of monstrous beasts with huge horns on their heads and wildly thrashing lizard-like tails. Other stories from the Congo-Angola-Cameroon region offer different descriptions, but all without exception tally remarkably with our ideas of what prehistoric saurians must have looked like. Most of these tales naturally come from natives, which does not make them any the more credible; but here and there they are alleged to have been confirmed by European settlers. For instance, there was "a Portuguese truck-owner" who, together with some natives, tracked down one of these rumours and in fact found traces of a struggle and the dismembered remains of a rhinoceros. An "animal-trapper" named Hagenbeck claimed to have been hot on the trail of an actual monster. A M. le Page stated that, in 1920, he came face to face with a prehistoric creature. And a "German scientist" (name not known!) said that he had photographed one. (Unfortunately, the photograph never saw the light of day, although it would have provided the strongest possible "scientific" proof.) A "Negro chieftain" repeated his grandfather's description of a giant lizard that was said to have died during the old man's day. Similar stories were told to a German expedition in the Cameroons in 1913. Frau Ilse von Nolde, who lived for a long time in Angola, collected a number of more or less credible reports from native sources. These were frequently contradictory, but that need not be taken as a total disproof of their truth, for such an encounter in the midnight jungle would be enough to addle the descriptive powers of anyone lucky enough to return to tell the tale.

It is difficult to say what, if any, truth there is in such stories. It is not simply a matter of ascribing the reports of Europeans to the psychological effects of living in the tropics, and dismissing the native tales as the lies of "children of nature", lacking in judgement and prone to exaggeration. But, inherently, there is little probability in any of these tales. It is significant that they only tell of encounters with individual saurian descendants, and over quite a number of decades the total of such adventures has been remarkably small. We might expect that a group of animals that had survived through 60 million years to the present day would be in a flourishing state and existing in considerable numbers. It would be really too extraordinary if the very last representative of a dying race were to be seen only in the twentieth century, as the "native chief" claimed. Nor is there any confirmation of the rumour that certain cave-drawings in South Africa, unlike those in Europe, depict these prehistoric beasts. The location of the caves in question has never been divulged, so it is impossible to investigate the assertion.

It is true that, even today, there are swamp areas in the interior of Africa which are almost entirely unexplored; they are full of secrets, perils and—perhaps—unknown species of animals. But, broadly speaking, one can hardly talk any longer of the "dark Continent". The insatiable hunting-lust of foot-loose adventurers, the desperate search for mineral treasures, the invincible curiosity of scientific expeditions, have all left scarcely a blank spot on the map, so that it would be really remarkable if reliable observers—and which of them is not armed with a camera these days?—had not obtained at least one "snap" of an extinct saurian, particularly since the outlines of the territory in which these interesting beasts are supposed to disport themselves are fairly definitely demarcated.

It goes without saying that official science gives no weight to these rumours. If it were otherwise, obviously every museum in the world would regard as its bounden duty the capture alive of one of these prehistoric relics. This particular possibility seems, on the whole, not to have worried the museums'

curators. Only when, in 1938 and after, the famous coelacanths were netted from the sea, did the romantic cherishers
of these legendary rumours spring into action again. Here
was a precisely analogous case! Until the first coelacanth was
caught, scientists were convinced that it had been extinct for
the past 60 million years. And now the fact that it "is"
instead of "was" has forced them to think again.

Thinking again can certainly do no harm, but the case of
the coelacanth is exceptional. The immense masses of water
covering the globe have been far less intensively explored
than the much more accessible land surfaces. Life in the seas
has now yielded up its proof of prehistoric survival. If the
land were to do likewise, science would be grateful and
jettison a theory that at present denies such a possibility.
Until that happens, "chipekve", "coje ya menia" and the
other fabled animals with their widely varied native names
cannot be taken seriously.

Yet how are the closely similar stories of dragons, which
appear among peoples widely separated in place and time, to
be explained? How did the idea arise that Siegfried slew a
dragon, when there apparently never existed a dragon to
slay? Well, it is safe to say that no legends have ever sprung
from the "communal consciousness" of a people; they have
always been the product of the poetic imaginations of a few
especially gifted individuals whose intellectual powers enabled
them to perceive more, to sense more and to invent more
than the mass of their fellow beings. Any small, vividly
persistent memory from childhood may help the reader to
understand this.

From the homely lizard could be elaborated tales of terrible
fights with dragons; the very small magnified into the
monstrous. There are, indeed, sub-tropical forms of lizards,
such as the Agamidae—a family including frilled lizards with
"wings" on either side of the body—which by virtue of
their bizarre appearance provide a perfect model for legendary flying monsters.

At this point mention could well be made of the colouring
of the prehistoric lizards. Unfortunately we know little about
this, for fossilisation is not capable of preserving colours. But
there seems to be no valid reason for supposing that the early

saurians were in this respect fundamentally different from those we know in the world today—lizards, snakes and crocodiles. It must be admitted, however, that the colouring of all "reconstructions" of all fossil animals is really no more than guesswork—and the same is true of the amount and distribution of hairs, scales, etc., on their skin.* Even much of the outline (when it is influenced by muscle rather than bone structure) is the result of imagination, usually allied, we hope, with profound anatomical knowledge.

And our radio wave is still racing through space. It is now little more than 60 million light years away, a mere nothing compared to the distance which it has already traversed. Nevertheless, it is still on the far, far side of the Milky Way.

* It is very rarely indeed that the fine surface details are preserved, as did however happen in the case of the ' mummified ' *Edmontosaurus*.

CHAPTER FOURTEEN

The New Age Begins

EARTH'S modern era—the Cainozoic—is subdivided into
two parts, the Tertiary and the Quaternary. These names are
survivals from the oldest geological nomenclature in which
the Palaeozoic was called the Primary Era, and the Mesozoic
the Secondary Era. The Quaternary, which includes the
Pleistocene and the Holocene, is the most recent, extending
right up to the present day and going back some 1,000,000
years. The other 70 million years belong to the Tertiary,
which, being earlier in chronological sequence, we shall
obviously deal with first.

The Tertiary is subdivided into the Palaeocene, Eocene,
Oligocene, Miocene and Pliocene Periods, each being differentiated by, amongst other things, the varying content of
present-day surviving life in its geological strata: thus in the
Palaeocene and Eocene there is roughly 10 per cent, in the
Oligocene 20 per cent, in the Miocene 40 per cent and in the
Pliocene as much as 80 per cent. These figures are of great
significance and clearly indicate the increasingly rapid change
of fauna with the approach of the modern age.

A similarly rapid transformation took place on the face of
the Earth, with the climax and conclusion of the Alpine folding movements which had begun in the Jurassic and Cretaceous. The final result was that by the time of the Pliocene
the proportionate division between land and water was
within 20 per cent of what it is today. This folding process
evidently began in the late Jurassic and raised up large
portions of the North American Rocky Mountains. The
South American Cordilleras followed in the late Cretaceous.
Whereas the ranges or chains of these foldings ran from
North to South, the young mountains of Europe and Asia
built up in an East-West direction. That meant the end of
the age-old Tethys Sea, from the floor of which were extruded

the Atlas Mountains, The Pyrenees, the Alps, the Carpathians, the Caucasus, and the mountain ranges of the Balkans and Asia Minor. The climax came during the transition between the Oligocene and the Miocene, and this world-wide crustal movement was certainly one of the most violent since the world began. Obviously, such an immense mountain-building process, which did not take place everywhere simultaneously but occurred in successive phases, made enormous differences to the general topographical picture. At first it caused extensive transgressions by both the Tethys and the Northern Euro-

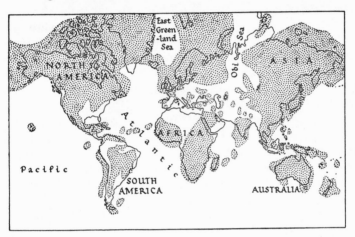

37. Map of the world at the beginning of the Alpine mountain folding

pean Seas. In the Palaeocene and Eocene, the Northern Sea flooded over the whole Anglo-Gallic basin and spread as far as Pomerania. In the Oligocene it extended across North Germany and Russia as far as the Aral Sea. At this period, too, the lowlands of the Upper Rhine were inundated and became an arm of the Tethys Sea, which thus was temporarily connected with the North Sea. The great land bridges of the northern continents—Ireland-Iceland-Greenland-America on the one side, and Alaska-Siberia on the other—subsided at numerous places, but were continually rebuilt until their final collapse in the Pleistocene of the Quaternary Period. In the Palaeocene the land connection between North and South America was broken, only to be re-established in the middle Pliocene. The final retreat of the oceans occurred after the Miocene, by which time all the chief mountain-foldings were completed. But there still persisted, for a long time, shallow basins and inland seas of varying extent. All these geological processes were accompanied by immense, primarily basaltic, eruptions and an intense increase in volcanic activity. Practically all volcanoes active today are the scattered relics of that period. Naturally, the Early Tertiary system of rivers was entirely disrupted and—mainly in the Miocene—completely re-distributed. It was only then that the Rhine, Weser, Elbe, Danube, Loire, etc., came into existence in Europe. Among the sediments there predominated sandstones, schist and marl—compositely known as Flysch. This is found bordering the Eastern Alps and the Carpathians, in Dalmatia, Greece and throughout South Asia, frequently associated with nummulite limestone.

The now extinct nummulites were protozoa which suddenly appeared on the scene, in incalculable numbers and exceptional size and built most of the chalk coasts of the Tethys Sea. We have already twice before encountered a similar sudden appearance, flourishing and disappearance of animals of this kind in the case of the orbitolites of the Cretaceous and, before them, Fusulina of the Carboniferous. Such spontaneous outbursts are one of the strangest phenomena in Nature, for they represent attempts to achieve immense effects by the repeated use of minute animalculae in a role identical to the one they had already played as "primal creatures" in the Pre-Cambrian. An interesting point about these protozoa is their repeated development of new types, for the nummulites did not exist before the Tertiary. It is precisely here, close to the very source of life itself, that vitality seems inexhaustible; for protozoa are enduring forms of life which, in spite of the extinction of numerous species, have been with us since the remote dawn of time and, quite apart from surviving, continue always to produce new varieties. Thus the stream of life flows on.

The climate of the Tertiary was generally warmer than that of today. It was warm enough to cause sub-tropical vegetation to spread to far northern territories. At the very start of the Tertiary the average annual temperature was probably 20° C.; in the following Eocene it was 22°. Then there began a gradual decline (Oligocene 20°, Miocene 19-17°, Pliocene 16-14°) until it reached roughly the present-day average.

The violent drop which led to the Ice Age no longer had any connection with the Tertiary. This steady lowering of temperature once more brings us up against the complex interaction of geophysical conditions. The folding of the gigantic European-Asian mountain chains must have brought about a local change of climate in the regions lying to the north. The masses of water which evaporated into the atmosphere from the constricted Tethys Sea could not easily cross these high ranges which had now become watersheds. The air currents, too, were diverted and their prevalence changed. The cooling winds from the Arctic now prevailed in all northern regions; and this could have brought about the fall in temperatures. What is, however, inexplicable, is the apparently sudden cooling of the poles—for, as has been mentioned, it is far from certain that they were always ice-capped. A pronounced tilting of the Earth's axis must again be considered a possibility; one result of this—apart from the exceptional case of the Ice Age—would have been our contemporary climatic zones, starting gradually and then becoming more and more sharply differentiated. The retreat of the warmth-loving subtropical flora first became evident in Central Europe towards the end of the Miocene, and finally, during the Pliocene, plant life in Europe took on approximately its present-day character. Coral deposits during the Miocene are only known as far north as the latitude of Malta.

Mineral resources originating in the Tertiary were primarily oil, salt and lignite (brown coal). About 50 per cent of all Earth's oil resources date from the Tertiary; the remainder is divided principally between the Cretaceous, Devonian and Silurian strata. Science is by no means clear as to how oil—of such vital importance to world economy—is actually formed. Like coal it is certainly organic in origin. Water saturated with salt and poorly aerated must be regarded as an essential factor. The chief organic source of mineral oil may be found in plankton, a collective term embracing all plant and animal life which leads a drifting existence in the seas and lakes, and comprising the microscopic protozoa, algae, jelly fish, certain snails and crustacea. If these animals die in waters such as those described above, they will not decay but will disintegrate, under the influence of anaerobic bacteria (which can exist without oxygen) into a mixture of hydro-carbons. A rapid covering with sediments will then induce a gradual transformation into mineral oil.

We have already seen, in the limestone seas of the Permian, how salt deposits were created. In the Tertiary the same pro-cess must also have taken place. The retreating Tethys Sea left behind it great inland lakes which, because there were no rivers and no rainfall to sweeten their waters, did not change to fresh water but very gradually evaporated as their channels to the open sea dwindled. A classic " contemporary " example is the Kara-Bogaz-Gol, a lagoon-like off-shoot of the Caspian Sea, to which it is only connected by a very narrow shallow channel. In this " Black Gully ", which is what its name means, huge salt deposits are forming. Today the salt content of the water is already 18 per cent (the average salinity of the open oceans does not exceed about 3.74 per cent). In Europe during the Miocene the Vienna Basin, for example, must have been just such a salt lake. From it came the gigantic salt deposits of Wielczka on the northern side of the Car-pathians where rock salt has been quarried for six hundred years, and the seemingly inexhaustible seam goes down to a depth of 900 feet. Here, as a consequence of a Tertiary inland sea, human moles have excavated a subterranean laby-rinth of caverns and passages which today stretch for more than 70 miles.

The first stupendous development of land plants culmin-ated during the Carboniferous. Now the Tertiary provided a second climax for the terrestrial flora. All that had been merely tentative during the Jurassic and Cretaceous matured during the subsequent 70 million years. The gymnosperms had been joined and were in the process of being ousted by the angiosperms, which flourished extravagantly on many different parts of the earth. Step by step, the covering of vegetation consolidated itself, stored up rain-water in humus-producing soil, and thus regulated the water supply of regions that for aeons had been barren. The period of scattered, oasis-like islands of vegetation was finally ended in the global sense. The sub-tropical climate produced extensive forests, which were not, like the Carboniferous forests, restricted to swampy regions around sea coasts, but stretched far into what had been predominantly dry areas. Of course the nature of the vegetation varied according to the soil, the land elevation, and climatic conditions. (For instance, jungles as luxuriant as the present-day Amazonian forests could only have flourished on damp and swampy terrain.) As a result of these conditions whole generations of plants sank into the ground and, after first becoming peat, commenced the old Carboniferous coal-building process and ended up as brown coal. It is quite possible that the vast lignite deposits we know of today *could* be transmuted into mineral coal by further tectonic convulsions in the distant future. But, so far as we can tell, after the main Alpine foldings there are unlikely to be any further major crustal foldings in Central Europe. Anyhow, the human race cannot wait that long, and men have therefore exploited brown coal as and where they have found it. It is far more accessible than the usually deep-lying mineral coal, for the few sedimentary layers from the Tertiary that cover it are easily penetrated. Indeed, it is often mined by opencast methods.

It was to be expected that the lignite deposits would prove rich treasure-houses of Tertiary life, at least of plant life, which was much easier to identify in the soft brown coal than in the hardened and chemically transformed mineral coal. And such was indeed the case. Seeds, fruit, remains of wood, well-preserved leaves, even whole tree-trunks, roots, etc., were found, which permitted the reconstruction of a complete picture of the flora of that period.

On the other hand, animal remains are practically non-existent, just as in the case of mineral coal. The main reason for this is that in the process of coal-formation humic acids are produced which destroy the lime in bones. (In mineral coal mines animal fossils have only been discovered over or under the actual coal seams; that is, in the surrounding sedimentary layers.)

But a sensational exception was provided by various brown-coal mines in the Geisel Valley near Halle in Germany. These

38. Typical lignite swamp clearing, with crocodile and primitive forms of tapir and flamingo (according to Z. Burian)

mines lie between Halle and Merseburg and are world-famed in scientific circles as being unique and superb repositories of animal remains from the world of the Tertiary. Apart from abundant forms of insect life, including the larvae of flies and the most delicate structures conceivable, there are, especially, skeletons of vertebrates with marvellously preserved fragments of skin, muscles, pelts, which seem to emerge in almost inexhaustible quantities from their brown-coal sarcophaguses after 40 million years—and the Geisel valley brown coal must be as old as that, since it dates from the Eocene. One particularly fortunate circumstance was a decisive factor in this unique preservation of Tertiary life. The Geisel valley Tertiary adjoins layers of shelly limestone—the Triassic Muschelkalk—as a result of which the ground water, containing dissolved lime, penetrated the brown-coal beds and prevented almost completely the formation of the destructive humic acids. Thus, after the Jura Mountains, the Geisel valley turned out to be the richest source of fossils in Europe.

The vegetation of the area, as revealed by the Geisel valley discoveries, was sub-tropical to tropical. There were swamp-

39. Amber containing insects and plants

cypresses and giant sequoias, such as we know today only in the sparsely surviving giant trees of North America. Forests of rubber-trees, interspersed with palmetto thickets, laurel and cinnamon trees, and of course palms of the most varied kinds, all grew alongside oaks and other deciduous and coniferous trees. Tropical rain forests alternated with swamps and steppe-like regions, seemingly in rather sudden juxtaposition. Thus a sharp division between dry and rainy periods is by no means out of the question and, indeed, suggests a comparison with the present-day conditions in the South American Matto Grosso.

With negligible variations the Geisel valley flora covered every region of the then surface of the Earth and especially the lowlands and foothill jungles of Eocene Europe. Date and coconut palms grew along the Rhine. In England, tree-ferns, *Nipa* palms and *Pandanus* trees (screw-pines) flourished. The lotus grew in Southern France; North Italy had eucalyptus, sandalwood, camphor, and dragon-trees. In Greenland and Spitzbergen the remains of oaks, planes, vines and laurels have been discovered.

At this period, too, there flourished coniferous trees whose resin, exuded in vast quantities, is now the semi-precious amber. Not only was amber highly esteemed by the ancients as an ornamental material, but it is today of considerable importance to the palaeontologists. The original sticky, fluid resin, which only hardened subsequently, frequently enclosed insects, spiders, leaves and small mosses, and preserved all these objects in an ideally fossilised condition. Two thousand species of insect alone have been discovered and identified in their amber settings.

This tropical exuberance retreated in Europe gradually as the average temperature dropped. In the Lower Miocene the vegetation in Central Europe had changed but little. But by the Upper Miocene palms were to be found only in the still very favourable climatic area around the Lake of Constance.

The tropical climatic conditions which today prevail north and south of the equator were in the early Tertiary spread well into the northern latitudes and similarly the animal world of the present-day tropics then inhabited territories far

40. *Phororhacos inflatus*, a giant running-bird from the Miocene in Patagonia. Length of head: 1 foot

to the north. The Geisel valley "treasure house" has yielded up numerous remains of crocodiles, turtles, precursors of giant snakes, tropical lizards, early primates, relatives of the tapir and the Andean condor. It is certainly a curious thought that hippopotamuses once swam in the Rhine. And rhinoceroses seem equally out of place in Mongolia, not to mention camels in North America. Yet that was the appearance of the world in the Tertiary Era. For now we have reached the age of the fast-evolving fauna which became the occupants of the regions abandoned by the extinct saurians.

Nothing more was any longer to be seen of those grotesque Cretaceous monsters. Of course it is possible that here and there a few surviving specimens lasted into the beginning of the Tertiary; but we certainly do not know of this for a fact. Very much more slowly, and now plainly surpassed by the mammals, the reptiles as a class pursued their modest way until they attained their present status. In this connection, it is remarkable that the snakes themselves are the only ones to have evolved further in any respect. For a very long while they were non-poisonous. Fangs with poison channels and grooves are only known from the Miocene, and with this deadly weapon these elegant and beautiful creatures recaptured some of the awesomeness of their ancestors.

Of the turtles, the predominating types were land and fresh-water animals. Fossil examples (in the Siwalik strata) from the East Indies have been discovered up to 9 feet in length. Generally, however, they never achieved the monstrous size of their Mesozoic ancestors.

The birds developed very rapidly. Possibly the lack of enemies in the air helped. As far back as the earliest Tertiary toothless forms had appeared. A striking feature in many fossil types is the loss of ability to fly owing to the stunting of their wings. Numerous fossil discoveries in all parts of the world have brought to light running and walking birds resembling our present-day ostriches, nandus and cassowaries. For the greater part these were giant animals. The skeleton of the elephant-bird (*Aepyornis maximus*) from Madagascar was 9 feet tall. This inability to fly seems to have had no adverse effect on the powers of survival of these creatures, since their descendants still exist today in the same climatic

regions and have only to fear extinction at the hands of man.
But here, indeed, they have a bitter and merciless enemy;
for even in historic times, probably as late as the fourteenth
century, there lived in New Zealand the moa (*Dinornis*), a
huge, flightless bird that reached a height of 9 feet. To judge
from kitchen refuse—broken skulls and bones—the Maoris,
who settled in New Zealand, must have made short work of
these birds. Their extermination was rapid and complete, for
the first human settlers in the islands ate the eggs of the surviving moas and thus decimated their progeny. The same fatal
ending befell the dodo, a bird about the size of a turkey, also
flightless, which inhabited the islands of Mauritius, Bourbon
and Rodriguez. Sailors always need meat and eggs — and thus the fate of the bird was sealed.

41. The moa (*Dinornis maximus*),
extinct in historical times

To consider for a moment the origin of such fantastic legendary birds as the roc, etc., one may reason-
ably assume seafarers in the early Middle Ages must have encountered the elephant-bird of Madagascar or even the moas of New Zealand. The Arabs in particular were great ex-
plorers, and it was in one of their legends re-
lated in the *Thousand and One Nights* that the roc first appeared.

Generally speaking, circumstances were not particularly favourable for the fossilisation of birds. The only excep-

tions were provided by swamp and aquatic birds. Dead forest
birds would almost inevitably be devoured quickly by carrion-
eating beetles, ants, etc. The hollow bones, gnawed clean,
usually decayed and seldom survived to sink into the protection of a preservative soil where they could become fossilised.
Nevertheless, discoveries up to now have sufficed to show that,
compared to mammals, present-day forms of bird life were
earlier on the scene and more fully represented.

With the insects we are far better—almost completely—
informed. The wealth of amber, the fossil El Dorado of the
Geisel valley, and numerous discoveries in other places have
yielded, at least in Europe and North America, a rich variety
of insects which is hardly exceeded by those known to exist
today. The amazingly highly organised social insects—bees,
ants and termites—now also inhabited the land.

We left the amphibians at the point when the kingdom of
the reptiles came into its own and the large armour-headed
Labyrinthodonts were about to become extinct. Their
departure was not, however, fatal to the amphibians, for the
vitality of this whole class of animals has always remained,
and still remains, undiminished. Today, frogs, toads, salamanders, newts, still hop, crawl, climb and creep, having developed into a wide and varied assortment of
creatures, diurnal and nocturnal, inhabiting the most diverse
territories. The Earth in the Tertiary swarmed with such
creatures, as well as giant leaping frogs and toads which have
long since died out. In this respect, too, the Geisel valley has
contributed its quota, for in addition to the four known sub-
orders existing today, it has produced 14 other species. And
the remains of more than 260 salamanders have also been
found.

The first discovery of a Tertiary amphibian belonging to
the group of giant salamanders came to light in 1726 and—
just like *Mosasaurus*—in rather humorous circumstances. In
that year the successful Swiss collector Scheuchzer (1672-1733)
found in the Miocene limestone near the town of Constance
a fossil which he described as the remains of an antediluvian
man. In contemporary verbiage he wrote: "This likeness,
which is presented in an excellent wood-cut for the scrutiny
of the learned and curious, is an undoubted and veritable

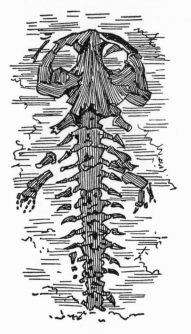

42. Scheuchzer's "antediluvian man", a fossilised giant salamander

survival from the Biblical Flood; there are to be found not merely a few lineaments which suggest to the fertile and ingenious imagination resemblance to Man, but an absolute correspondence to the various parts of the human bone-structure, the complete symmetry, indeed, of the bones embedded in the stone; even the softer parts, too, have survived *in natura*. This Man, whose sepulchre exceeds in antiquity and authenticity all those of the ancient Romans and Greeks, as well as of the Egyptians or other Orientals, is seen from the frontal aspect."

The worthy Scheuchzer was, of course, a firm believer in the Flood and probably took a naively sensational pleasure in being able to present to his contemporaries a fossil from the days of Noah. Nevertheless, he was a physician; and it is somewhat difficult to understand the (certainly unconscious) mental blinkers he wore in his further detailed anatomical description of his discovery. Other anatomists expressed their opinions, until at last—as so often—Cuvier (in 1811) spoke the final word on this extraordinary object, which had meanwhile ended up at a Haarlem museum. He prepared it properly as a specimen and recognised it indisputably as an extinct giant salamander. In spite of the comical mis-diagnosis, the fossil bears, in honour of its discoverer, the name *Andrias scheuchzeri*. It was closely related to the present-day Japanese monster salamander. Since numerous similar finds have subsequently been made, there can be no doubt that in the Tertiary these amphibians enjoyed a new hey-day, having, in their giant form, suffered a severe decline during the Triassic Period. It may also be assumed that, overshadowed by the competition from reptiles during the Mesozoic, they did not flourish as they might well have done if they had had the field to themselves. In this connection, the rapid advance of the birds in the Mesozoic is noteworthy, for they, being able to fly through the air almost free from danger, found conditions for development far more favourable than those confronting the mammals, who only started their effective evolution after the total disappearance of the saurians. Then, however, the habitable regions of the Earth became gloriously free of enemies and the highest class of vertebrates was able at last to give full rein to its suppressed vitality.

CHAPTER FIFTEEN

Transformation of the Animal World

T H E period that now ensued was one of unparalleled development and diversity in the animal world—or, if one must have
a parallel, it can be compared to the conquest of the Earth
by the saurians. One cannot even say that the parallel fails
in regard to duration and final extinction. For we do not
know how long the era of mammals will last, since the 70
million years that we can survey come up to the present day
and it is obviously impossible to calculate or even to guess
how long it will continue into the future. But although we
cannot definitely predict the eventual extinction of the
mammals, it is clear that mammals, as the predominant form
of life in this world, are definitely declining. This is a fact
that can be supported by figures. In the Tertiary, so far as
we know, there existed a total of 32 orders, with 2,864 genera
and 15,000 species. In the present day there are, by contrast,
only 18 orders, with 1,932 genera and 6,000 species known.
All the rest have already died out! Admittedly, present-day
orders include the few (4 or 5) mammalian orders which are
believed to have existed in the Mesozoic Era. But this does
not alter the total picture, which shows a definite, general
decline in the world of mammals.

The anatomical revolution in the development of mammals
lay primarily in the increasing differentiation and final per-
fection of their method of bringing young into the world.
This development was in three stages. The first mammals
were merely animals which laid eggs like reptiles, and then,
unlike reptiles, suckled the young after they were hatched.
The classical example of this is the duck-billed platypus of
Australia, which is a living survival of this transitional stage.
In its outward appearance alone, with its beak-like snout and
thick fur, it is a grotesque in the present-day animal world.
Its suckling ability has not developed into the form of actual

teats. The milk is spurted at its young through sieve-like areas in the skin. The platypuses are known as Monotremata because the ducts leading from the ovaries or testes, from the bladder and from the digestive tract, all open into a single cloaca or common outlet. Undoubtedly the platypuses are related to the Multituberculata among the primal mammals which, in their later forms, died out in the beginning of the Tertiary.

The next step upwards led to the marsupials. These are animals which no longer lay eggs, but give birth to incompletely developed young and suckle them in a pouch until

43. The duck-billed platypus

they become independent. The best-known contemporary marsupials are the kangaroo, opossum, phalanger and koala bear. They were fairly widespread as far back as the Cretaceous, and in the early Tertiary they were distributed over almost the whole of the Earth. But after that they became confined to the Australian archipelago and South America, as a result of domination elsewhere by those mammals which achieved the third and highest step in embryonic evolution —the Placentalia, to whom Man, in this particular sense, belongs.

Among the Placentalia the embryos, until actual birth, are nourished from the mother's blood by a form of osmosis through the wall of the uterus.

Other rapidly developing anatomical features of the mammals which contributed to their powers of survival were: a great variety of tooth formations; complete adaptation of the foot to every sphere of life until, in the case of monkeys and men, it became a prehensile hand; and, most important of all, the increasing emphasis on the brain in a correspondingly expanding cranium. Growth in physical size was also widespread. Whereas, in the Jurassic, the Multituberculata

44. *Uintatherium*, an amblypod from the Middle Eocene of North America (according to Scott)

and Marsupialia were still tiny animals, by the time of the Eocene they appeared prolifically as quite sizable creatures.

Naturally, the road of general development ran, broadly speaking, from the simplest to higher and finally the highest types, in chronological sequence. In spite of their immense variety of forms, it is certain that all the higher mammals (the Placentalia) are descended from a common origin, the order of Insectivora which number today such odd small representatives as the hedgehog, mole and shrew. From their ancestors sprang all living forms that are included among the Placentalia—even Man.

The first great group which developed during the transition from Cretaceous to Eocene was the Creodonta, primitive carnivores which have long since died out, but from which are descended all true present-day carnivores. At this early stage the creodonts were equipped with few carnivorous teeth. Their intelligence, too, must have been far inferior to that of present-day cats and dogs; and their average size was quite small. It was not until the Eocene or Oligocene (in Wyoming and Mongolia) that full-scale beasts appeared, when, for instance, *Andrewsarchus,* a carnivore discovered in Mongolia, probably reached 12 feet in length.

The first recognisable ungulates, the Condylarthra and the Amblypoda, were contemporary with the flesh-eating creodonts. All of these early ungulates had very small brains; the Condylarthra were also small in body, being no bigger than sheep. The amblypods, which had emerged in the Palaeocene and disappeared again by the Lower Oligocene, resembled in their early forms the hippopotamus. As in the case of the latter, their teeth were so constructed that they served only for severing, crushing and grinding their vegetable food, being entirely useless as weapons. In this case, as so frequently happened with other animal species, lop-sided specialisation could easily lead to early extinction.

The Middle Eocene, which now followed with its "paradisal" annual mean temperature of 22° C., was a period of exceptional fertility, and both the Middle and Upper Eocene brought forth some giant creatures of remarkable form. North America and Mongolia produced *Uintatherium,* an animal the size of a rhinoceros but resembling an elephant, with a massive skull adorned with horn-like growths and projecting incisor teeth. Another odd ungulate was *Arsinoitherium,* from the Lower Oligocene in Egypt, a beast with a 10-feet-long elephant's body and a pair of huge forward-projecting horns on the head. As far as is known neither the Condylarthra nor the Amblypoda were ancestors of the present-day ungulates; these latter must have descended from the common stock which also produced the creodonts.

The trend towards the conquest of the water—not their natural element—which was so characteristic of the reptiles, also made a very early appearance among the mammals. As discoveries from the Middle Eocene in North America, Egypt and West Africa show, there were already at that period whales—it would be more accurate to say, primitive whales—which must have evolved in direct line of descent from the monstrous creodonts. They were true carnivores with fangs, and in no way inferior to the horrific mosasaurs of the Cretaceous. Since they reached lengths of from 40 to 60 feet (*Zeuglodon* and *Basilosaurus*), there can be little doubt that

45. *Basilosaurus*, a primitive whale from the Eocene in North America. The name is misleading, for this beast was not a saurian but, like present-day whales, a mammal

they dominated those ocean hunting-grounds where once the mosasaurs had reigned. Not until very much later, perhaps in the Oligocene, did their descendants such as the right-whale, having lost their teeth, change over to a predominantly plankton diet, whereby they adapted themselves to a form of food supply that was virtually inexhaustible and thus could continue to develop their own giant forms with impunity. Of this family, the blue whale has been known to reach a length of over 90 feet, thus being the largest recorded animal, exceeding even the giants among the dinosaurs. In intelligence they are among the cleverest of animals, probably the equal of dogs and maybe chimpanzees, so that they should normally be able to enjoy unchallenged mastery of the seas for an illimitable time to come. But they too have encountered a fearful enemy—Man. The sight of the floating factories of the present-day whaling fleets, with their super-efficient modern weapons, will make it plain to anyone that *Homo sapiens* is well on his implacable way to the eventual extermination of these ocean mammals. It will not take much longer. All the "close seasons" and restrictive regulations can no longer avert their extinction. The toothed whales, too, which have predominantly taken to feeding on fish and cephalopods, as did the ichthyosaurs in the Upper Cretaceous, and therefore frequently have to dive much deeper, still must come to the surface in order to breathe, and there they are caught.

Among the later terrestrial ungulates in the Eocene there developed a division into two orders, the even-toed and the odd-toed, of which the odd-toed seems to have appeared somewhat earlier. This distinction, based on anatomical peculiarities, needs a little explanation. Even-toed ungulates are animals whose toes are always arranged in pairs—2 toes or 4; never 1 or 3. The original 5-toed structure disappeared in all these animals due to the total atrophy of the fifth toe. Present-day animals belonging to the even-toed order are the hippopotamus, camel, pig, all cattle, deer and the giraffe. Among the odd-toed, living examples include the tapir with 4 toes on its forefeet but only 3 on its hind ones, the rhinoceros with 3 toes on each foot and the horse with only single-toed hoofs.

For an excellent picture of the evolutionary development of a group of mammals, an ideal subject is the horse—or, rather, the whole family Equidae, since the wild ass, the donkey and the zebra are all descended from the same stock. In this instance, science has at its disposal fossil material so complete that it reveals, step by step, almost the whole process of development from primitive, dog-sized, four-toed little horses up to those of the present day.

The evolution of the horse is characterised by three impor-

tant features: a gradual increase in size, a reduction in the
number of toes, and the transformation of the teeth to their
present-day long-crowned form. This process of development
can be seen at every intermediate and transitional stage
throughout the duration of the Tertiary. The discovery of
prehistoric horse-like creatures completely confirmed Darwin's
basic assumptions; for here emerged a picture of the very
gradual transformation of a species, by means of quite minor,
hereditary changes (mutations) and by natural selection,

46. *Arsinoitherium* from the Lower Oligocene in Egypt

which finally arrived at a form best adapted to coping with
its environment.

Of recent years a biological theory was propounded which
claimed that, instead of continuous development through
countless tiny mutations, there occurred instead sudden,
violent mutations which took place at epochal turning points
in the evolution of flora and fauna and which radically and,
so to speak, overnight created a new animal form, according
to some higher scheme of evolution. And indeed the family
tree of the horse in particular—though only in its older form
as Haeckel knew it—seemed to have gaps demanding a very
definite jump from one stage to another. However, modern

geneticists have long known that the majority of mutations in fact produce quite pointless changes in a species. Successful "bull's-eyes" from a biological point of view are very rare. According to Darwin there is also the vital factor of selection, which plays its part in weeding out the useless mutations and only permitting the survival of those equal to their environ-

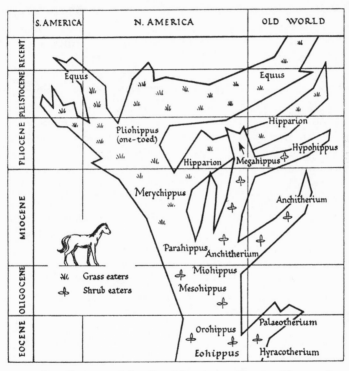

47. Family tree of the Equidae (according to Simpson)

ment. A jump-mutation of any considerable magnitude would mean that in the evolutionary process certain hidden forces were at work which would inevitably and unfailingly produce improvements in the species' capacity for survival. Practical science, however, has no need for such esoteric forces, and finds the generally accepted principles entirely adequate, providing satisfactory explanations for all phenomena in question. Thus the idea of a purposeful macro-evolution has

yielded gradually in favour once more of the older theories
of Darwin and Haeckel. Nevertheless, a new lesson has been
learned: that the straightforward course of evolution, hitherto
accepted as a fact, is in reality something far more complicated. The steady upward march of evolution is not just a
matter of developing along a single favoured line; instead,
it takes place along a large number of parallel or diverging
lines, all interconnected, but some of them sterile and doomed
to extinction, revealing—if every detail were known—an
extremely tangled complex of biological experiments. Just as
present-day atomic physicists in ascertaining natural facts do
not depend on the observation of single events within the
electron envelopes of a group of atoms, but instead draw their
conclusions from the statistical average of an enormous
number of such events which must yield an answer inevitably
correct for the individual event, so the modern palaeontologist must of necessity ignore the many thousands of infinite
gradations along the highway of evolution and concentrate
on the fossil-milestones which here and there provide sure
markers at intervals throughout the millions of years of this
process. We realise, indeed, that our knowledge of the almost
complete ancestral tree of the Equidae presents a very rare
exception, and it is therefore worth following the course of
some of the equine "milestones".

It is not definitely certain in which region of the Earth the
primal, tiny horse first appeared. As *Eohippus* it is known
from the Lower Eocene in North America, and in the form of
Hyracotherium from the same period in Europe. Both
resemble each other so strongly that they can be regarded as
identical. Since the chance simultaneous development, in two
widely separated quarters of the Earth, of animals so completely identical physically is most improbable, and since—
as is known today—North America was the cradle of all the
Equidae, it is reasonable to assume that Eohippus migrated
across the then existing land-bridge to Europe to give rise to
colonies of animals now known as *Hyracotherium*. These little
primitive horses were still rather clumsy, timid forest-dwellers
about the size of a terrier. There was as yet no suggestion of
our present-day graceful, muscular race-horse. Nevertheless
these animals migrated across a quarter of the world; a fact

by no means startling provided it is borne in mind that there was no question of a sudden, spontaneous departure or of regular, continuous daily treks; for what took place was simply a gradual dispersion throughout which—and this must be remembered—time played no relevant part. Even though the road from America to Europe may have taken 50,000 years, that was still a rapid migration. It was not just a single generation that migrated, but the countless descendants of a whole race.

The Geisel valley has also yielded up a superb specimen of a complete primitive horse from the Middle Eocene, than which no finer example could be desired. This miniature jungle horse, from the Eocene brown-coal forests, had already attained a length of about 28 inches. As is evident from the increased size of this Geisel valley horse, the descendants of *Eohippus* in Europe developed into a variety of forms. At least six of these are known from the Middle Eocene. One of them was *Palaeotherium,* from whose fragmentary fossil remains in the gypsum of Montmartre Cuvier made such a masterly reconstruction.

All these primitive European horses died out in the Lower Oligocene. It was only several million years later, in the Lower Miocene, that once again new and more highly developed types emerged. Since the evolution of the Equidae in Europe had so evidently come to an abrupt end, a further wave of migration from North America must be assumed. World-wide migrations are known to have occurred extensively during the Tertiary Period, the horse, in particular, becoming more and more mobile. For example, during the Miocene and Pliocene *Hipparion* spread in vast herds over Asia and Europe. The fact that South America was entirely devoid of horses until well into the Upper Pliocene is due to the subsidence of the land-bridge between the two American continents. Evidently South America was ill-suited to these belated equine immigrants, for they survived only a short time, and when America was discovered they were as unknown in the southern continent as they were in North America, their original birth-place.

Although North America must be regarded as the birth-place of the Equidae (numerous finds in Nebraska and South

Dakota and elsewhere) and the chief centre of their evolution, whence they spread continuously into almost every quarter of the world, the history of these odd-toed ungulates was not without its crises. For instance, at the period of transition from the Oligocene to the Miocene there is a quite evident regression of the hitherto dominant types, *Miohippus* and *Parahippus*. These two (and others, such as *Mesohippus*) had already become agile inhabitants of steppes and savannahs, since the evolutionary path of all Equidae led from the foliage-eaters of the forest to the dwellers in open country who grazed on coarse herbage and rich meadow-grass. This

48. *Hipparion* from the Pliocene

emancipation from the shelter of the Eocene jungle is reflected in a gradual change in their teeth, and also in their feet, which eventually developed into the single-toed hoof of present-day horses, so eminently suited to fast running in open country. Abel has pointed out that contemporaneously with *Miohippus* and *Parahippus* there also appeared the notorious tsetse fly which, today, being a carrier of trypanosome diseases, causes such tremendous havoc among domestic animals in certain parts of Africa. It must be borne in mind that, with the appearance of warm-blooded creatures, the bacterial and protozoic parasites found fresh feeding-grounds, and consequently there must have been the possibility, even at that time, of large-scale epidemics which may have killed off the mammals wholesale. Only the gradually increasing defence of natural immunity in surviving individuals, combined with an ultimate weakening of the trypanosome stock, or lucky migrations of the mammals concerned into non-infested territories could have defeated this menace. However, the primitive horses successfully survived whatever crises there may have been, as is clearly evident from their widespread and prolific development during the Miocene when two invasion waves swept into the Old World (Europe and Asia): *Anchitherium* during the Lower Miocene, and *Hypohippus* between the Miocene and the Pliocene. Both forms became extinct without evolving further. But North America was inexhaustible. In the Pliocene there appeared the type known as *Hipparion,* of which it has been said that it literally swarmed all over Asia and Europe. But in spite of this fertility, *Hipparion* also proved to be merely another dead-end. Its zebra-like appearance led, for a long time, to the assumption that it was the ancestor of our present-day zebras. But that is probably not so, for *Hipparion* was always three-toed. Then, almost at the same time as *Hipparion,* there appeared in North America the one-toed ungulate, *Pliohippus,* which must be regarded as the ancestor of all the present-day Equidae. *Pliohippus* also migrated to South America. (Of all the quarters of the world, only Australia is totally devoid of any equine remains, in consequence of its complete geographical isolation throughout the whole of the Tertiary.) Gradually, during the Ice Age, all American forms of the horse died out. Then the Spaniards of Columbus's day reintroduced these animals into the country of their own origin, to the complete astonishment of the natives, who had never seen them before.

Nowadays, horses, in man's estimation, are among the finest and noblest of creatures, and even their small ancestors would certainly be regarded as "delightful". But the grotesque and repulsive appearance of the dinosaurs in the Mesozoic animal world had not altogether disappeared with the extinction of these creatures in the Tertiary, as is evidenced by the canine teeth of the hideous amblypods, the primitive whales—and, strangely enough, by a particular

group of odd-toed ungulates from North America—the
Titanotheria. These, too, originated in the Eocene, but at
first were only about as large as sheep: then they increased
to the size of rhinoceroses and finally to that of elephants. In
the Middle Oligocene they died out completely. Their proto-
type is *Brontotherium*.

The Brontotheria were powerful, clumsy animals, somewhat larger than a rhinoceros. Their skull was unusually
broad, constructed of extremely thick, durable bone. The
brain was still very small, and their power of sight—as in the
present-day rhinoceroses—not very well developed. Powerful

49. *Mesohippus* from the Oligocene

forked bony projections from the muzzle must have given
these animals a stupid, unwieldy appearance. Of similar
structure and resembling *Brontotherium* were other titanotheres, such as *Brontops, Diploclonus* and *Megacerops. Brontops* grew to a height of over 7 feet at the shoulder. Its
native territory was chiefly North America; but remains discovered in Mongolia prove that migrations in this direction,
too, must have occurred. The comparatively abrupt demise
of the whole of the titanotheres—not unlike that of the Cretaceous saurians in its sudden completeness—again led Abel
to look for a trypanosome epidemic as the cause; for during
the Oligocene the relative of the tsetse-fly, *Glossina oligo-*

cenica, appeared and could have been the carrier of any form of plague. All circumstances considered, this is probably the most likely explanation.

The greatest of all known land mammals, however, finally appeared in the shape of the odd-toed rhinoceroses. The name rhinoceros—nose-horn—was taken from the present-day forms we know. But in the Tertiary there were several members of this family without any nose-horns. The mighty *Baluchitherium* was such an animal. Specimens so far discovered

50. *Brontotherium* from the Oligocene of South Dakota

have all been confined to Asia. (The first was found in Baluchistan: hence the name.) An Oligocene skull found in Mongolia in 1922 was of such a gigantic size that anatomical reconstruction resulted in an animal standing nearly 18 feet at the shoulder on very stout legs indeed. This Mongolian giant must have been, therefore, the greatest land mammal in the history of the Earth.

On the whole, the rhinoceroses (with or without horns) have survived successfully over the long period from the Eocene to the present time. Even if—like very many other mammals—their evolution had reached its climax long ago, their powers of survival were still strong. Indeed, by developing thick, shaggy coats they managed to cope with the subsequent Ice Ages. After that, however, the battle for survival turned against them. This change in the tide was started by the Ice Age men, who found a favourite object of the chase in the woolly rhinoceros, as is evidenced in numerous cave-drawings. Yet the senseless mass slaughter of animals, leading

51. *Baluchitherium*, largest of all land mammals

to rapid extinction, remains a prerogative of contemporary, civilised man.

Rhinoceroses, for example, are represented as vicious and treacherous, though every zoologist knows that they are neither. They are merely timid, and consequently attack blindly when they feel themselves threatened. By this instinctual behaviour they have managed to survive on the Earth for a longer time than mankind has existed. But now their days are numbered.

While the few remaining rhinoceroses survive today only

in Africa and South-East Asia, in the Tertiary they were far more widespread. With the exception of Australia in its isolation, and South America which, in the Oligocene, was equally isolated from North America, they roamed over the whole Earth.

Equally widely dispersed were the tapirs, who evolved almost simultaneously with the rhinoceroses. Their physical development was less striking; for apart from variations in size, their form in the Miocene was much as we know it today, in both the New and Old Worlds.

In contrast to the odd-toed ungulates which culminated in in the horse, the vertebrate order of the even-toed ungulates evolved, from the Eocene onwards, into a remarkable variety of widely differing forms, resulting in a multiplicity of present-day species. These include the camel, swine, hippopotamus, and all the ruminants, comprising cattle, giraffe, deer, prong-horned antelope and other animals. Camels put in an appearance from the Upper Eocene onwards and were at first confined exclusively to North America, one place where they no longer exist. The development of their hoofs and teeth, as well as their increase in size, closely parallels the history of the horse. The original little creature (*Protylopus*) was no larger than a hare; its descendants grew during the Oligocene to be as big as deer, then, by the Pliocene, they became the size of camels today. It was at this period that they started migrating, the dromedaries to Asia over the bridge across the Bering Straits, and the llamas via the Panama isthmus to South America. The present-day forms have been found as fossils in North America. Like the horse, the camel survived the Ice Age in the land of its birth, and then died out there completely. In their new homes they have not yet lived long enough to evolve into different species.

In the great deer family the most striking feature has always been their horn formation. Today the variety of horns is enormous. Countless shapes and sizes adorn stags, elks, reindeer and many others. There are also hornless types, such as the musk-deer and water-deer. At first, their primitive forms in the Upper Eocene and Oligocene (for example, *Amphibragulus*) were, without exception, hornless. Only later, after frequent modifications, did there appear the horns and antlers

52. *Alticamelus altus,* a camel from the Colorado Miocene (according to Scott)

which we know and admire today. Their climax was reached by the giant Irish elk, whose antlers, with a spread of over 10 feet, have been found in, among other places, the marls and peats of Ireland. Such discoveries indicate that these beasts survived the Ice Age and only died out in historical times.

A particularly interesting group of extinct even-toed ungulates are the anthracotheres. Literally translated this means, roughly, "coal animals". In fact, they had nothing at all to do with coal, but were typical swamp-dwellers who were merely discovered in the brown-coal region—which is why they got their name. Many were as large as rhinoceroses, but looked rather like pigs. They flourished chiefly during the Middle Oligocene in Central Europe. Remains from the later Miocene have been discovered in North America and in the East Indies. It is possible that from certain offshoots of this family there may have descended the hippopotamuses, which are externally quite dissimilar animals. The Siwalik strata of the Tertiary Period in the East Indies are exceedingly rich sources of this fauna and have yielded the oldest known hippopotamus from the middle Pliocene. The hippopotamuses never got beyond Asia, Europe and Africa.

Another offshoot of this family may have given rise to the Old World pigs, which appeared during the Oligocene. Like the hippopotamus, the Old World pigs never invaded America. The New World pigs, which were called peccaries, are an entirely separate and parallel lineage.

Typical Old World animals—that is, those not originating in North America where so many animals were evolved—seem

53. *Megaceros euryceron*, a giant stag from the Pleistocene

to be the giraffes. Their home was probably Southern Asia, whence they migrated to China and Southern Europe. Not until late in the Pliocene did they move into Africa. One of their Pleistocene side-branches gave rise to *Sivatherium*, an immense animal with a skull eighteen inches broad and bony projections and horns on the head.

With the exception of the Baluchitheria, which were rhinoceroses, all the largest Tertiary land mammals belonged to the Proboscidea, e.g. elephant-type. Apart from the early

Eocene forms, the various families all bore a close resemblance to one another, trunks and tusks being their particular characteristics. Their home ground appears to have been North Africa, if one can judge from the discoveries of a primitive beast named *Moeritherium*. This creature was discovered in the Eocene layers of an ancient sea in the Egyptian oasis of Fayum. It was still a tiny animal, no more than three feet tall, with a full set of teeth in the upper jaw. As yet, it had no tusks. Even the trunk was a mere suggestion and gave it a tapir-like appearance. Probably these creatures lived sluggishly in the swampy lowlands of early Egypt and never left North Africa. The urge to migrate must have seized later forms which then, in the Oligocene, moved out into Europe and Asia. Whether *Moeritherium* can really be regarded as the ancestor of the dinotheria, mastodonts and elephants, has been hotly and frequently disputed, by Abel amongst others. If not, there must have been other early forms, having a close evolutionary relationship to the *Moeritherium*, about which we have hitherto no knowledge. It certainly seems that North Africa, and particularly Lower Egypt, was the cradle of all Proboscidea, since in the Lower Oligocene—that is, very far back in time—there have been discovered remains of primeval mastodons (*Palaeomastodon, Phiomia*) which were already true proboscideans and achieved a wide geographical distribution as a family. During the Miocene they wandered from Africa throughout Europe and Asia, and in the Pliocene finally crossed the Bering Straits bridge to America, where they started to flourish extensively. They must have been extremely numerous and lived in great herds for even though their various stages of evolution up to their final forms—the changes in jaws, teeth, trunk, tusks, size—have been deduced chiefly from European discoveries, the wealth of mastodon fossils in North America is just as important as the ichthyosaur treasure in the European Jura. It was in America, too, that these cumbrous ancestors of the true elephants survived the longest. Whereas in the Old World they died out before the Ice Age, it has been proved that in America they were hunted by Indians in historical, pre-Columbian times. They must also have moved as far south as Ecuador, as finds in 1894 and 1928 have proved.

Discoveries of coeval pottery fragments, typical relics of human culture, are an irrefutable proof that man and mastodon came face to face. While fossil mastodons have been known to science for over 150 years, a particular deviation of their group has been discovered only quite recently (from 1929 onwards). The animals in question, *Platybelodon* and *Amebelodon*, were found in the Upper Pliocene of Mongolia and the Kuban region of Southern Russia and in the Plio-

54. *Syndyoceras cookii*, a primitive ruminant from the Lower Miocene in Nebraska (according to Horsfall)

cene of Nebraska. Among all the types known hitherto, trunks and tusks had developed steadily, through many transitional stages, towards the elephant-stage. But in these "newcomers" a trunk-like appendage was combined with the tusks of the lower jaw to form a broad, curved, shovel-shaped snout, 15 inches wide and over $4\frac{1}{2}$ feet long, which, together with the downward-pointing lateral upper tusks, must have given the brutes a grotesque appearance. These were plainly cases of entirely un-elephant-like aberrations; specialised forms which had developed in response to particular feeding conditions which have not yet been wholly explained.

From the mastodons descended the elephants, who first appeared on the scene about 7 million years ago, during the Pliocene. They developed 27 species in all, of which 3 survive today. More will be said later about their well-known Ice Age relative, the mammoth.

A closely related offshoot from the mastodon-elephant line was *Dinotherium*, the "terrible beast". This sobriquet, which suggests an object of frightful appearance, was scarcely

55. *Platybelodon* from the Asiatic Pliocene

deserved by these herbivorous animals. They were far from terrible to look at. In fact, they closely resembled elephants, but they certainly grew to a gigantic size during the Pliocene. Fossil remains discovered in Roumania in 1890 revealed an animal which stood 15 feet high at the shoulder, not very much smaller than the record-holder, *Baluchitherium* of Mongolia. Whereas the tusks of elephants and mastodons are elongated upper incisor teeth (some mastodonts also had small tusks in the lower jaw, making four in all), the Dinotheria developed powerful tusks in the lower jaw only. Since the extremity of the jaw turned down at almost a right angle, the slightly curved tusks consequently pointed directly towards the ground, which must have presented an unusual sight, to say the least. In contrast to their other relatives among the Proboscidea, the dinotheres were not particularly migratory, which again is difficult to explain. The first types are known from the Lower Miocene in Europe. Later they appeared in East Africa and the East Indies. But they never found their

56. Mastodont (*Trilophodon*) from the European Miocene

way to North America, as the mastodons certainly did. In the Pliocene they reached their climax, though a few survived in Africa until the Pleistocene.

In connection with the Dinotheria there was, also, an amusing incident. As early as 1613 a doctor in Southern France dug up several bones and teeth of these monsters and calmly asserted that they were the remains of the Germanic king, Teutobod, who was defeated and killed at the battle of Aquae Sextiae by the Romans under Marius in 102 B.C. The doctor travelled the bones from town to town and exhibited them for money. For a while he apparently did very well out of it. But he eventually succeeded in setting the learned world of Paris, who were not inclined to accept his "Teutobod", in an uproar. Unfortunately, as a result, his discovery was entirely discredited, and it was even considered that the objects were not bones but "freaks of Nature". So not until Cuvier's day was justice done, when the great man himself identified the animal, from its teeth, as being an extinct giant tapir. That was no small accomplishment, even though, for once, it was not quite accurate.

The early history of the carnivores is not so precisely known as that of certain other orders. Here there is a lacuna in the treasury of fossils which has still to be filled in. Obviously, their chances of preservation were not as favourable as those of the herbivores, who were generally larger and, moreover, far more numerous. Extensive herds of elephants, horses, gazelles and buffalo had always been the rule. Herds of lions, tigers or bears never existed. In contrast to the gregarious animals, the carnivorous mammals mostly lead an unsocial life, their largest group being the family. (Even roving wolf-packs can hardly be regarded as herds.)

All the known species of carnivores are descended from the Creodonta, the primal carnivores of the earliest Tertiary times. One of the first divergent lines to develop from the parent stock dates as far back as the Eocene: it is the largest carnivore found so far, measuring 12 feet in length and 6 feet in height, and having a skull 3 feet long. It was discovered in Mongolia by the eminent American palaeontologist, R. C. Andrews, leader of an expedition for the New York Museum of Natural History, and was named *Andrewsarchus mongoliensis* in his honour. In the Oligocene the distinction between felines and canines became quite clear, their different bodily structures determining their different methods of hunting. The canine species developed a very delicate sense of smell and an exceptional turn of speed, with great powers of endurance, their claws being of little use as weapons. The felines became extremely sharp-sighted, were equipped with powerful claws, crept up on or lurked in wait for their prey, and were capable of sudden, violent exertion, but lacked stamina. The bears are descended from ancestors closely allied to the canines. From the European Miocene came an animal known as *Amphicyon*, with teeth between those of a wolf and a wild dog, which attained the size of a bear and was once thought to provide the common link. The true bears appeared later from another divergent line. At

57. *Dinotherium giganteum* from the European Lower Pliocene (according to Abel)

first they were small animals; only during the Ice Age did they grow to an exceptional size in the form of cave bears.

The feline line achieved its largest form in a no longer extant offshoot, the celebrated sabre-tooth tigers. In North America their origins can be traced back to the Tertiary. In Europe and Asia they reached their fullest development in the genus *Machairodus*; in North America, principally, with *Smilodon*. At the end of the Pliocene they also spread over South America. Thus they followed the normal migration route taken in so many cases by their prey.

As on several similar occasions in Earth's history, there existed during the Tertiary one particular death-trap for animals, which has yielded an immensely rich treasure to the palaeontologist. This was the famous Californian asphalt swamp at Rancho La Brea, which is now within the city limits of Los Angeles. During the Pliocene and Pleistocene it must have been covered with a sheet of water which attracted countless thirsty animals. Most of them did not stop and drink at the edge; instead they went right in and were caught by the tenacious, sticky, porridge-like asphalt bed and sank to inevitable death. Whole herds of bison, elephants, mastodons, horses, camels and deer have been dug out; not to mention tapirs, wolves, rodents, birds of prey and, above all, 3,000 sabre-tooth tigers. This mixture of carnivorous and herbivorous animals suggests that the predatory ones could not resist the sight of helpless prey sitting there sinking into the mud, and therefore jumped to their own death after them.

The sabre-tooth tiger was a little larger than our present-day lions, but in their powerful, downward-projecting upper canine teeth they possessed fearsome weapons by means of which they could probably inflict deadly wounds at their very first attack on even the largest victims.

Generally speaking, the carnivorous mammals have survived very well. They have far more families and species living today than have the ungulates. Their powers of self-defence, their toughness and intelligence, together with an almost ubiquitous, inexhaustible supply of prey for food, enabled them to spread over the whole world and multiply without hindrance. Only Australia in its geographical isolation is devoid of placental carnivores. (The dingo is a dog that was introduced by man and then ran wild.)

A certain obscurity surrounds the origin and evolution of the seals, who are also carnivorous mammals. It is known that seals and walruses existed in Europe and North America from the Miocene onwards but no intermediary fossils have been found from before that time. Now these flourishing marine creatures are threatened with extinction. They have the misfortune to yield fur (in the case of the seals), leather, meat, blubber and train-oil, and are mercilessly hunted and decimated for these products. Many species have been already destroyed in our day, and others are on the verge of vanishing.

Undoubtedly one of the most striking characteristics of mammalian life during the Tertiary were the migrations of fauna from one part of the world to another. This process can almost be described in terms of modern economics. For example, North America produced and exported horses and camels; North Africa produced mastodons and dispatched them to Asia and North America. The pre-requisite for this traffic was, naturally, a solid land connection to enable such

58. Weasel-like dog (*Cynodictis*) from the Oligocene

migrations to take place. For that reason Australia—geographically isolated since the Cretaceous—has remained to a great extent unaffected by the stormy course of mammalian evolution and is inhabited to this day by a very ancient primeval fauna whose development has been largely arrested; only animals already evolving on the old Gondwana continent, principally the marsupials, exploited their full potential in a rich variety of evolutionary forms. This conservative state of affairs may have been greatly contributed to by the unchanging nature of the Australian landscape and the absence of tectonic disturbance throughout the whole of the Tertiary. So this remnant of primeval Gondwana may still today resemble its appearance some 70 million years ago. The stimulating effects of changes in climate and flora of the northern continents were here almost wholly absent.

In South America this situation was remarkably paralleled, this area of the Earth's surface having also been isolated from an early period (in the early Tertiary) by the disruption of the Panama land-bridge. Up to the Eocene the principal forms of mammals which had migrated into South America were the primitive and as yet unspecialised ungulates; no placental carnivores had gained entrance. And such the position remained for perhaps 100,000,000 years until the land-connection with North America was restored in the Pleistocene. From these early immigrant ungulate forms there subsequently developed an entirely distinctive fauna which is not found anywhere in the rest of the world. South America thus became a unique example of how groups of animals can evolve quite differently in different environments even though descended from a similar ancestry; indeed South America became an isolated and independent region, inhabited by a flora and fauna dating from the earliest Tertiary times. (Because of the physical inaccessibility of the South American forest and mountain regions, it is understandable that the Argentine pampas and parts of Patagonia were the first to be thoroughly explored from the palaeontological point of view; but here there are, in certain Tertiary beds, rich fossil deposits which give an excellent picture of the prehistoric fauna, although the evolutionary sequence of events is still very much a closed book.)

For instance, the Miocene strata yielded the ungulate *Thoatherium*, which not only physically resembled the horse but also was one-toed just like the true horses which appeared in North America very much later; yet this animal had in fact no connection at all with the horse family-tree, representing instead a particular type of ungulate which existed only in South America. Another similar case is *Pyrotherium*, from Oligocene times, equipped with forward-pointing tusks and a short trunk. But there was no connection with the Proboscidea, nor was the animal related to the dinotheres. There were also the toxodonts, belonging to the extinct South American order Notoungulata, which were beasts resembling the rhinoceros, but larger, and not connected in any way with the latter animal.

The South American carnivores were of marsupial, rather

than of placental, descent, but among them were large predators that were strikingly similar to the placental wolves, bears
and cats of the northern continents. There was even a South
American marsupial carnivore which bore a remarkable external resemblance to the sabre-toothed tiger. These parallel
biological types probably led rather similar lives despite their
different genetic origins. Very remarkable, also, is the tendency
towards the evolution of llama-like forms (*Macrauchenia*), a
characteristic of South American fauna. But it should be noted
that this is merely an outward resemblance, for the llama, so
closely related to the camel, migrated to South America from
the north only in the late Pliocene, after the Isthmus of
Panama rose from the sea and linked the two continents.

Characteristic present-day examples of the distinctive South
American fauna are the sloths, armadillos and ant-eaters
which occur in this sub-continent only, and nowhere else in
the world. Very well known, and also known for a very long
time, are the giant sloths of the Ice Age. The first skeleton
was discovered in 1789, in pampas loess near Buenos Aires.
From Cuvier it received its name of *Megatherium ameri-
canum*. These creatures were as large as elephants, being
more than 20 feet in overall length. Remains were also found
subsequently in North America, whither they must have
migrated. Another related animal, *Mylodon,* did not attain
the size of these huge monsters, who probably crawled along
ponderously on the outer edges of their feet. Although the
name "giant sloth" has become attached to them, from the
evolutionary aspect they are more closely connected with the
ant-eaters than with the true sloths who seem to have
appeared very late in the history of the world. The Megatheria must also have been herbivores, for they lacked the
extended trunk-like snout and the very long, extensile, sticky
tongue with which Nature had endowed all true ant-eaters
to enable them to get at their natural food.

No less distinctive and strange among the fauna of this
region of the world were the glyptodonts, the giant armadillos. They were clearly related to the true armadillos, but
the armour of their ancestors had become grossly exaggerated,
giving a curious superficial resemblance to the armoured

dinosaurs of the late Cretaceous. Whereas the armadillos are protected by a number of movable, bony, transverse bands, the glyptodont developed a high, humped shell like the tortoise. In certain types the head was also armoured and the tail was equipped with spines, and others carried at the end of the tail a defensive—and doubtless aggressive—weapon that resembled a medieval mace. Since these animals grew to a length of over 12 feet, they must have been extremely formidable. They, too, migrated to North America over the Panama land-bridge

59. Glyptodont from the Pleistocene in Argentine

at the end of the Pliocene, but did not reach as far north as the Megatheria.

Nature's one attempt to make mammals at home in the air, as well as in the other elements, succeeded with the bats. There is something unique about these odd, gregarious, twilight and night fliers. They were already fully evolved as far back as the Eocene, and thus have flourished undisturbed for about 50 million years and are now spread all over the world in about 1,000 different species. While in the case of canines smell became the most important sense organ, and with cats sight, bats developed an extremely delicate sense of hearing. Here—as with the previously mentioned armoured fish with electric organs—Nature anticipated man in the invention of a radar-like ultrasonic echo device. Bats orientate themselves by emitting high-frequency sound waves, inaudible to humans, which are reflected back from solid objects and are picked up by their large ears. Thus they can avoid obstructions in flight. Since they are predominantly eaters of insects and fruit, food has always been plentiful for them. The specialised blood-sucking types—vampires—have also never lacked for nourishment. The bats' habit of hiding during daylight enables them to escape enemies, and so, obviously, these animals are one of Nature's more successful and enduring products.

The rodents—the largest order of all land mammals—developed quietly and unsensationally during the Tertiary. They, too, began their existence at the very start of the Tertiary, with their typical feature, the pronounced incisor teeth which were so vital to them; and in the course of time they evolved into countless new forms. One of their most striking characteristics is the lack of any increase in size. Mice, porcupines, guinea-pigs, squirrels, etc., are all small animals and have remained so since their inception. Of all the 3,000 living types, the largest among them, the South American water-pig, grows to little more than 3 feet in length. Only the exuberant South American animal world seems, in the Pliocene, to have produced gigantic animals from the group of the present-day porcupines. And bear-sized beavers existed in the Pleistocene.

So far we have had to content ourselves with imaginative reconstructions of the physical forms of primeval animals, their habits, origins, and relationships. Little has been said about their intelligence.

Only the tiny brain pans of, for example, the dinosaurs offered slight and not very encouraging hopes for the mental future of living creatures. Of course, it would be wrong, looking back from our present intellectual eminence, to be didactic on the subject. Up to the end of the Cretaceous, Nature managed with beings which led a predominantly vegetative existence. For them, instinct and unconscious reflex reactions to the world around sufficed for survival in an environment in which every other living creature survived in the same way. The new "weapon" of survival, in its higher form which we call intelligence, first appeared in the Tertiary.

Unfortunately there is not sufficient material to enable us to trace the cerebral development of animals in the way we can follow their physical evolution. Failing actual observation, it is impossible to make any assertions, however general, about the degree of intelligence of fossil-animals, known only as fossils. Only the skull capacity—and that is not always known—can offer even the vaguest indication. So we are dependent upon contemporary forms of life for our knowledge of animal psychology. And we know little enough of that, opinions about animal intelligence differing as widely as they do. Earnest efforts are still being made to ascribe every possible action connected with feeding or reproduction to that magic word "instinct". This is certainly correct to a very large extent, but in the case of the higher animals there is somewhere a point where intelligence takes over and lays down deliberate plans of action which are not wholly instinctive. This elaboration of the intelligence must have progressed in all the main groups during the Tertiary, thus leading to the more mentally advanced present-day species. Obviously, the primitive *Eohippus* can scarcely be considered to have had the same degree of intelligence as its present-day descendant, the horse. The early Proboscidea were certainly mentally far inferior to the amazingly gifted elephants. The domestic hound and our hearthside cats must be enormously in advance of their ancestors in the Tertiary. So here we have a definite upward trend, the significance of which must not be overlooked. Perhaps the examples mentioned may be absolute end-products of their groups, incapable, so far as intelligence is concerned, of further evolution and simply continuing to exist alongside the intellectually developing human as aimlessly as many old fossil forms survive alongside their contemporary animal descendants. But can one be certain of that? The stimuli of new environments nearly always lead to far-reaching changes, and this may be particularly so in the case of animals living in the community of man, where there are endless incentives to adapt to new experiences and to learn fresh ways of self-preservation.

Yet it must be admitted that we still know extremely little about this subject. The possibilities of carrying out scientifically controlled tests on many of these animals are small. The process necessitates lengthy, difficult observation such as Karl von Frisch so devotedly and successfully dedicated to his bees. One thing that can be taken as absolutely certain is that a great many animals, some of which have scarcely been observed, are clearly possessed of considerable and unexpected mental capacities.

CHAPTER SIXTEEN

The Advent of Man

WITH the chimpanzees and their astonishing accomplishments we now come to the highest order of animals—not hitherto mentioned in a palaeontological context—the primates, the supreme animal species to which belong the lemurs, the apes and man. They form the evolutionary line along which Nature has developed and consummated her greatest weapon—the brain.

It would be ridiculous to treat the emergence of Man as one of the great mysteries of the universe. It is far from being that. Man developed just like all the other animal species hitherto discussed, influenced by the same causes, obeying the same laws and rules which have governed the animate world right up to the present day. There is nothing to contradict this view, and everything is in its favour. The first pieces of fossil evidence appertaining to the advent of Man were found, quite logically, at a point in the Tertiary when the whole evolution of the mammals and particularly the apes had reached such a stage that the deviation in the direction of Man was simply inevitable.

At this point it must be once more emphasised that in this purely factual book only the results of practical investigations are mentioned and discussed. Even where the causes of the stupendous processes of biological development are considered, every effort is made to keep to the solid ground of known facts. Philosophical and religious views and conclusions on this matter are far beyond the scope of this book, and they and their widely accepted validity will not be touched on at all.

Present-day investigations, particularly into the problem of Man's origin, are based mainly if not exclusively on the principles of Darwinism. So here a word must be said about this much misunderstood "ism".

When Darwin's famous work *On the Origin of Species* first appeared in 1859 and precipitated a world-wide intellectual upheaval, the fundamental concept of the natural evolution of living creatures had, hitherto, been only very discreetly mooted. The actual "theory of evolution" was not originated by Darwin and is not identical with "Darwinism". The fact that, despite a very considerable passage of time, the two phrases are still generally regarded as synonymous is an indication of how little the broad mass of opposing opinions really understand what it is all about. The doctrines of evolution have grown up organically with palaeontology itself. Admittedly, intuitive strokes of genius were needed to give these bold concepts their first foundations and outlines. The milestones on this road were set up by Jean Lamarck, Erasmus Darwin—Charles Darwin's grandfather—Etienne Geoffroy Saint-Hilaire and—a fact that is far less known—by the great poet and thinker Goethe. (In this matter Cuvier was a crank, refusing absolutely to abandon his Catastrophic Theory which could not accept a continuous, steady process of development in Nature.) There must also have been quite a number of geologists and palaeontologists who took a process of gradual evolution so much for granted that they made little fuss about it and therefore never fluttered public opinion.

Darwinism is something quite different. Darwin assumed the fact of a common origin of species and simply explained how this had come about. The inexorable competition between the various species produced by mutations and the elimination of the less promising types in the process of the "Survival of the Fittest" has already been described—and this is the real meaning of Darwinism. What actually upset people was the inevitable conclusion that Man, too, must be part of the general line of biological descent, subject to the same influences in his development, and appearing on the scene at a time solely determined by the stage of evolution reached by the race of primates. This plainly meant—only Darwin did not express it quite so crudely—that the apes lived on Earth before man, and that from their stock, from their immediate relatives, descended first the ape-men and then Man himself, a conclusion actually first drawn by

"Darwin's bulldog", Thomas Huxley the naturalist. In Germany it was Ernst Haeckel who became the chief protagonist of this doctrine.

It has often enough been said—but it can bear repetition —that neither Darwin, Huxley, Haeckel, nor any other contemporary or later scientist has ever asserted or believed that "Man is descended from the apes", that is, *descended from apes as we know them today*. That theory has simply been thrust upon Darwinians by people who cannot or will not understand what the scientists meant. We have already seen how contemporary science conceives the evolution of species as an intricate combination of minute changes, some simultaneous, some consecutive and some overlapping. Present-day Man, too, has not developed in a straight line, but is the result of an immense variety of mutations flourishing aimlessly in all directions within the primate family, and from these the process of natural selection has only permitted the survival of the mutation that exists today as *Homo sapiens*.

Darwinism is just over a hundred years old; during those years it has been the subject of endless attacks and discussions. Dozens of times its opponents have claimed to have finally refuted it. Nevertheless, today it is regarded as an indispensable element in modern scientific research, and the soundness of Darwin's original theories is becoming more and more appreciated.

The apes—like all Placentalia—have their biological origins in the insectivores. They descended from some offshoot—though of what species or genus of this order it is quite impossible to say, for there were an enormous number, the majority of which are not even known to us. The treeshrew family is a possibility, as it includes a number of small arboreal insectivores looking somewhat like squirrels but showing decided anatomical resemblances to the higher primates. Related to the tree-shrews is the tarsier, another rather primitive primate—also an insectivore. It is not out of the question that evolution towards the lemurs began as far back as the late Cretaceous. Certainly in the Palaeocene, even more so in the Eocene, the first lemurs, together with tarsiers, flourished in Europe and North America. From North

25. Miniature 28-inch-high primaeval horse—and a crocodile; both from the Eocene of the Geisal valley near Merseburg, Germany.

26. Neanderthal group at Gibraltar.
Diorama in the Chicago Natural History Museum.

27.   Solutrian and Aurignacian cultures.
(*Above*) Scratching an engraving on stone.
(*Below*) Painting the wall of a cave.
Dioramas by R. Blaschke and C. S. Corwin in the Chicago Natural History Museum.

28. (*Above*) Coloured representation of a bison in Altamira in northern Spain. (*Below*) Rock-engraving of a mammoth in Les Combarelles, Dordogne, France.

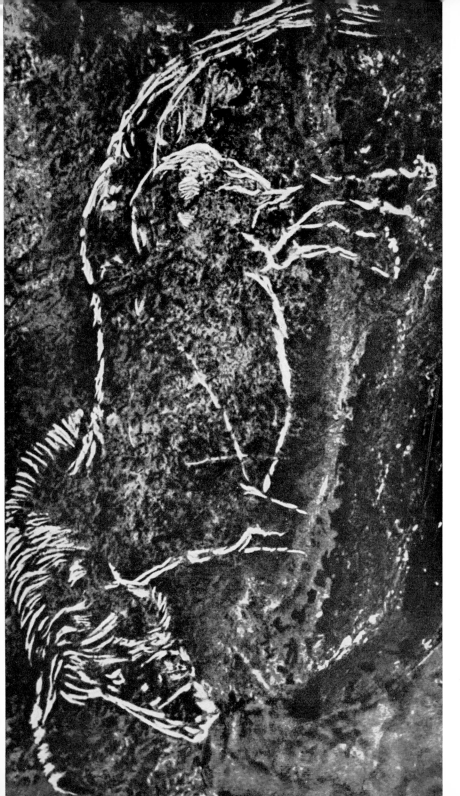

29. Wild horse. A rock-engraving in La Bastide, Hautes Pyrénées, France.

30. Roof of the Lascaux cave, covered with painted animals. Dordogne, France. (This picture should be viewed from the right.)

31. Coloured paintings at Lascaux.
(*Above*) Small wild horses.
(*Below*) A bison pierced by a spear, with a prone human figure.

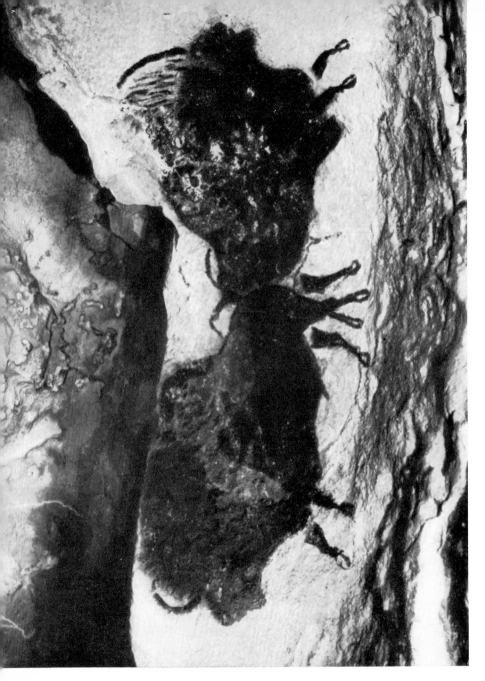

32. Two bison bulls. Coloured paintings at Lascaux.

America they made the usual migration to the South American continent and there, after the disappearance of the Panama land-bridge, led an isolated existence. The fact that they are no longer to be found in South America immediately suggests that they died out. But it is probably safer to assume that they simply evolved into the forms of the broad-nosed (platyrrhine) New World monkeys which today are characteristic inhabitants of those parts of the New World. Their evolutionary potential was presumably incapable of anything higher.

At the end of the Eocene the lemurs also died out in North America and subsequently were no longer found there. Today they are still widely distributed in Madagascar, however, and rather less numerous in Africa and the East Indian Archipelago. Whether the early lemurs and tarsiers can also be regarded as the direct ancestors of the Old World narrow-nosed catarrhine monkeys or as a parallel branch from a communal stem is still not clear. The first assumption is the more probable, for the lemurs are in fact somewhat more primitive, appear rather earlier in fossil strata and prove themselves, in the case of the South American monkeys, to be capable of a higher development. Anyway, there is no more likely explanation for the origin of the New World monkeys.

As in the case of other mammals, geological conditions on the whole were not generally propitious to the preservation of ape fossils. Until recently such fossils were among the rarest of discoveries, and as a result there are considerable gaps in our knowledge, which even today have not been satisfactorily filled and are particularly evident in the human line of descent during the Tertiary.

True apes most certainly existed in the Oligocene, and were spread over Africa, Europe and Asia. The earliest apes known are *Parapithecus* and *Propliopithecus*, both from Egypt. (The suffix "*-pithecus*" is one that we shall come across frequently: it is derived from the Greek word for ape.) These early apes evolved direct from the Eocene lemurs and tarsiers, without going through any "monkey" stage at all. Of the aforementioned types, *Parapithecus* (meaning "standing alongside the anthropoid apes") was still a very small animal, but already possessing anthropoid characteristics. *Propliopithecus* clearly anticipated the present-day gibbons and may perhaps be regarded as their ancestor. The true anthropoids (Pongidae) appeared in the Lower Miocene. Equatorial Africa in particular seems to have been very rich in a great variety of forms, most of which died out long ago. Remains from a later period have also been found in Europe and Asia. Unfortunately, these have almost always been merely fragments of skulls, jaws and limbs, as well as teeth; but they have sufficed to enable the expert anatomists to reconstruct with some precision the appearance of the former apes.

The most widespread group of fossil anthropoids is provided by the Miocene and early Pliocene genus *Dryopithecus*. These lived not only in Africa, but also in Europe and India (Siwalik fauna). All anatomical discoveries indicate that from their group descended the present-day anthropoids—orang-utan, gorilla and chimpanzee. The orang-utan probably came from the Siwalik forms, and the other two from the African representatives. All three are late-comers in the Tertiary development of anthropoids. Most recent of all are the chimpanzees, who first appeared at the end of the Pliocene. It is quite clear, merely from the time at which they appeared, that Man could not possibly have descended from these apes, for in the Pliocene there had long been in existence types which had progressed far beyond the chimpanzee stage along the road towards Man. Nevertheless, the chimpanzees are by far the most "human" of all living creatures. Their whole anatomical structure and physiological functions resemble ours. Blood characteristics are the same, as well as numerous physical particulars which do not occur in any other animals. So probably there is a close relationship, and if one is searching for the original point of divergence of the human line from the animals, it should obviously be sought where the ancestors of the chimpanzees first appeared on the world's biological scene. So it is astonishing to discover that *Dryopithecus* was, in small anatomical details, more man-like than were the chimpanzees. And *Dryopithecus* lived in the Miocene, between 25 and 30 million years ago.

What was there, in fact, lacking in the anthropoids, at the climax of their physical development in the Tertiary, that would have transformed them into hominids, beings of the human type? Certainly there was nothing physiologically deficient, as we can see from the example of the chimpanzees, who, in this respect, are not in the least inferior to us. The sole, but decisive, distinction of fundamental importance as between ape and Man is the differing size of the brain. This difference was a result of changes in the shape and size of the cranium and of the whole skull. These changes also included the mouth which, in the case of almost all animals up to this stage of development, had been their chief prehensile organ. This loss of the mouth's ability to grasp things made it consequently necessary that other organs, in this case the hands, should take over such duties. In order to free, for this purpose, the hands and arms which hitherto had been used as means of support and for running, an upright posture was necessary. Thus the actual development of Man certainly began with the holding of the body erect. We must therefore seek for fossils of anthropoid apes most closely resembling chimpanzees, which, to judge from their anatomical structure, may have adopted an upright posture. This is easier said than done, for in this respect fossil formations leave us sadly in the dark. The comparatively numerous discoveries from the Upper Pliocene in South Africa reveal types which had long ago adopted the erect posture. But what we want to know is when the first step, the actual " jump " from animal to Man, took place. With our present-day ideas and theories it is not so very surprising to find that we have to go back as far as the Tertiary, at least to the *Dryopithecus* stage of the Miocene —perhaps even further.

For a long time it was popularly assumed and regarded as "proved" that the fossil apes were just jungle animals, like their present-day descendants, whose life consisted entirely in hanging and swinging from the branches of trees. It was believed that an erect posture was assumed by those who gave up a jungle life in order to become creatures of the open country. But fossils of *Dryopithecus* and other species raise considerable doubts as to whether these creatures were in fact solely forest dwellers. The physical developments

necessary for hanging and swinging may well have been a
later specialisation which actually prevented a section of the
anthropoids from ever rising above the level of apes. This is
a view which is prevalent today. The pronounced and accomplished agility of present-day anthropoids in swinging and
hanging depends on an exceptional lengthening of the arms
which is not evident in the case of their fossil prototypes. So
the Miocene anthropoids may be imagined as animals which
certainly clambered about in the forests, but were equally
at home in steppes and savannahs and even rocky terrain.
The "urge to the upright" must have been present more
naturally during the early stages of development than
after specialisation into pure forest-dwellers had taken
place.

This leads to the conclusion that all contemporary anthropoid apes are forms which, after the branching off of the
human line, have descended from an origin common to them
and *Dryopithecus*. They are therefore comparable to *Hipparion* among the Equidae, who was a descendant, like
Pliohippus, of the original *Merychippus* ancestry, but
developed into a three-toed deviation incapable of further
evolution, whereas the one-toed *Pliohippus* eventually produced the modern horse.

Where is one to find the "*Merychippus*" of the human
line, that fertile original form which produced both anthropoids and hominids? Almost certainly further back than
Dryopithecus, and in forms which had not yet undergone a
one-way, irreversible development by acquiring the specialised characteristics of pure forest-dwellers. The scarcity of
helpful fossils is extremely frustrating, and one can only hope
that future lucky finds will produce the proof we require.
For that reason every fresh discovery must be regarded as a
priceless treasure.

A major piece of luck occurred in 1948. Dr. L. S. B. Leakey,
the anthropologist, found in the Lower Miocene in Kenya
the remains of a primeval ape whose lower jaw (having a
pronounced development towards a chin structure) and skull
(absence of frontal protuberances over the eye-sockets) marked
it as the most man-like animal yet discovered. This beast
must have been much more like Man than the chimpanzee

or *Dryopithecus*. Since it was the size of a chimpanzee, Leakey named it *Proconsul* after one of his house-trained chimpanzees which was called "Consul". Further carefully planned explorations revealed the existence of a whole group of these animals in the Lower Miocene. It is nowadays considered that they represent the vital offshoot which originated the line of descent that led eventually to Mankind. The other line of descent, via the *Dryopithecus,* culminated in the contemporary anthropoids. Whether *Proconsul* was already able to walk erect is still in doubt. Probably he was not.

From that point onwards, that is from round about 25 million years ago, there yawns a fossil gap of some 20 million years, during which we know nothing at all about the development of the hominids. A possible exception is an Upper Miocene discovery in Tuscany which was made as far back as 1870 and which until now has been grouped with the Cercopithecidae (Old World monkeys) as *Oreopithecus.* Recently, the Swiss palaeontologist Hürzeler has re-examined this fossil and believes that, from the characteristics of its teeth, it must definitely be regarded as belonging to the human strain.

This discovery, exciting though it is, is the only one known from a period of 20 million years and is far too inconclusive, particularly since it is very deficient and provides no evidence whatsoever about the creature's limbs or habit of progress. Naturally, this particular Tuscan deposit is being closely explored, with great hopes that other fossils may be found there; and, in fact, these hopes have not been disappointed, for in 1958 a further discovery was made, which at the present time is under discussion and on the palaeontological value of which the experts are not yet decided.

Welcome and, in certain respects, decisive as this second Tuscan find may be, the fact remains that it cannot bridge that tremendous hiatus in the fossil world. All that can be said about it is that it confirms what has been guessed—and does not contradict anything!

So there is nothing for it but to jump in time to the Upper Pliocene about 2 to 3 million years ago, for at this point South Africa proved to be an unexpected El Dorado. It all began in the year 1925, when Professor Raymond Dart reported the discovery of the skull and fragments of the lower jaw of an apparently four-year-old child, embedded in a limestone matrix in a cave at Taungs, Bechuanaland. The cranial capacity was about 500 cubic centimetres, this being considerably larger than the crania of present-day anthropoids of a comparable age and stage of development. Since the frontal ridges are less prominent than in the case of the apes, and the teeth very human, there seems to be here an intermediate form in the

60. Reconstruction of *Australopithecus*

line of human descent. Professor Dart named the species to which this young creature once belonged, *Australopithecus africanus*. Unfortunately, this discovery did not carry matters much further, since it is difficult to draw any definite conclusions as to the final adult form from an infant skull still in the process of developing.

Naturally the scientific world was now on the alert. But it was not until 1936 that Dr. Broom from Pretoria discovered further sources of fossil treasures which even today have not yet been exhausted. These were at Sterkfontein and Kromdraai—and, later, at other places such as Swartkraans and Makapan—which have yielded over a long period a great number of teeth, skulls, jaws and bones of all sorts, providing an invaluable contribution towards the building up of a more and more complete picture of this primitive creature. Broom gave different type names to his various discoveries, such as *Plesianthropus* ("near man") and *Paranthropus* ("next to man"). Nevertheless, all these South African fossil discoveries are now placed in the genus *Australopithecus*. These hominids were evidently widely distributed, as has been evidenced by subsequent finds in the region of Lake Victoria in East Africa.

(Quite recently Dr. L. S. B. Leakey discovered in the Olduvai gorge near Lake Victoria in East Africa the complete cranium of an apparent relative of the Australopithecines, together with what are believed to have been his tools. He has been named *Zinjanthropus,* and an age of about 1,750,000 years has been assigned to him.)

But when did the Australopithecines exist? That was a hotly debated question. The dating, which was far from easy to establish, varied between the Upper Pliocene and the Pleistocene. Finally, the decisive answer was provided by close investigation of the accompanying fauna. In this connection invaluable work was done by the famous French palaeotologist, Abbé Breuil, who made detailed examinations of the different places of excavation. All the discoveries concerned had been made, without exception, in limestone deposits riddled with caves—ideal conditions for the preservation of bones. The presence in the caves of great quantities of all sorts of animal remains leads to the conclusion that these were water-borne accumulations of dead creatures which had all been swept together with rubble and mud after heavy tropical downpours. Now this accompanying fauna was found to consist of animals that were no longer living in the Pleistocene. Thus the period of these hominids' existence must be placed in the Upper Pliocene, though it is impossible to say how far back. One thing is certain: the ages of the individual types vary. *Plesianthropus* is obviously older than *Paranthropus*. Probably it is safe to say, with wide margins, that the whole family of Australopithecines existed over a period from 2 million years ago until 750,000 years ago.

What sort of creatures were these, in which ape and human features were so strangely combined? That they were still merely anthropoid apes is extremely improbable. First of all, they walked erect, as is proved beyond doubt by anatomic discoveries (fragments of the pelvis and parts of limbs). Moreover the forward position of the opening at the rear base of the skull gives a clear indication of a correspondingly erect posture of the spine. Their height of about 5 feet was scarcely more than that of present-day Congo pygmies. The cranial capacity varied between 450 and 600 cubic centimetres and only very slightly exceeded the contemporary anthropoids (male gorilla 510 c.c., male chimpanzee 411, male orang-utan about 440 c.c.), though a skull excavated at Swartkraans had a cranial capacity of 900 c.c. Their teeth were in general more powerful than those of present-day Man, but had many characteristics not present in anthropoid apes.

All in all, there emerges a picture of a creature which in quite distinctive points has outgrown the anthropoid ape stage, but is still not a man. Broom always spoke and wrote of "ape-men", a clear unequivocal description which seems to characterise that intermediate stage. Scientists have disputed how far it is permissible to draw the distinction of an intermediate ape-man stage between the evolutionary level of the anthropoid apes and that of true men. It must be remembered always that Man is not descended from the anthropoid apes—he ·diverged from a common ancestry at some time back in the Miocene. It is still not known whether any of the Australopithecines lay on the direct line between the Miocene apes and Man as he is today; in all probability they formed a specialised offshoot. We can use several characteristics in deciding whether or not to group one of these primates with Man. We can say that if his brain is large enough he can qualify; but the brains of neither the Australopithecines nor the anthropoid apes were more than half Man's brain-size. Another approach, much in favour at the moment, is to regard the development of tool-making as marking the dividing line. It is, of course, quite impossible to pin-point an exact generation, and say "Man began here". Instead we

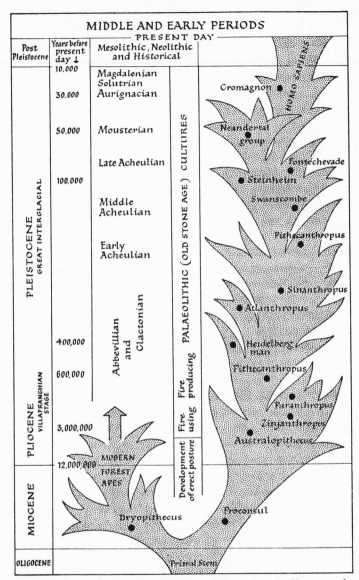

61. Man's probable family tree. The dots indicate only approximate, average dates for the existence of the individual types, based on geological data; they do not pretend to show either when a type first evolved or when it died out. Possible genetic relationships, being extremely uncertain, have been ignored

must remember that human evolution, like all other organic evolution, took place gradually, and at some period a slow change began to occur. First tools (in the form of loose stones, bones and sticks) were *used,* and then, bit by bit, they were sharpened and chipped and cut, and were ultimately deliberately *made.* Related to this is Man's use of fire—something which always frightens wild animals. Did the Australopithecines make tools, or use fire? There is no clear answer to these questions yet. There are certainly traces of fire in their cave deposits, and, as we shall see in a moment, there are also indications that they used stones for cracking skulls. But this does not necessarily amount to tool-*making.* It seems rather that, at the height of their development, the Australopithecines had just reached that critical level which characterised the emergence of Man—but along a different line of descent. Professor Weinert discovered yet another criterion for the level of human evolution among the Australopithecines. Unfortunately it is one rather unflattering to "human dignity"! Very frequently at the excavations in South Africa remains of baboons were found and all their skulls were cracked in the same manner. Broom concluded that this had been done by pointed antelope bones. Upon which Weinert comments: "To slay one's fellows, roast and eat them, is the way not of an ape but of a man! "

In fact—as we shall see later—cannibalism among primeval man was a quite common custom.

Before we leave the Tertiary, some mention must be made of mankind's place of origin. After all that has already been said, it looks as though only Africa comes into question. Both *Proconsul* and the Australopithecines of East and South Africa support this. Nevertheless, science is not yet entirely convinced. It may be pure coincidence that we have found these very early types in Africa only. No one can tell what surprises may be in store underground in other continents, such as Asia. But, for the time being, that is all we know.

To return for a moment to our imaginary radio wave which is still travelling through space at the speed of light: at the time of the existence of *Paranthropus,* it has reached the constellation of Andromeda—and it will take many thousands of years before it has passed through it. At the end of the Tertiary it will be speeding across the immense space which lies between Andromeda and the Milky Way. There are still only 600,000 light years to go. A mere nothing compared to what has already passed.

CHAPTER SEVENTEEN

The Pleistocene Ice Age

WITH the approaching Quaternary we have now reached the latest and shortest period in Earth's history. It is subdivided into the Pleistocene ("most recent period") and Holocene ("contemporary period").

The limits of the Pleistocene are clearly defined by the beginning and end of the Ice Age, give or take a few thousand years. It probably began about 1,000,000 years ago and ended about 10,000 B.C., according to the latest radio carbon dating. As has already been mentioned, it is not quite correct to speak of the Ice Age as though there were only one. In fact, there were four tremendous separate glacial advances which were interrupted by three, very lengthy, interglacial periods. These intervening periods were such an absolute contrast climatically that in certain regions the earlier Pliocene conditions of the Tertiary largely returned. Today we do not know for certain whether the Ice Age, in its totality, is really at an end or whether we are in fact living in an interglacial period which may be followed by a fifth glacial advance, probably due, according to careful calculations, if it comes at all, in about 50,000 years' time. To our way of thinking such a period of time is vast, far ahead in the inconceivable future. It is difficult to imagine what may happen before then. We feel we stand helpless before a monstrous span of time. But one must beware of yielding to this feeling, even when glancing backwards, for many things are much easier to understand if one realises that 50,000 years (a mere geological nothing) are, indeed, only 50,000 years.

Our knowledge of an immense and extensive icing-over of the northern hemisphere is about a hundred years old. Of course, observant students of nature had already discerned unusual features in the Central European landscape which required particular explanation. A very obvious feature of this kind is provided by the driftblocks, mostly gigantic granite blocks worn into a smooth rounded shape, which occur on level terrain. These are alien bodies in the framework of their geographical setting, for far and wide around there are no known granitic mountains. Charles Lyell suggested that they had originally been deposited in their present locations by drifting icebergs. But this theory was incorrect. The proper deduction was drawn in 1860 by a Swede named Otto Torell, who stated that these granite blocks came from the Scandinavian mountains. They had not been transported on drifting icebergs (how, indeed, could icebergs have acquired a freight of rock?) but had been swept down from Scandinavia to north Germany by the movements of glaciers. Torell correctly identified the geological surface structure of the North German plain as deposits of debris brought down by glaciers, and perceived that the chains of hills were in fact piled up moraines. Furthermore he contested the theory of an epoch of general glaciation. Since Lyell's day the study of the Ice Age has continued intensively—many geologists having made it their special subject—and has brought us to our present improved but still imperfect state of knowledge.

The circumstances that may have caused a radical and comparatively sudden change in climate, such as could precipitate an Ice Age, have already been touched upon in the discussion of the Permo-Carboniferous Ice Age. So at this point we can confine ourselves to presupposing a decline at the end of the Tertiary, of from 6° to 8° C. in the average temperature. The first result of this, particularly in the more climatically inhospitable regions, was tremendous downpours of rain, providing an inexhaustible supply of new ice. The snow level on all mountains also descended considerably. The process of glacier-building increased continually, and the ice-fronts moving down from the mountain heights spread farther and farther over the lowland regions, eventually linking up and even overlapping. In the end, this amalgamation of the different glaciers led to the formation of one solid ice-cap which, as in the case of Greenland and Antarctica today, buried the land under a continuous expanse of ice. Over North Germany the depth of this mighty ice shield

varied between 1,700 and 2,000 feet. The most extensive
surface areas were covered by the first two glacial advances.
These started from Scandinavia and the Scottish mountains,
as well as—moving in a northerly direction—from the Alps.
The southern limits of the glaciers descending from the north
were, in England, roughly in the latitude of London; while
on the Continent their furthest limits were the Southern
Netherlands, the south of the Harz Mountains which here
and there projected slightly above the surface of the ice as
rocky islands, the northern slopes of the Sudeten ranges which
put a stop to any further movement south in this area, the
basin of the River Oder and, in Southern Russia, the region
of Kiev.

All in all, over Europe an area of some 2.5 million square
miles was covered by ice, including the North Sea and the
Baltic, which at that time were dry land. North America
fared even worse. There, 5.8 million square miles were
covered by ice to an average depth of 4,500 feet, the southern
limits of the glaciation reaching down as far as the present
point of confluence of the Missouri and Mississippi rivers.

Of course the whole of the Earth was affected by such
cataclysmic events. How far the south polar ice-cap extended
north is difficult to determine, owing to the surrounding
ocean. Certainly, Tierra del Fuego was completely glaciated.
The snow level in the Andes was as much as 4,200 feet lower
than it is today. And similar conditions prevailed in New
Zealand, Australia and Tasmania. Siberia, to a great extent,
was one sheet of ice, with the Central Asian mountains far
more covered with glaciers than they are today. In the
equatorial regions there prevailed periods of rain of inconceivable intensity. Even on Mount Kilimanjaro the snow
level descended to well below 3,000 feet. The Earth's supply
of water was so impoverished by transformation into ice that
the surface levels of oceans and inland seas sank by 200 to
250 feet.

As a result, many shelf-regions were left high and dry.
In particular there must have emerged extensive land connections between Australia and South-East Asia by way of
which primeval Man could have populated this hitherto
isolated continent.

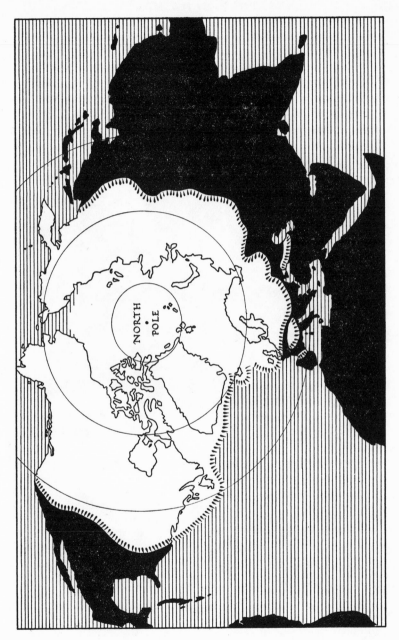

NORTH POLE

62. Extreme limits of Pleistocene glaciation in the northern hemisphere

63. Ice-Age mammoth (according to Z. Burian)

Within each successive advance of the ice-caps there were also subsidiary variations, with a perpetual shifting of the limits of the glaciers; as a result, climatic disturbances on Earth, caused by sensitive reactions to every change in temperature, must have reached an almost unbelievable intensity. It was inevitable that the plant and animal worlds should also have been affected violently by this revolution in their environment. The flora of the Pliocene disappeared completely from the glaciated areas, and the Arctic tundra vegetation moved far to the south under the influence of the spreading ice-fields. Only with the melting of the glaciers and the considerable increase in temperature during the interglacials did the freshly exposed areas once again become covered with plant life, and then in a vast way which culminated in an immense extension of forest regions. These extreme variations in flora were repeated a number of times, as each glaciation was succeeded by an interglacial phase.

With the fauna a similar upheaval occurred, and now real animal migrations must have taken place, lasting for a very much shorter period of time than the leisurely waves of dispersion during the Tertiary. To begin with, the retreat was to Southern Europe and Africa, the latter being easily accessible over a number of land-bridges. There remained behind only those animals who today are the chief representatives of northern fauna: reindeer, musk-ox, marmots, lemmings, wolves, elks, bison—the zoological counterparts of the Arctic tundra flora.

During the intervening warm periods, the picture once again changed strikingly. Most of the warmth-loving creatures returned northwards; which does not, of course, mean they were the identical animals who had migrated south, for the total duration of the first Ice Age was about 50,000 years. The length of the first Interglacial Period was some 70,000 years (see table on page 279), and during this period even tropical animals, such as forest- and steppe-elephants, rhinoceroses, hippopotamuses, sabre-tooth tigers and others moved north again.

This whole ebb and flow repeated itself rhythmically during every advance and retreat of the ice, until gradually more and more tropical animals gave up their northwards migration. The sabre-tooth tigers soon died out completely from the face of the Earth. The rhinoceroses and steppe-elephants apparently followed their example after the second glaciation, and the forest elephants after the third. Specialised forms of these creatures, and of the rhinoceros, emerged in the mammoth and the woolly rhinoceros, both of whom bore long, thick coats and actually flourished in the icy regions. Bears, hyenas and lions acclimatised themselves to living in the shelter of caves and became distinctive Ice Age fauna.

The nomenclature of the main Ice Ages and the warm

intervening periods varies from country to country. In Germany the four main advances (starting with the oldest) are generally known as the Günz, Mindel, Riss and Würm Glaciations. The geologists Penck and Brückner named them after small rivers in the northern Alpine foothills and, as far as correlations can be made, these names are in general use throughout Europe. In North America the names given to these same events are: the Nebraskan, Kansan, Illinoian, and Wisconsin Glaciations. The names for the interglacial periods follow in consequence: the first interval G/M (between

64. Woolly rhinoceros from the Pleistocene

Günz and Mindel) and then M/R and R/W. America has quite different names for these, so that it is safest to refer to them as the first, second and third Interglacials. The second (M/R) Interglacial is also known as the Great Interglacial, though it is not certain that it actually lasted longer than the others.

It must here be said that the course, duration and number of the glaciation periods are far from being known for certain. In spite of much research and a great expenditure of effort and ingenuity, there still prevail views which differ widely from the outline given here, mainly as a result of increasing sub-division of the phases of glacial advance. A further complication is that each glacial phase was composite in detail, and consisted of several minor advances and retreats of the ice-front. It is not so easy to survey a "mere" 1,000,000 years! This must be honestly admitted, in order not to discredit the possible validity of other opinions.

Thus, particular excitement on the subject of Ice Age investigation has been aroused by the Yugoslav M. Milankovitch. Being an astronomer, he considered the Earth primarily as a planet. The characteristics of the Earth's orbit, such as its periodic variations in distance from the Sun, the slight deviations from its truly elliptical track and changes in the inclination of its axis were all, to him, data on which to base calculations whereby he proposed to explain the origin of the Ice Ages. Since the three above-mentioned variables in the Earth's course are all of different duration, there could only be certain points in time when all the most unfavourable values coincided—i.e. the greatest distance of the Earth from the Sun (the perihelion), the greatest inclination of the Earth's axis, and the maximum deviation from its orbit (eccentricity). This gradually accumulating (and equally gradually diminishing) combination of circumstances must undoubtedly (so he claimed) have led to a diminution in the intensity of the Sun's radiations received on Earth. Summer would have become increasingly cooler, with all the consequent effects of a lowering of the snow-line, heavy rainfall, etc. The result of his calculations coincided remarkably with the periodic glaciations of the Earth, thus offering an astronomical solution for a great geological problem. However, subsequent accurate checks revealed discrepancies which could not be explained, and therefore Milankovitch's theories must be regarded with reserve. Logically, also, his theories, if correct, should be equally applicable to Earth's earlier history, with the consequent implication that there must have been a long series of glacial and interglacial periods starting from at least as far back as the Tertiary—something that is not confirmed by geology. Another glacial phase (called the Donau, after the Danube) is dated by Milankovitch as far back as 800,000 years and is placed with the Villafranchian deposits at the very base of the Pleistocene.

Naturally, the revolutionising events of the Ice Ages left

their mark on the surface of the land. The piled-up walls of debris of the end-moraines have already been mentioned. The final glaciation left behind it the tremendous, long Baltic ridge, which runs from Denmark across North Germany into Russia. It shifted and deposited not only granite blocks, but also massive layers of sand, gravel, marl and chalk. For instance, the area of the Lower Elbe near Hamburg is a 600-feet-deep layer of Pleistocene material.

One characteristic of the Pleistocene was the formation of loess. The loess areas of China, Russia, Central Europe, North America and the South American pampas all originated at this time. Loess, a very fine, silty material, largely composed of minute quartz grains, was produced from the outwash fans of the great rivers flowing from the edge of the ice-sheet. The wind, driving down from the glaciers, must have carried this light material over the exposed land in tremendous dust and sand storms and continuously deposited it so that the loess is now often of great thickness (as much as 550 feet in China). Steppe grasses held the loess firm and thus produced today's fertile territories. In these ways, the character of extensive areas of the Earth's northern hemisphere was decisively formed by the Ice Ages. There are certain regions of Siberia, Alaska and Canada which, as a direct result of the glaciation, are still frozen by the so-called "Perma frost" to a depth of several hundred feet and only thaw out for a few feet down during the summer. Many of the important valleys of Central Europe have been cut through glacial ground-moraine deposits, and almost all the river systems, both there and in North America, have been greatly influenced by events in the Pleistocene. The numerous lakes of North Germany, Russia, Finland, Southern Sweden and the lowlands surrounding the Alps are mostly survivals from the melting of the ice-masses, whilst the present form of the Great Lakes in North America was largely determined by the position of the ice-front at different stages of glaciation.

The advance of the ice must indeed have been a terrifying phenomenon. The solid sheets of rain descending, the storms of sand obscuring the Sun, the crushing, irresistible power of the slowly encroaching glaciers which sent out before them their own icy zones fatal to flora and fauna—they must have induced an actual end-of-the-world atmosphere. Once again it must be stressed that none of this happened with any rapidity. Nevertheless, an average human lifetime would have been sufficient to discern definite changes in the world around and to sense unmistakably the approach of the ice. The movements of glaciers in our present-day Alps are small; but in Greenland they are about 60 feet a year. Probably, during the Ice Ages, the ice advanced considerably faster.

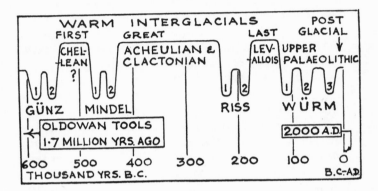

The Pleistocene Ice Age, showing interglacial periods. The Villafranchian Stage—now regarded as being the base of the Pleistocene—occupies the period from the end of the Pliocene (1,000,000 years B.C.) up to 600,000 B.C.

CHAPTER EIGHTEEN

Further Progress in Man's Development

IT was during these unsettled times, with their alternating extremes between barren steppes and tundra and warm, lush forests and grasslands, between predators hardened to the cold and their defenceless, harmless prey, that mankind emerged and evolved. We have seen already, in the remote Permian, how unfavourable external circumstances had a far more beneficial influence on the upward progress of life than a period of unruffled, paradisal calm. The Tertiary and Quaternary also in their different ways confirm this phenomenon as clearly being the rule. For whereas the human stock took at least 25 million years during the Tertiary to traverse the road of evolution from the ape-like *Proconsul* to the man-ape *Australopithecus*, the Ice Age hastened the tempo towards the final appearance of *Homo sapiens* so enormously that this far greater stride was accomplished in an incomparably shorter time.

In the Pleistocene we now encounter quite different types of beings from those that have gone before. It is very remarkable that for this period source material comes predominantly from Asia and Europe. Africa lags far behind. It seems as if Man's further evolution needed the rigours of the north. Yet even so apparently obvious a picture can mislead: for some of the higher types have also come out of Africa. The greater wealth of fossil finds in Europe may be due to more thorough exploration of the Pleistocene in that area, as well as to the preservative qualities of the limestone strata in Europe and Asia, which are considerably more favourable than any to be found in South Africa. Also, of course, the greater number of finds could be partly attributed to the numerical increase of individuals in these territories.

The first discovery of this entirely new type of pre-man proved an object of wonder and curiosity. It dates from the great days of Ernst Haeckel, who considered the growth of the tree of Man as being rather more straightforward than it has proved to be in reality. He was content merely to postulate a "missing link", an ape-man a stage higher than the anthropoid apes, who walked erect and was the direct ancestor of primeval man. As we know today, this view is fundamentally correct, though not in the sense that he conceived it. Haeckel was so unshakably convinced of the justification and necessity of this intermediate stage that he named the creature *Pithecanthropus erectus* before it had even been proved to exist. He paid no heed to the scorn and ridicule that was heaped on him. One day, he said, those fossils would be found. And found indeed they were.

A Dutch army doctor, Eugen Dubois, was so convinced of the correctness of Haeckel's ideas that he had himself transferred on colonial service to Java and Sumatra in order to settle the question of the "missing link". He had a particular reason for selecting this area for his researches. At that time —it was 1898—Haeckel claimed that the closest relative to man was not the chimpanzee but the gibbon. Since these East Indian islands were the home of the gibbons, it was a very reasonable assumption that here also was the birthplace of those types which developed beyond the anthropoid ape stage. Actually this assumption was basically fallacious since the gibbon is today no longer included among the anthropoid apes proper. Yet in spite of this mistake, the wildest coincidence in the whole history of science led to Dubois' carefully calculated plans being crowned with success. He began excavating at a place called Trinil in Java, where numerous fossil remains of mammals had already been discovered. At varying intervals he unearthed two molar teeth, the roof of a skull and a left upper thigh-bone, which were quite sufficient, anatomically, for the reconstruction of a primitive, man-like creature which walked upright and was, to judge from its brain-capacity (935 cubic centimetres), exactly half-way between anthropoid ape and Man. The hypothetical *Pithecanthropus* of Haeckel had been found.

The sensation caused by this discovery rocked the whole scientific world. On the one side were triumphant cheers, on the other obdurate disbelief. Such a thing simply could not be true, said the latter; it was preferable to believe in the existence of an outsized fossilised gibbon! But the proof could not be argued away.

It was exceedingly difficult to fit this Trinil discovery into its chronological place in the scheme of things. Only much later did the palaeontologist von Koenigswald succeed in identifying so precisely the accompanying fossilised fauna in the Javanese excavations that it proved possible to allocate the existence of *Pithecanthropus erectus* to the second Ice Age, that is, about 300,000 years ago.

All those doubts, which prevailed for so long, have now been completely dissipated; for subsequent finds of fossils of the same or similar kind confirmed the original discovery. The lucky finders were once again Dubois and von Koenigswald. Fossil remains dug up in Central Java between 1936 and 1939 brought to light another type of this species which Franz Weidenreich has named *Pithecanthropus robustus*. This second creature was certainly older than the first type found, and probably lived during the first interglacial period; so its antiquity can be estimated at a good 500,000 years. Reconstructions have produced a very ape-like being, with a flatly sloping forehead and low skull, accentuated brow-ridges over the eyes, a muzzle-like protruding mouth, and a recessive chin. Its height must have approximated that of present-day man. Its distribution in the world is tolerably well defined by other discoveries in Asia, Europe and Africa.

One of the most important and richly informative of all archaeological sites proved to be a limestone area at Choukoutien near Peking. The ancient magic of secret medicines and protective amulets, which played an important part in traditional Chinese culture until quite recently, strangely enough proved the signposts to this discovery. Since the dawn of civilisation, probably, Chinese physicians have been acquiring fossil bones, teeth, etc., and selling them either in powdered form or whole as amulets. A German doctor named Haberer was the first to recognise the palaeontological value of these medicaments, and he did science an enormous service by buying up, at considerable financial sacrifice to himself, whole collections from the apothecaries of Tientsin and Peking and sending these trophies to experts in Germany for examination. One of these objects was a molar tooth which was held to be of very early human origin. Since whole hordes of local people were engaged in collecting these fossils for the apothecaries, it was impossible to conceal their source, and the attention of the anthropologists was soon drawn to the limestone area around Choukoutien. Then, in 1918, a Swedish scientist found two more teeth. This event alerted the Americans, who organised an ambitious, well-financed programme of excavations which lasted from 1927 until 1937, with a large international assortment of experts participating. Once again a tooth provided the vital evidence. Davidson Black, a Canadian —the "Cuvier" of the expedition—recognised it as belonging to primeval man and, with the same audacious assuredness that the old Frenchman always displayed, he inferred from it a being which he named *Sinanthropus pekinensis*. Such an apparently hasty deduction was, in this case, brilliantly confirmed; for in the years following not only were further teeth discovered but also quantities of skulls, jaws and portions of limbs. All told, the remains of about fifty individuals were recovered from this source. The process of reconstruction revealed a surprising fact—that *Sinanthropus* was so similar to *Pithecanthropus* that it should perhaps be placed in the same genus, with the consequence that nowadays this early man is sometimes referred to as *Pithecanthropus pekinensis*. Variations from the structure of Javan Man are, from the point of view of classification, relatively unimportant. Plainly the Chinese specimens lived at a later date than *P. robustus*, but earlier than *P. erectus*.

The actual site where all these precious remains were discovered was a collapsed limestone cave filled with gravel, sand and clay. The fact that the remains of so many individuals were assembled in this confined space has led to a horrible conclusion. In the case of almost every skull the occipital bone had been cracked and the spinal bones crushed. These obvious results of violence could only have served one purpose—to get at the brain and the marrow. So it looks as if what was unearthed was a primeval robbers' cave, to which *Sinanthropus* had been dragged as a victim, slain and devoured. Who were the cannibals? His own fellow men? That is possible. But it is equally conceivable that at that time there were early men considerably in advance of *Sinan-*

thropus. Indeed, this possibility must definitely be taken into account, for the whole *Pithecanthropus* group were not necessarily representative of the highest evolutionary stage which Man had reached by that time. However, since we do not yet know definitely of any superior contemporary being, we can only theorise; but it is ironically tragic that the relics of such bestial deeds should first put us indirectly upon the track of a hypothetical "higher Man".

Unfortunately, the whole of these priceless Chinese finds disappeared on the outbreak of war with Japan in 1941. By agreement, they were the property of the Chinese Government. An attempt, at the request of the Chinese, to transport them to the United States was made too late and failed. Since, after the end of the war, they did not reappear in Japanese hands, it must be feared that they were destroyed by the ignorant soldiery.

In Europe so far there has been only one find related to the Javanese and Chinese types of men. This is the famous, extremely well preserved lower jaw from Mauer near Heidelberg. It was found in 1907 in a chalk pit from which road metal had been excavated for a long time and which had already yielded numerous fossil remains of animals from the early Pleistocene. Here too—as in the Geisel valley—the physical circumstances were favourable, the strata being saturated with lime-rich ground-water which checked the formation of destructive humic acids. Otto Schoetensack, the palaeontologist who for decades had watched, with infinite, dedicated patience, over the salvage of the fossils, was overjoyed to be able to identify this powerful lower jaw as belonging to primeval Man, and he designated its former possessor *Homo heidelbergensis*—Heidelberg man. As far as we know today, it belonged in fact to the *Pithecanthropus-Sinanthropus* group, so that its placing in the genus *Homo* is possibly not entirely satisfactory. Judging by the contemporary fauna, Heidelberg man must have lived during a warm period. Therefore he has been assigned to the first Interglacial of about 550,000 years ago, making him contemporaneous with *Pithecanthropus robustus*.

Naturally, this valuable source of fossils received the closest attention thenceforward, unfortunately without any success

until, after the end of the
Second World War, a com-
plete skull was dug up near
by. And then something inconceivable happened: the
workmen who found it
secretly destroyed the skull
because they were afraid of
"trouble with the police".

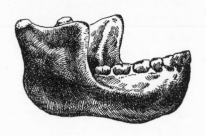

Since prehistoric skulls are
so exceptionally rare, this loss
to science is incalculable.

65. Lower jaw of the Heidelberg man, discovered at Mauer

The very wide dispersion of this early group extended also
to Africa. Here we must rely on the great expert, Dr. Weinert,
who, from a mass of fossilised fragments discovered by Dr.
Ludwig Kohl-Larsen by Lake Eyasi in Tanganyika, described
an extinct type of man, somewhat resembling *Pithecanthropus*. He named it *Africanthropus*—but this name cannot
be used, since it had already been given earlier to an entirely
different kind of fossil human skull. "*Africanthropus*" was
probably a relict group—it became extinct towards the end
of the Ice Age.

It is indeed by no means extraordinary that there should be
distinct variations of type among primeval men at different
periods and in different parts of the world. Even among contemporary forms of *Homo sapiens* there are tremendous
differences between a North European and an Australian
aboriginal, a Japanese and an Ethiopian. The process of
fragmentation into races may equally well have taken place
among early mankind, and even the very scanty discoveries
that have been made reveal, again and again, hybrid types
suggesting just this. Thus, it is difficult to decide where
Telanthropus capensis, discovered by Broom at Swartkraans,
should be assigned, although he betrays obvious relationship
to *Pithecanthropus*. Another hybrid type is the Ngandong
man, eleven of whose skulls were discovered in fragmentary
form at Ngandong in Java during the 1930's. Although he
must still have closely resembled *Pithecanthropus,* certain
characteristics assign him to a somewhat higher place in the
ladder of evolution, already approaching the later Neander-

thal man. These discoveries, too, bore indications of savage
head-hunting, for most of the skulls were smashed in at the
back, and the fact that they were all found within a limited
area indicates that the victims must have been dragged there.

There is equal uncertainty with regard to the classification
of the Modjerkerto child from Eastern Java, whose cranial
capacity was 700 c.c. at the age of four or five and who might
therefore correspond to a young *Pithecanthropus*. This, however, is far from certain.

Another type is represented by *Atlanthropus mauretanicus*,
of whom two lower jawbones—probably of a male and a
female—were found in Palikao in Algeria in 1954. The very
pronounced and almost fully-toothed male jaw is said to bear
a remarkable resemblance to that of the Heidelberg man,
while the less well preserved female one resembles *Pithecanthropus*. Contemporary fauna dates them as living at the
beginning of the second glaciation period, thus making the
Atlanthropus somewhat younger than Heidelberg but older
than *Sinanthropus*, which accords very well with their type.
Certain physical variations from other roughly contemporary
finds suggest that here was a deviation from the main line of
development.

Really sensational discoveries were made in Java by von
Koenigswald in 1939 and 1941. These were fragments of
lower jawbones more than twice the size of that of the Heidelberg man, which itself was already massive. Since these jaws
are human, von Koenigswald was forced to deduce from them
the existence of a race of giants, which he called *Meganthropus palaeojavanicus*. These discoveries linked up with
some fossilised teeth which the same scientist had bought
before 1939 when rummaging through Chinese apothecaries'
shops in Hongkong. The teeth were of such a size that at first
he hesitated to ascribe them to human beings, and he therefore named their owner *Gigantopithecus*, indicating the ape-
element. It was Weidenreich who first decided that the teeth
should be regarded as human, and hence inferred that there
must have been a race of men over twelve feet high. Then
Weinert found among Kohl-Larsen's collection of fossils—all
of which came from East Africa—upper jawbone fragments
and two molars of a similar huge size. Weinert attributed

these remains to giants and called the African type *Meganthropus africanus.*

Strangely enough there is little agreement in the scientific world on the existence of such giant types. It has been pointed out, not unfairly though with considerable vigour, that the size of a chin, let alone a tooth, is not sufficient evidence on which to base conclusions as to the stature of the being to whom they once belonged. But giantism has been a quite normal phenomenon throughout the animal world at all times, and we have already encountered numerous examples of it. Why, then, should the human race form an exception? Naturally, this line of argument does not constitute a proof. One can only wait for the earth to yield up further fossilised limbs which will justify the advocates of the existence of prehistoric giants.

The whole group of Pleistocene primeval men so far described, belonging to *Pithecanthropus* (or closely related to it), must now be compared with the *Australopithecus* group of the Pliocene and very earliest Pleistocene. Neither of these two great groups lay on the direct line of human evolution—each progressively developed structural features not found in present-day Man. Each became extinct during the Pleistocene—but the *Pithecanthropus* group lasted longer, and produced some descendants which lived in Europe contemporaneously with more highly evolved forms of true men.

The most striking and the best known example of these parallel forms is the famous Neanderthal man. He is, also, the Ice-Age relic who has been longest known to the world of science.

In the year 1856 quarry workers in the Neander valley near Düsseldorf came across fragments of bones and heedlessly shovelled them down on to the valley floor about sixty feet below. By a lucky chance the foreman arrived just in

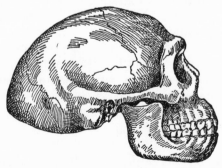

66. Reconstruction of a Neanderthal skull

time and had the bones collected (they were subsequently found to consist of the roof of a skull, humerus, ulna, radius, etc.). The owner of the quarry gave them to a Düsseldorf schoolmaster called Fahlroth, and he handed them on to Professor Schaafhausen, who recognised in them the remains of a fossil man. Much controversy followed this decision—at that time no one knew of Ice-Age man, as investigation of the Ice Age had scarcely begun. Even the possibility of the existence of prehistoric fossil men had been banished from the realm of scientific thought by the lapidary pronouncement of the mighty Cuvier: *"L'homme fossile n'existe pas."* The first well-justified excitement caused by this discovery focused the attention of the world of international science on the thesis which Fahlroth and Schaafhausen elaborated. But both were defeated by the superior weight of world scientific opinion. Dr. Pruner-Bey of Paris rejected Fahlroth's "fantasies": at most, these discoveries were the remains of an ancient Celt, or—as Wagner of Göttingen opined—some old Dutchman. Professor Mayer of Bonn, on the other hand, offered the suggestion that they were the bones of a Cossack who had hidden there during the Napoleonic wars. Again and again Fahlroth drew attention to the very pronounced frontal ridges over the eyes, the receding chin and other skeletal features all characteristic of primitive Man. But on this very point Virchow, the leading authority of his time, demolished all Fahlroth's ideas. To Virchow it was as clear as daylight that here was a case of pathological degeneration of the bones. The individual concerned had contracted rickets in early youth and later developed gout. So that was that. Virchow, unfortunately, was as dictatorial and stiff-necked as Cuvier. *"L'homme fossile n'existe pas!"* and the matter was settled. The unfortunate schoolmaster was overwhelmed by such devastating opposition, and had to suffer the stigma of being dubbed the victim of an over-active imagination.

However, support came from England. Professor William King, the geologist, was not to be shaken: he believed that this *was* a fossil man and called him *Homo neanderthalensis*, a name still valid today. Sir Charles Lyell, too, was firmly of the same conviction. But even the views of these two scientists could not stand up against Virchow's abuse of his authority.

Such grave errors coming from an eminent physician are extremely difficult to explain. (It is also well known how Virchow slightingly rebuffed Robert Koch—the little doctor who later became so famous—when Koch suggested to him the idea of the existence of microscopic creatures which caused tuberculosis.) But progress can only be delayed, never truly halted. Inevitably there will be subsequent discoveries to confirm the first. And so it came about.

A hundred years ago the general exchange of news and information, including scientific intelligence, did not function

67. Reconstruction of *Pithecanthropus* (left) and *Homo neanderthalensis*

nearly so efficiently and swiftly as it does today. Any discoveries, unless they were of immediately obvious importance, were, at most, published in the local newspaper and then vanished into the archives. It required a good memory to recollect earlier discoveries which might perhaps tie up with new finds. So it was not until eight years after the Neanderthal discovery that someone remembered that as long ago as 1848 a skull had been found at Gibraltar which in structure corresponded to that of the Neanderthal skull. With increasing attention focused on the subject, people now began to collect material hitherto considered of little importance. But knowledge about the early existence of primeval man did not appreciably increase until the vital, break-through year of 1886. In that year a cave at Spy in Belgium yielded skulls, lower jaws and remains of other bones of a number of individuals who were indisputably of the species *Homo neanderthalensis*. Contemporary fauna proved to consist of Ice-Age animals, such as the woolly rhinoceros and the mammoth. In addition, there were considerable quantities of worked stone implements. So that was the end to "pathological degeneration" of the bones of modern men. Here were representatives of an extinct human race that had ceased to exist in Europe about 40,000 years ago. Nevertheless, it was not until the end of the last century that the eminent anthropologist Gustav Schwalbe found the "courage" to recognise publicly the fact that the world had stumbled upon the track of the oldest true men, and in accordance with his convictions he named the type *Homo primigenitus,* "the first created man". As we know today, the claim implicit in the name is wrong, for Neanderthal man was *not* the first true man; and in any case the name *H. neanderthalensis* had been given to this species first. The present century has brought to light, from numerous sites in France, Moravia, Croatia, Spain, Italy, Southern Russia, Palestine and South Africa, so many fossil remains that we now know a great deal about the nature, appearance, habits and geographical distribution of Neanderthal man.

As was frequently the case with other groups, the Neanderthal men, too, in their differing environments, were by no means uniform in their characteristics, the Palestine finds in particular showing considerable deviations. A real "super" Neanderthal specimen was Rhodesian man (*Homo rhodesiensis*) who was discovered in 1921 in a zinc mine at Broken Hill in Rhodesia. Enormously protuberant eyebrow ridges must have given him the appearance of a gorilla, yet the proportions of his limbs were more "modern" than those of the European Neanderthal man. Like *"Africanthropus"*, Rhodesian Man was probably a local race which was isolated from the main stream of evolution. Many of these early men are in fact best thought of as representing separate races in the modern sense. It now is known that Neanderthal man existed as far back as the third Interglacial, perhaps 180,000 years ago. During the fourth glaciation they were, in fact, the only Europeans who for tens of thousands of years dwelt in those inhospitable regions as true Ice-Age men.

Frequent attempts have been made to reconstruct their outward appearance, but so far no consistent view has been agreed on. Despite a smallish average height of about five feet three inches, their bone structure was immensely strong, and their muscles probably correspondingly powerful. The original belief that they waddled about with a bow-legged gait is discredited; this was a mistake originating from the discovery of a bandy-legged type in La Chapelle in France. The skull with its receding forehead and projecting frontal ridges was on the whole more massive than that of the present-day European, for which reason savants in Virchow's time spoke also of water on the brain as a further indication of sickness in the "modern" specimen. The cranial capacity was very high—1,500 c.c. The lower jaw was strongly formed, but the chin, on the contrary, was only very weakly developed. Like the vast majority of primeval men they went about naked (clothing was only invented incredibly late in Man's history) and were probably—particularly during the Ice Age —heavily haired. By present-day standards they could hardly be regarded as handsome. If, in addition to the above, one bears in mind the fact that they undoubtedly indulged in cannibalism, the total picture is of a repulsive semi-dwarf with a bestially savage nature.

Indeed, the Neanderthal men could hardly be otherwise, for the world in which they mostly lived was anything but friendly. There were animal enemies galore; starvation was a perpetual threat which necessitated resourcefulness. They must threfore have been gifted with extremely acute senses and almost animal instincts.

Our knowledge about their origin, how long they existed, and when they finally disappeared, is still very uncertain. If they originated far back in the third Interglacial, they lived, to start with, for a very long time in exceptionally favourable circumstances. They suffered their first hardships with the beginning of the fourth glaciation, when their homelands became desolate and they themselves were forced back into the tundra and steppes of the marginal regions. From that time onwards, of course, things became harsher and harsher for them. While their remote ancestors in the Interglacial had been able to enjoy vegetable foods in plenty, now they were forced to become predominantly flesh-eaters, a change requiring cunning and desperately bold hunting, for the wild animals who were their prey were fleet of foot and, moreover, well able to defend themselves. Thus "drives" by a number of individuals led to an increase in the strength of communal life and tribal feeling. Consequently their dying out is somewhat extraordinary. Plainly they were a deviation from the main evolutionary course, and it is quite certain that they were not the ancestors of present-day Man at all. Even during their time, and possibly before them, there existed primeval types of Man which, from the point of view of development, were considerably in advance of them, as we shall shortly see. So it is conceivable that during their later period they were relentlessly pursued by "higher" men pressing up from the south and finally suffered complete extermination, which could have come about quite easily in view of their numerically small strength (at most 2,000 individuals per generation). Furthermore, the discovery of numerous hybrid forms with persistent Neanderthal characteristics suggests a process of absorption through interbreeding with other types. (We shall return later to their cultural legacy.)

Whereas Neanderthal fossils are plentiful (over 100 individuals), we are lamentably lacking in specimens of their far more interesting contemporaries. Indeed, there are up till now only four sources of information about them: the Ilm valley in Thuringia not far from Weimar, Steinheim on the River Murr, Swanscombe on the Thames, and Fontéchevade in France.

Of these, the individual deposits that have been known longest are the chalk deposits of Taubach and Ehringsdorf in the Ilm valley, which have proved rich sources of fossils from the last Interglacial. As long ago as 1871 a human skull was discovered here; unfortunately it was submitted to Virchow for judgment and immediately suffered the fate of being rejected as non-prehistoric. Over lengthy intervals the area yielded up molar teeth, lower jaws, fragments of bones and, in 1925, another broken cranium. Although resemblances to the Neanderthal man are unmistakable, the formations of the forehead and the curvature of the skull in particular appear to suggest a higher type. However, opinions on this are still divided.

Nearer to unanimity is the view taken of a fairly well preserved skull which was discovered in a gravel-pit near Steinheim in Württemberg. It obviously belonged to a young woman, as is indicated by the smaller brain capacity, which always (even among anthropoids) is less than that of the male. The Steinheim skull shows several resemblances to Neanderthal man, but the heavy brow ridges of that species are not so well developed—in fact it is in general less specialised. It probably lay near the common source of both present-day Man and *Homo neanderthalensis.* All the contemporary fauna in this fossil-rich gravel pit, as well as the loess deposits, indicate the third glaciation as the period in which they were laid down, which means that these early men must have lived 200,000 and more years ago.

In the case of the Swanscombe man, the characteristics of *Homo sapiens* are even more pronounced. Here, too, only skull fragments survive, which were dug out of gravel pits near the Thames in 1935 and 1936. The brain capacity—and in this case, too, it was a woman—must have measured about 1,325 c.c., clearly indicating that it was of "late" origin. Nevertheless the Swanscombe type is older than the Steinheim man. The accompanying animal remains belong to a warm era, so must be assigned to the second Interglacial, indicating an age of at least 250,000 years. Furthermore, numerous stone implements were found, which—as we shall see—are infallible indications of early Stone-Age cultures and in this case correspond with the period mentioned.

The most recent finds of this nature were made in 1947 in a well-known and already thoroughly explored cave at Fontéchevade in France. Here, remains of two skulls revealed the existence of primeval men who had evolved beyond the Neanderthal stage and very clearly anticipated the anatomical characteristics of present-day Man. This Fontéchevade man, also, is assigned, in point of time, to the last Interglacial.

The exceptional rarity of such discoveries is certainly very disappointing. Even carefully organised exploration cannot help, for it is almost impossible to devise any sort of scheme likely to be productive. Obviously, every Pleistocene gravel-

pit must be regarded as promising territory, particularly if
fossilised animal remains have already been discovered there;
but the impossibility of knowing where the scattered groups
of primitive men may have wandered and died seriously
limits any sort of systematic investigation.

The now discredited Piltdown man (named after a place in
Sussex in the south of England) used to be placed amongst
these earlier fossil hominids. This find consisted of assorted
fragments recovered between 1908 and 1915. The English
lawyer Charles Dawson, who bore the cost of the excavations
and directed them himself, reconstructed from these remains
the Piltdown man, who was named in his honour *Eoanthropus
dawsonii*. Certainly it seemed to be one of those rare and
precious fossil treasures which had been so much sought after,
as it combined in a most desirable way the many characteristics of several stages in the evolution of Man. It was, in fact,
a perfect "missing link"—too perfect though, for in 1954,
after many expert palaeontologists and anthropologists had
carried out a series of exhaustive investigations, the conclusion was reached that the "remains" were nothing more nor
less than an extremely clever fake. The perpetrator has never
been identified, but the one certain thing is that Dawson himself was in no way to blame. The lower jaw was revealed as
belonging to a contemporary ape, probably an orang-utan. It
had been "fossilised" with the utmost skill; and the teeth,
too, under the delicate application of a file, had been worn
down to simulate the teeth of a primitive man. The associated
roof of the cranium was indeed that of a man, coming from
a late Ice-Age skull, and therefore nothing like as early as was
claimed for the fossil as a whole. So, unfortunately, Piltdown
man has turned out to be simply an anthropological hoax,
by a person or persons unknown.

Another similar palaeontological mystery had a more inno-
cent solution. As long ago as 1913 there was discovered in the
Olduvai gorge in East Africa the skeleton of an undoubtedly
genuine *Homo sapiens*. But it lay among layers which clearly
belonged to the Middle Pleistocene. The inevitable conclusion to be drawn from this was that Man had reached his full
development in Africa a quarter of a million years before he
did in Europe. This sensational, indeed revolutionary, claim

was not, it need hardly be said, accepted forthwith; and indeed subsequent finds of a similar sort provided the solution: the Olduvai man was not in any way older than the European representatives of his kind. He had in fact died in his appropriate stratum, but had subsequently been shifted by earthquakes into a deeper and therefore earlier geological environment.

The time-error in this case was a result of the determination of age from surrounding geological strata, a method which, generally speaking, is most reliable. Indeed, it is a method that is impossible to dispense with, but which should, if possible, be confirmed by other means of proof. Recently there have become available additional means of checking, and these have proved very valuable within certain limited time-spans.

One of these is the fluorine test. This test is based on the tendency of the calcium phosphate content in the bones of animal and human skeletons to absorb fluorine from the moisture of the soil in which they are buried. The longer the bones have lain in the ground the greater, naturally, is the quantity of fluorine absorbed; and thus it is possible to ascertain their age. But the factors of error in this method are quite considerable, so that it can only be regarded as moderately reliable.

Considerably more accurate, and increasingly so as the technique improves, is the radio-carbon clock. This is one of the most brilliant attempts to make use of certain natural characteristics for the purpose of absolute determination of prehistoric time. Once again—as in the case of the uranium-lead clock—radioactivity plays the decisive part. The radioactive carbon isotope C^{14} has been known since 1940. It has a half-life of 5,568 years, with an uncertainty factor of 30 years, more or less. The American Professor Libby, in conjunction with the famous Nobel Prize winner Anderson, discovered that in the upper atmosphere this isotope is continuously being produced, by the action of ultra-radiations on nitrogen, in quantities that compensate exactly for its own loss through radiation decay. This is an astonishing fact, and provides significant evidence of the state of absolute equilibrium prevailing in the power-conflict perpetually being waged between the outer atmosphere and hostile cosmic influences. Now C^{14} does not persist in an independent state; it combines with free oxygen in the air to form carbon dioxide. As a result, the proportion of carbon dioxide in the atmosphere, which has been constant for a very long time, contains an equally constant though very minute proportion of radioactive C^{14} carbon dioxide, which is assimilated in the same way as "normal" carbon dioxide into the tissues of plants and, indirectly, through the ingestion of plants, into the bodies of animals, thereby making all plants and animals slightly radioactive. While a plant or an animal is alive, the carbon-14 is maintained at a constant level. When the organism dies, however, the supply of C^{14} ceases and the amount of radio-carbon diminishes at its fixed rate of decay.

On the basis of these facts Libby began, in 1949, a series of experiments with the radio-carbon clock which—with progressively increasing refinements—have been carried out ever since in many countries. The methods involved are both complicated and time-consuming. At the present, one single measurement takes at least 48 hours. Originally Libby worked with solid carbon. He obtained this by burning the object under investigation and collecting the resultant carbon-dioxide gas; the gas was then, by means of reduction with magnesium (separating the oxygen content from the CO_2), changed into carbon which could be tested by a Geiger counter for its radioactive intensity. Nowadays the tendency is more and more towards investigating gaseous and fluid forms of carbon-hydrogen compounds whose carbon contents are naturally derived from the object under investigation. Acetylene gas (C_2H_2), with the aid of which a great deal of research is now being done, has proved particularly practical and time-saving. But even the famous Geiger counter has now been forced to retreat into the background, for this extremely sensitive instrument unfortunately reacts to every chance radiation in the atmosphere or from surrounding objects, and therefore requires especially elaborate precautions as regards shielding, the taking of measurements and their ultimate interpretation—all of which difficulties tend to make the eventual results inaccurate. In preference, therefore, use is made of the scintillation-counter which, in 1902, was introduced in its primitive form by William Crookes into the field of atomic physics for the purpose of counting elementary particles and measuring their electrical charges. This apparatus consists principally of a fluorescent film which reacts to each impact of an elementary radiation particle with a tiny scintillation which can then be photographed.

Marvellous as the functioning of this radio-carbon clock appears to be—and it will become even more so with further development—it suffers from one severe handicap: a far too short half-life. What are a mere 5,568 years to palaeontology? After this period its radiations, which even to begin with were extremely weak, have sunk to half; which means that after roughly 28,000 years it will radiate at only one thirty-second of its original strength, barely sufficient to provide a basis for any reliable calculations. For this reason, during the early years when this method was used, the upper limit of absolutely reliable dating had to be restricted to 20,000 years. Only after the scintillation-counter had been brought into use was it believed possible to go back, theoretically, to 44,000 years. Optimistic opinions from the United States are hopeful of covering periods of as much as 60,000 years, and although this would be of invaluable assistance in investigating the later Pleistocene and subsequent periods of Man's development, the *Pithecanthropus* period still lies hopelessly beyond the reach of this method of dating. So far only archaeology has made any significant use of it, covering the prehistorical period as far back as the "new men".

Now extremely recently a new and almost unbelievably accurate method of dating has been brought into use. This, like the radio-carbon method, is a type of atomic clock; but it spans millions of years. The working of this clock is based on the excessively slow decay of the radioactive isotope potassium-40 into calcium-40 and the stable isotope argon-40, and it is from the quantity of potassium that has changed into argon (an inert gas) that the lapse of time is calculated. To discover the date of a rock by this method it is only necessary to establish the number of potassium and argon atoms in a potassium-bearing element in the rock in question. But for the purpose of dating fossils it is essential that the rock in which they have been found was actually formed at the time these fossil beings existed. In the case of the Olduvai gorge, in the dating of *Zinjanthropus* (see p. 265), the perfect rock existed—volcanic tuff or ash containing the necessary potassium-bearing mineral. The accuracy of this means of measuring time is indicated by the fact that the quantity of argon in a rock sample can be measured, by means of an instrument called a mass-spectrometer, to within a ten-thousand-millionth of an ounce.

One striking thing about these latest measurements of prehistoric time is the shortening of all hitherto accepted timespans. Thus, in the Haua-Fteah cave in Cyrenaica (North Africa), a Neanderthal lower jaw was found which, according to the C^{14} method, must have been about 34,000 years old. Hitherto anthropology had dated the extinction of Neanderthal Man at about 60-64 thousand years ago. But the more remote datings by the radio-carbon method still show a fairly wide potential margin of error, and too much significance should not be attached to allegedly precise values. However, certain changes in the time-scale may well become necessary in the light of future datings.

Virtually nothing is known about the line of genetic descent of the "new men" from the older types. We have already seen that these early men—with the exception of the Neanderthalers—have left very scanty fossil remains. Even the Neanderthal group is extremely diverse in detail, and skulls from different places show their own local peculiarities. Ehringsdorf and Steinheim man were not identical, any more than, amongst present Man's true ancestors, Swanscombe man was identical with Fontéchevade man. Each species or group shows diversification into local races. Therefore these later men as we know them are not homogenous; instead, they vary widely in size and in form of skull and skeleton. The one thing they have in common is the disappearance of primitive characteristics in a process of thorough "modernisation" which, in the case of many finds, goes so far that they are almost indistinguishable from *Homo sapiens*. The transition to this final stage took place from the different races so smoothly that even today there are ethnic groups which can only be regarded as pure, direct descendants of those "new men". Indeed, some individuals at the present day have skulls of a shape quite identical with those of some of their Pleistocene ancestors.

From the "new men" onwards we are richly endowed with fossils. Ice-Age Europe, in particular, has been thoroughly explored and has provided evidence of complete, distinct lines of descent. The African and Asian territories have so far proved less rich in remains, although Asia in particular is regarded as the original home of these higher stages of Man's development. But this deficiency is obviously attributable to less prehistoric research having been carried out in those remoter regions.

One outstanding racial type is the Cro-Magnon, a name deriving from a cave near Les Eyzies, a village on the River Vézère in the Dordogne region of France. Up to 1868 the cave was entirely unknown. It was exposed by railway builders laying a new stretch of line, and in the cave were found human bones. The building contractors were public-spirited enough to hold up further construction work until archaeologists could arrive on the spot and make an expert appraisal of this find. To judge from their bones, the Cro-Magnon men were tall (about 6 feet), had high, vertical foreheads, well-rounded skulls, scarcely any trace of frontal ridges above the eye-sockets, predominantly narrow noses and pronounced chin formations. This description so much resembles present-day types that the obvious descendants of the Cro-Magnon men are those who live in the Dordogne today, the Basques of Northern Spain, early occupants of Hesse and Westphalia in Germany, the Dalarnians of Sweden, as well as the Guanches, the primitive inhabitants of the Canary Islands. Numerous later finds, and—as was only subsequently remembered—many earlier disregarded discoveries, indicate a very widespread distribution of this type. They were, in fact, the talented representatives of the most highly developed Ice-Age culture, the creators of the numerous cave paintings which date from the last great Glacial Period.

Closely allied to them, even though racially distinctive— a point that is, however, strongly debated—is the Grimaldi type. These take their name from the Grimaldi grottoes near Monte Carlo. Altogether there are nine not very deep caves eroded out of the limestone, from which, since 1872, a total of sixteen well-preserved skeletons, obviously ceremonial burials, have been recovered. These have included men, women and children. Their average adult height was about 5 feet 4 inches, generally well below the Cro-Magnon size. On the other hand, one male skeleton is 6 feet 4 inches tall. The shapes of the skulls strongly suggested negroid affinities, but this is now considered to be the result of faulty reconstruction. A number of characteristics seem to connect them with Cro-Magnon man; but others suggest a resemblance to contemporary North Italian, Lombardic types, so that it is far more likely that they are related to early ancestors of the latter.

Other racial types too are known from this period in Europe, differing somewhat in skull proportions, and clearly the ancestors of present-day racial groups. Some of the specimens of Cro-Magnon man show rather pronounced brow ridges, and some anthropologists have tried to suggest that these forms represent intermediates—hybrids—between the two groups of Neanderthalers and "new men". It is almost certain, however, that such heavy-browed individuals were merely deviations from the standard Cro-Magnon form, and in no way represent hybridisation with the Neanderthal stock.

The finds of "new men" have in recent times become very widespread geographically. England, Germany, Italy, Russia, Siberia, North, Central, and South Africa, Palestine, China, Java, Australia, have all contributed specimens. In every case, the "new men" have very clearly outgrown the stage of the "old men". From time to time characteristics reminiscent of Neanderthal man appear—and, as in the case of the Piedmont form of Cro-Magnon man, it is probably best to regard them as deviations from the normal form rather than as evidence for interbreeding with Neanderthal man. From the chronological point of view, of course, such interbreeding would have been possible, as Neanderthal man lived contemporaneously with the "new men"—especially in, say, North Africa, where isolated populations of Neanderthalers lived on after their relatives in Europe had died out. In the present state of knowledge of Man's ancestors, it is probably best to discount interbreeding of this kind until we have more evidence.

The transitions to the present-day races of *Homo sapiens* are so imperceptible that no hard and fast lines can be drawn anywhere. Indeed, the diversity of all human types starts from a date far back in time, an unknown date, when the process of racial differentiation began and the features of present-day Man were first delineated.

CHAPTER NINETEEN

Robinson Crusoe Cultures

I T was in July 1704 that the English galley *Cinque Ports* dropped anchor near the island of Mas a Tierra, which lies in the South Pacific far off the coast of Chile. Mas a Tierra is one of the Juan Fernandez group—a cluster of completely uninhabited islands which had provided, ever since their first discovery, a welcome retreat for pirates on account of their remoteness. Here water could be replenished, booty shared out, and a period of recuperation enjoyed before embarking on fresh buccaneering expeditions. On this particular occasion a twenty-eight-year-old Scottish sailor, Alexander Selkirk, had fallen foul of the master of the *Cinque Ports,* a highly dangerous thing to do in the harsh sea-faring conditions of those days. The master disposed of Selkirk by simply marooning him on the deserted island. The trouble-maker might thereafter fend for himself as best he could. If he were fortunate, he might possibly be taken off by another ship; if not, that would be his bad luck.

Now Selkirk had sailed all over the world and happened to be a man of resourceful character. He knew very well that he could not depend upon the opportune arrival of a chance pirate ship whose crew were in need of relaxation. Years might pass before this happened (in fact, he was not rescued until February, 1709). Certainly he would have perished miserably in a very short time, had he not immediately and most energetically done everything possible to ensure his survival for an indefinite period. He possessed nothing but the strength of his bare hands, the courage of desperation and an intelligent mind. Thus equipped, he took up the challenge of the wilderness and became the world-famous model for Daniel Defoe's *Robinson Crusoe.*

The persistent popularity of the Crusoe story undoubtedly derives from the almost unique drama of one defenceless

man's fight for naked survival against the primitive world
around him. We all know how Crusoe, in the book, took
refuge in a sheltering cave, made fire by the primitive method
of savages, shaped stones and pieces of wood to form implements, collected fruit and stored up supplies, hunted wild
animals with courage and guile, made his own clothing,
improved on his weapons, and did and invented a hundred
other things which finally made him master over the wilderness and its animal inhabitants. A triumph of the human
mind and its abilities.

Quite unconsciously Defoe had, in fact, compressed into
the course of a few years in a man's life the whole story of
the development of primitive Man who, in important respects,
resembled Crusoe to an astonishing degree. Naturally Crusoe
and Selkirk enjoyed one appreciable advantage: they came
from a culturally advanced society, and—the cultural level
of the individual plays no part here—were endowed with a
knowledge inherited and accumulated from the experience of
countless preceding generations. Primitive Man, in contrast,
had to fumble his way to this knowledge, discovering it and
acquiring it by infinitesimal stages. Crusoe knew what he
had to rediscover in order to deal with this or that situation,
an advantage that was denied to early men.

It has already been mentioned that during the Tertiary
the physical evolution of Man proceeded at a snail's pace,
while during the Pleistocene it raced headlong forward.
Exactly the same happened in the case of his mental and
cultural development. This is particularly noticeable if we
consider Man's progress during the 600,000 years of the
Pleistocene that followed after the Villafranchian Stage, that is
the actual period of the Ice Ages. It seems as if, about the beginning of the Ice-Age era, the pre-hominids of the Tertiary
had not yet surpassed the animal-ape level of existence. It is
well known that a great many apes recognise clearly which of
the fruits among the great variety growing in their native habitats are enjoyable, and which are not. They know what kind
of birds lay the largest eggs, which insects can be approached
without risk of poisonous stings, and they also understand
clearly the optimal conditions for survival in their own
environment. They use cudgels for getting their prey, stones

for knocking down nuts and also as effective weapons. Some decades ago a film of an expedition in Africa showed a herd of baboons fleeing from a leopard. In the course of their flight they crossed a stream strewn with boulders and one baby baboon was left behind helpless on a rock in the middle of the torrent. With furious chattering, the tyrannical patriarch stopped his herd, and, as if at a command, they all started bombarding the leopard on the far bank with an absolute barrage of stones, until finally the beast was forced to turn tail. Under this "covering fire" the leader rescued the baby, and then the whole herd continued on their way. Obviously, the use of hard, handy stones as a throwing weapon is not a prerogative of early men. Similarly, the herd and family instinct, the impulse to help each other, is deeply rooted in the animal nature. Thus the use of fire is probably the only advantage that the Australopithecines had over their ape contemporaries. For at that stage of evolution speech cannot have developed beyond conventional noises which are to be found throughout the animal world in a thousand variations and gradations. The chimpanzees, in particular, are credited with using widely differentiated vocal sounds.

So the primitive culture of evolving Man started at the point when fire was first deliberately used as a source of light and warmth in the night and in the darkness of caves and when conscious fashioning of tools began. This latter process commenced, so far as our present knowledge goes, in the late Tertiary, since stone tools were found in the same rock layers as *Zinjanthropus,* which the potassium-argon method dates as considerably more than one million years old. With regard to that other criterion of awakening cultures, the technique of producing fire artificially, it seems certain that it was not discovered widely and simultaneously. So far as we think we can tell, knowledge of it spread extremely slowly, and fire appears to have been regarded as a normal cultural asset only when the Neanderthal level had been reached.

Hitherto stones, also, had only been used casually and then discarded. When and where the first attempt was made to shape stones, and to keep them for prolonged and repeated use as tools, will never be known. It is possible that the first step in this direction was made by some single primitive genius who was then imitated by his kin and members of his tribe, who recognised the usefulness of his invention. More probably, however, a great number of such "geniuses" existed; for the rapid spread of stone-working over the whole of the inhabited world could not have resulted from one single point of origin, the numbers of primeval men being too small for continuous contact to be maintained over the whole of the world's vast land areas. The attainment of a certain mental level was all that was needed for the phenomenon of the Stone Age to appear wherever primitive men dwelt. The fact that the technique of stone-working developed, by and large, along roughly similar lines in different places is a result of the limited number of possibilities of shaping stones, which were very much the same the world over.

The question: "What can be done with a mere stone?" has been probably answered as exhaustively as possible by early men. They produced all the basic hand tools which are still in use today, such as knives, hammers, saws, files, planes, drills, chisels, as well as weapons for striking, stabbing and throwing. Certainly for more than half a million years the stone was Man's most powerful aid to cultural and intellectual progress. This was especially the case with the flint, which enjoyed great popularity because of the ease with which it could be split. Its property of emitting sparks when struck hard also made it the most important means of producing fire artificially. Indeed, right up to comparatively recent times it was used as the means of "firing" flintlocks.

Stone artifacts have proved to be vitally important in tracing the course of Ice-Age cultures. We have already seen how exceedingly scanty are the surviving traces of the men themselves who used these implements. We would know desperately little about the evolution of Pleistocene Man if the vast quantities of stones they worked had not told us so much that we need to know. Everywhere, over and over again, it is stone implements which have revealed where men lived and how they lived. Their bodies may have decayed, disintegrated and vanished, but the flint traces of their days on Earth still survive after all those eons.

Naturally, such a wealth of sites and finds cannot be surveyed without some systematic arrangement. Therefore the main periods are comprehensively and clearly divided into Palaeolithic, Mesolithic, and Neolithic. Of these the Palaeo- lithic is by far the longest. It lasted from the beginning of the Pleistocene until about 10,000 B.C.—that is, well after the appearance of *Homo sapiens* on the scene. This extent of time necessitates a further subdivision into Lower, Middle and Upper Palaeolithic. The individual cultures fit into these main divisions. The use of the term "culture" is widespread in scientific circles, but to the layman it may seem rather strange when used in connection with the semi-anthropoid *Pithecanthropus* or the barbaric Neanderthal man. It must therefore always be borne in mind that we are not speaking of "culture" in its contemporary grandiose meaning, but in the much more limited sense of the range of activities of Pleistocene Man. Another term with a specialised meaning is "industry"—used by anthropologists for the stone imple- ments made by a particular group of people, living in an area at a particular time. The names of the cultures are taken from the first site where industries belonging to that culture were described. If on subsequent occasions more industries belonging to the same culture are found in remotely separate parts of the world, they are still given the same name. As the most intensive work has been carried out in Europe, we find that the names of cultures are mostly taken from localities in Europe, whilst in contrast the separate industries bear local names. This scheme or system goes back to the French scientist Gabriel de Mortillet who worked it out towards the end of the last century. It attained its final form after many improvements, which were chiefly due to the eminent French archaeologist, Henri Breuil.

The oldest true stone artifacts come from Africa, and it is doubtful whether they date as far back as the Pliocene. It is not really astonishing that Africa seems to lead the way here, for the spread of the human race in Europe, from whatever directions immigrations may have come, was, at the least, considerably delayed by the advance of the ice right at the beginning of the Pleistocene. Africa, ice-free and subjected only to periods of intense rain, had a 50,000 years' start over Europe so far as the advancement of early Man was concerned, anticipating many developments in the technique of stone-working which only became common in Europe very much later. The sole possible exceptions are provided by discoveries made in the 1940's along the Portuguese coastal areas, which could be dated as far back as the Günz glaciation. These areas were never even threatened by the ice, and in fact were so far away that they would have provided favourable conditions for settlement. Generally speaking, however, the earliest European cultural groups must be allocated to the first Interglacial, a warm period that lasted for 70,000 years.

This first culture was the Abbevillian, named after the town of Abbeville on the River Somme in Northern France. (The

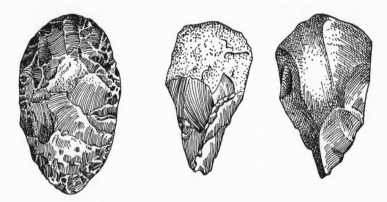

68. Hand-axes: left, from North Africa; centre, from
Abbeville; right, from the early Acheulian

Abbevillian includes the so-called pre-Chellian and early Chellian cultures.) By coincidence, this is not only the earliest European culture in the historical sense, but also the first ever to be discovered. It was round about 1837, a time when the existence of prehistoric men was violently disputed, that Jacques Boucher de Perthes (1788-1868), the chief of customs in Abbeville, came on the scene. He was an extremely versatile and gifted man with the vivid imagination of a Jules Verne. In his time there had been discovered in South France the skeletal remains of our old friend the Tertiary anthropoid, *Dryopithecus*. From that moment he was obsessed by one fixed idea—as was his contemporary, the lawyer Edouard Lartet, later a famous cave-explorer—that men must have existed during the Tertiary. Therefore it was necessary to search for remains, in the way that one looked for animal fossils. And so he searched. The area he chose was the Somme valley where he knew quantities of bones of mammoths, wild horses, cave bears and stags had already been discovered. In addition to further animal remains, he also unearthed a number of very oddly shaped stones, such as had always been found here and there and had been dismissed casually as freaks of Nature. Now even though Boucher de Perthes was no expert in geology and managed to confuse Quaternary and Tertiary strata, he was far from stupid. Suddenly these stones caught his attention: their shaping was no "freak of nature", but the result of purposeful work by the hands of men. This was his brilliant idea, which he boldly made public. Unfortunately he went somewhat too far, for he attributed the stone artifacts to the Tertiary System, attempting thus indirectly to prove the existence of Tertiary Man. He was, as a result, ridiculed to death by the official world of science and sent back to his pigeon-holes. The stones continued to be regarded as "freaks of nature" until Sir Charles Lyell looked into the matter and shattered the narrow-minded complacency of his contemporaries. Artificially worked stones had, of course, been found here and there, at various times and in various places, but his opinion was that none of these were Tertiary—they were all of Pleistocene origin.

With that the conception of the Stone Age was born; and the cultural achievements of those still hypothetical primitive men were thenceforward known to science as the Ice-Age cultures. The actual nomenclature accepted today was established by Breuil when he set out the chronology of these various Ice-Age cultures.

Fresh ideas in the world of natural sciences always have great difficulty in making their mark and becoming generally accepted. A stone fashioned as an implement presupposes a prehistoric man who must have made it. But acceptance of this fact only gained ground during the second half of the last century. (One only has to think of the fate of the Neanderthal discovery, which was made at about the same time as bitter battles were being fought over the recognition of Boucher de Perthes' stone implements.) Decades passed before the immense value of these "freaks of nature" in elucidating prehistory was gradually appreciated, and then Pleistocene sites all over the world were plundered for their treasure. Slowly there arose a school of specialists who studied the now vast quantities of stone implements that had been unearthed, and classified them and finally were able to recognise the different techniques of working and to distinguish and appreciate their ever-increasing refinement.

It may not be immediately obvious how such apparently trivial differences can be sufficient to enable the archaeologist to distinguish between widely separated cultures. But here science has given full credit to the mental abilities of primitive Man. To us, today, their achievements may seem a mere nothing (and they would assuredly have seemed so to Robinson Crusoe, who at least knew what he wanted): but for the Ice-Age men, behind every new tool, every new form, every fresh method of chipping stone, there was an idea, a new discovery of things which hitherto had never existed, things without precedent or prototype in Nature. What does an animal know of the usefulness of a pointed stone axe for stripping the hide off its prey, of the advantage of thin stone blades for chopping up meat or splitting bones and wood, of the use of handy scrapers for cleaning a desirable pelt, or the increased power of a pointed flint when secured to a piece of wood with sinews or fibres? Yet all these advantages became known to Man. And every new device reflects a corresponding intellectual advance.

This problem of "handling" stone was not, however, tackled in exactly the same way by the various types of early men in different parts of the world; nor was it always solved in the same way. Although the *effect* of the usefulness of the manufactured implements must have been much the same in every case, quite distinct methods of working were developed, which are clearly characteristic of the cultures concerned.

Two important kinds of tools are known—those such as the hand-axes and choppers or cleavers, based on the central core of a flint from which flakes have been removed, and those where the flakes themselves are utilised. It is impossible to produce a core tool without also making flakes, and it was usually the case that in any industry some of the flakes would be used for small ancillary tools such as scrapers. The relative importance of the core and flake tools varies from culture to culture. Hand-axes were stout lumps of flint which fitted comfortably into the hand and were pointed or sharpened on one or both sides by beating on an anvil formed by a bigger stone. Most likely they served as general purpose tools. Some, with a straighter transverse cutting face, were probably mostly used for chopping, and equivalent tools survive to the present day in primitive societies. In general, the evolution of flint utilisation progressed more and more in the direction of the finer and more delicate working of flint flake-tools, which reached a climax in the very slender blade-like flakes of the Upper Palaeolithic.

The Abbevillian was a purely hand-axe culture which, outside Western Europe, is known to have existed chiefly in North and East Africa. In South Africa it is represented by the Stellenbosch stage, one of those local appellations which crop up so frequently. In Europe this culture spanned the whole of the first Interglacial Period (about 70,000 years), and its bearers, from all that we know, must have been those early hominids hitherto familiar to us as Heidelberg man, *Pithecanthropus* and *Sinanthropus*.

Out of the Abbevillian there developed in Africa, and spread subsequently to Europe, the Acheulian, naturally a hand-axe culture also. It is named after Saint-Acheuil, a suburb of Amiens in the north of France. To a certain extent the Abbevillian was a very primitive culture, covering a period when the use of stone was first discovered—stoneworking being inefficient, crude, almost haphazard, and the implements mostly fashioned on one side only: whereas during the Acheulian stone tools were in general use and manufacture, and the quality achieved was high. Indeed, within their physical limitations, these later, extremely versatile, double-sided hand-axe implements were finished to such a degree of excellence that a certain cultural stagnation actually set in, which was dispelled only by subsequent mingling with other cultures. In comparison with the Abbevillian, the Acheulian lasted for a very long time, roughly 250,000 years, and has, in consequence, been divided into Lower, Middle and Upper Acheulian. Of these, the Upper

Acheulian is already modern enough to form part of the Middle Palaeolithic, while the first two round off the Lower Palaeolithic. From what we know of the development of mankind, the culture-bearers of the Lower Acheulian were still pithecanthropines who, from the Middle era onwards, must have been gradually superseded by true hominids of the Swanscombe and Steinheim type. So far as Europe is concerned this characteristic line of development is chiefly in evidence in the west and in Southern England. It becomes rarer in Central Germany, and the more so the further east. Africa, being the home-land of these types, is almost everywhere rich in hand-axes of this epoch; and, since they are also found in places in the Sahara which today are most inhospitable to man, it must be concluded that the Pleistocene pluvial phases—rainy periods corresponding to the northern glaciations—turned this area into a comfortably habitable region, something which men today are vainly striving to bring about again. Discoveries have shown that further waves of the Acheulian spread across Palestine and into India, and this is no matter for surprise. The abundantly fruitful strip of oases forming Egypt seems to have been continuously settled ever since the days of the Acheulians, a period of about 480,000 years.

In the group of the flaked-tool cultures, which did not possess the hand-axe, the chief European representatives are the Clactonian and Lavalloisian. Although the main discovery site after which they were named—Clacton-on-Sea, a coastal resort in East Anglia—belongs, on the evidence of contemporary fossil fauna, to the second Interglacial, this culture may perhaps be traced back even farther, to the first Interglacial, in which case it would have been, in part, contemporary with the Abbevillian. Its main characteristics are simple flaked-implements, most of them with a broad, one-sided striking face. Double-sided examples are unknown. Further shaping of the flake after it had been split off was, at first, slight and primitive, and only during the Middle and Upper Clactonian did the process become more elaborate under the influence of other stylistic elements, finally achieving a highly finished result. This technique undoubtedly lasted until the end of the third glaciation. In Africa it is only sparsely in evidence; but it is considerably more common in India and Java. It is very unlikely that any sort of cultural cross-fructification between these two widely separated regions (Eastern England and Eastern Asia) could have taken place during the Lower Clactonian. Furthermore there was quite clearly no close contact and obviously no intermingling between the Clactonian and the hand-axe cultures of near-by France. So it must be accepted as a fact that the same discoveries were made independently in different parts of the world.

A particular stone-working technique is characterised by the name Lavalloisian (named after a place near Paris). By this method it was possible to produce flakes that were so perfect for their intended purpose that scarcely any further work on them was needed. The typically Lavalloisian technique of striking flakes off a so-called "tortoise-core" may quite possibly have been developed independently in different parts of the world.

Another further development of the Clactonian may well be the Tayacian, in which the techniques and basic styles of various cultures are mixed, with the Clactonian predominating. The time-sequence of these cultures is still in dispute.

The important Mousterian culture belongs to Neanderthal man. It seems to have developed from the Clactonian, but was apparently influenced at times by the techniques of the Acheulian and Lavalloisian industries. The first industries leading to the Mousterian tradition belong to the third Interglacial, associated with, for example, Ehringsdorf man. There is some doubt as to whether Fontéchevade man was responsible for the Mousterian implements associated with his skull, or whether these tools belonged to early Neanderthalers who happened to surprise and kill the Fontéchevade individuals.

At this point it is hard not to pay a small tribute to these "barbaric cannibals", the Neanderthalers. They were the first men of whom we know for certain that they "stayed at their posts" when the glacial periods approached, breathing a chill over the hitherto warm continent of Europe; and they survived during these inhospitable times in the rock shelters where their remains are now found. All other discoveries of human remains in Europe have, without exception, been assigned to one of the warm periods. Those two types, the Swanscombe and Fontéchevade men, who were on the evolutionary line of the true men and were already superior to the Neanderthalers, certainly shared Europe with the latter during the Great Interglacial. After that, however, they must have vanished. The possibility of a migration south into warmer regions suggests itself. But is this really tenable? It must be borne in mind that the glaciers of the Würm advance did not simply take a single generation by surprise. Hundreds of years must have passed before the approach of the ice became apparent. The probably short average age of the men of that time would not be sufficient to register any deterioration in the climate. Even the oldest and wisest grandfather would scarcely have had any recollection that in his youth

69. Stone implements from the French Mousterian

the days somehow seemed to be warmer. Moreover, at the Neanderthal level the capacity for speech would have been still very limited so that complicated communications were ruled out. Also lacking, of course, was any knowledge of far away, climatically more favourable regions which could be reached by migrating. Every new-born generation was aware only of the climate in which it grew up and knew nothing of former, earlier conditions long ago. In so far as it is permissible to make any firm assumptions about a subject on which so little is known, it may be assumed that these warm-period types simply died out. At all events, the Neanderthal men dominated Europe during the cold periods at the start of the Würm glaciation.

The Mousterian itself was a pure flake-tool culture, but was no longer uniform throughout all the regions it covered (as far off as South Russia, Syria and Palestine). The influence of other cultural elements seems unmistakable here and there. Almost always the stone implements are very carefully and neatly finished off, so that the workers may have possessed a certain artistic sense. On the other hand, it may have come about that a group of craftsmen developed a certain facility for the work. This would have meant a division of labour within the clan or horde, and thus the discovery of organisation as such, a discovery which had to be made suddenly sooner or later and which would certainly have been possible at the Neanderthal stage. Hitherto mankind would only have known the division into man and woman as decreed by Nature. Man's life was taken up with the effort and hazard of hunting, as well as with occasional battles; women tended the children, kept "house" and undertook the lighter work such as gathering fruits. The fashioning of stone implements was certainly the task of everyone. But later, possibly, men who were crippled or had become unfit for hunting or fighting, would have specialised in stone-working and thus brought about such a division of labour. There comes to mind Wieland, the skilled smith of the Nordic sagas, for whose hideous, deformed figure a Neanderthaler might well have been the perfect model.

With the Neanderthal men the Mousterian culture in Europe flourished and died. About 60,000 years ago, still in the middle of the Würm glaciation, the Upper Palaeolithic began. The hand-axe and flake-tool cultures, in the original Lower and Middle Palaeolithic sense, were superseded by the true, genuinely artistic blade-cultures which emerged with the new men of the Cro-Magnon type. The great era of the Ice-Age cave-men, with its astonishing wealth of genuine works of art, had begun.

CHAPTER TWENTY

Wonders of the Ice-Age Caves

THE Upper Palaeolithic Era which now follows coincides roughly with the second half of the Würm glaciation. Its span is generally assumed as extending from the close of the Mousterian, about 60,000 years ago, down to the disappearance of the glaciers in the far north of Sweden, about 12,000 years ago. During this period there existed three great cultures: the Aurignacian (named after Aurignac in the French Département of Haute-Garonne), the Solutrian (after Solutré in the Rhône valley) and the Magdalenian (after the semi-cave of La Madeleine in the Dordogne). Within the framework of these cultures, the systematology of prehistory has been still further elaborated and distinguishes a whole series of cultural gradations which are identified by Roman numerals and sometimes by individual names. For our purposes these extremely fine distinctions are little to the point, their existence being mentioned only to show the intensive care and attention to detail devoted to research on the subject.

While the division between the Lower and Middle Palaeolithic is hazy and far from obvious (for which reasons certain prehistorians do not recognise it), the dawn of the Upper Palaeolithic is as clear as daylight. At this point there really lies a dividing line as distinct as that which separated the Tertiary from the Pleistocene at the time of the first advance of the ice. It is distinct because, with the end of the Mousterian (Mousterian II), the culture-bearer *Homo neanderthalensis* for some reason disappeared from the scene and made way for new men of the Cro-Magnon races. The latter, with their highly developed technique, supplanted all former Stone-Age culture, replacing it with their own. Where they came from is difficult to say. Africa, which gave Europe the hand-axe culture, seems the most likely place. But it may have been from the east or even possibly the north-east, for the direction of advance of the fluctuating ice-cap during the Würm must be taken into account as a powerful motive for migration. No people would voluntarily migrate from a favourable climate to an unfavourable one. Only the reverse process would be reasonable. Therefore, during the Aurignacian, the area covered by Spain, France, Southern England, Southern Germany, Austria, Hungary and Southern Russia must have offered more attractive living conditions than homelands which perhaps lay much farther to the north. Some authorities consider Hungary as the place of origin of the Solutrian, and regard the Magdalenian as nothing more than a natural subsequent development of the Aurignacian in territories already settled.

Mention has already been made of the physical development of the Cro-Magnon types. Their mental evolution and level is reflected in their cultural legacy. The cave regions of Southern France and Northern Spain are one vast prehistoric museum, containing treasure houses full of works of art which testify to the maturity of their creators. But it would be quite wrong to conclude from this that the late Palaeolithic men were predominantly cave-dwellers. Of course they did inhabit caves—wherever they could find them, as in limestone or Alpine regions. But generally they lived in the open country, even during the hard winter months. The attraction of having a "roof over one's head" has, since the days of earliest Man, been expressed in the building of huts of all sorts and sizes and of increasing complexity, constructed from twigs, animal skins and wood. Caves—often very deep and labyrinthine, and oppressive and frightening in their absolute darkness— were not such desirable dwelling-places. On the other hand they were ideally suited to mystical cult-rites and were, indeed, as we shall see, widely used for this purpose. But for living in, only the entries and passages accessible to daylight were used. For this reason the numerous semi-caves—*abris*, as they are called in French—were very popular. These *abris* were formed by running water washing away easily soluble rock from beneath hanging masses of harder rock.

The intellectual level, compared to that of the Neanderthal, rose sharply, the most important single feature being the development of speech, which finally became a fluent and

expressive means of communication. Up to the early Neanderthal, the capacity of mankind as a whole in this respect had
probably been extremely limited. From simple sounds with
different intonations there developed, very gradually indeed,
childishly imitative but consistent monosyllables indicating
definite objects, which from the beginning, by reason of having originated in widely separated regions and among many
different races, led to clear differences of dialect. Only with
the numerical increase of mankind, which brought about
increased contact with neighbouring tribes, must there have
occurred an intermingling of languages, an exchange of
vocabularies and, in consequence, an enrichment of the means
of expression. What was certainly lacking up to and including
Neanderthal days was any linking of elementary expressions
into coherent sentences. For this the intelligence of the
Cro-Magnon was necessary, an intelligence which rose above
purely factual, earth-bound concepts; for suddenly the
"higher", abstract conceptions were there. We know that
Neanderthal Man only very occasionally buried his dead.
Upper Palaeolithic Man, in contrast, was familiar with a
regular, ceremonial interment complete with food supplies,
ornaments and other sacrificial gifts. He had, therefore, discovered the "Beyond" and was already thinking about the
world behind the reality. His speech must, consequently,
have had definite expressions which brought such abstract
ideas as gods, spirits, demons into common usage.

A further striking difference from primitive mankind
appears in the increasing use of clothing. Since the first bone
"needles" date back to the Aurignacian, we must conclude
that clothing first became "the fashion" at this period—
exclusively to keep out the cold! There is no support for the
theory that with the awakening of human intelligence there
grew up a feeling of "modesty", which at any rate at this
stage of mankind's development would have been quite
unnatural and totally unknown. It is much more likely that
clothing was later associated with the desire for adornment
and also with an attempt at magical concealment, a trace of
which is found among civilised man today in masked and
fancy-dress balls. The fact that clothing was first invented in
Ice-Age Europe and Asia is surely indicative. It never occurred

to the inhabitants in warmer regions to festoon their bodies with animal skins; and such is the case even to the present day. Nevertheless, the late appearance on the scene of this elementary protection against the cold is rather extraordinary, since it must have been almost a matter of instinct to wrap oneself during daytime in a skin under which one must certainly have lain during the night.

But this again is "thinking back" from our own secure present. A skin wound about one means, first and foremost, an unaccustomed impediment to free movement. It must also be secured in order to stop it slipping off the body. And how is that done? Crusoe would have been in no doubt. With his stone knife he would have cut two arm-holes in the right places and worn the skin as a coat. Then it would certainly have occurred to him to bore some "button-holes" in the region of the hips, through which he would thread deer-sinews, securing the ends with knots and loops. It is as simple as that. But Robinson Crusoe knew what he had to reconstruct; whereas primitive Man had to discover all this. So we must try to understand what a really difficult problem must have been posed merely by the tricky connection of knots and loops. A thousand such apparently minor obstacles had to be overcome by early Man; so there is little point in amazement at the "late" discovery of such elementary things (in our contemporary view), and it is better to

conclude that probably at every stage in Man's intellectual development there were more stupid people than clever ones, more opponents of progress than advanced "geniuses".

Stone-working reached its culmination in the Upper Palaeolithic. The Aurignacian is sharply distinguished from the Mousterian by its tools, which were predominantly fashioned in blade form. Probably bone and wood were extensively used for hafts. Narrow, pointed and delicate blades indicate, by their shape alone, the existence of particularly adept and "experienced" craftsmen. Bone, ivory and horn appear with

70. Aurignacian spear-head

increasing frequency among the implements. Needles have already been mentioned. Snail-shells, animal teeth and ivory, with holes bored through, must have been used in the manufacture of ornaments. During the Solutrian the so-called leaf-point culture had a sudden revival; it was typified by the very beautifully formed and finished chipped stones in the shape of a spear-point which had already appeared here and there in the last Interglacial, chiefly in East Europe. In style the Magdalenian based itself on the Aurignacian. As we shall see, it represented in every respect the high point of the Ice-Age cultures. The use of bone, horn and ivory during the Magdalenian became so extensive that these materials almost overshadowed stone in importance. Novelties in the range of weapons were the one- and two-sided harpoons. Engraving and decorative carving on bones and ivory, which had already been practised in earlier times, now became common.

In the case of all Pleistocene men the struggle for existence centred on the hunt. By its success or failure life stood or fell. The captured prey yielded all that was needed: food for sustenance, bones and horns for tools and weapons, and bones mixed with dried dung for fuel in the ice-bound, treeless tundra and steppes. Skins provided protection against wind and weather, a cushioning against hard ground, and a covering during the night.

It is very probable that an exclusively meat diet was restricted to climatically unfavourable periods and areas. During warm periods and in sub-tropical regions plants would undoubtedly have been the staple food. But even here there is widespread evidence of hunting, so that it must be regarded, in general, as mankind's most important activity. For this reason methods of hunting were already well developed at the early stages of Man's history, so much so that the "higher" man of the Upper Palaeolithic could not have been, in this respect, far in advance of his earlier ancestors of 100,000 years and more ago. Practically everything that could be slain by spear or stone weapon was hunted. Obviously, men quickly learned to pursue young animals and the less aggressive beasts. But the stout hides and gigantic bones of elephants and rhinoceroses or bears proved irresistible, so that they were attacked and killed as frequently as easier prey. The pit-trap, skilfully disguised with skins, was invented early on; and the device of the battue (driving game) was used almost from the first—it was indeed an absolute necessity for catching fleet-footed prey.

A famous, now classic, example, of a battue area was discovered near the French village of Solutré which lies in the Rhône valley, in the neighbourhood of Mâcon. Here, a slope rises gently up and ends suddenly in an abrupt drop of more than 1,000 feet. At the foot of this rocky cliff were discovered, in 1866, enormous numbers of bones of wild horses. According to recent estimates at least 50,000 horses must have died here, not to mention wild cattle, reindeer and mammoths. The obvious conclusion to be drawn from this charnel house is that the Cro-Magnon hunters must have driven hordes of horses up the slope and forced them to plunge over the top to their death; then, if necessary, they could be conveniently finished off. Not a very sportsman-like proceeding—but this was, after all, the Stone Age.

However, figures in this case may be misleading. A total of fifty thousand horses is a tremendous lot and suggests some wild, insensate mass slaughter almost amounting to local extermination. But the fact is that this region of Solutré was settled over a very long period. Excavations here have unearthed one of the richest finds of stone implements and tools from all three Upper Pleistocene Periods. Assuming that the lapse of time from the beginning of the Aurignacian to the end of the Magdalenian was 50,000 years, which it could well have been, this would mean that, in effect, an average of only one horse a year fell over the cliff, which could quite well have been no more than pure accident. But a calculation of this sort is almost certainly fallacious; for all the circumstances point to this being the site of a battue, even though the huge number of animals becomes less astonishing when spread over such a considerable period of time. Cro-Magnon Man would certainly have had enough sense not to indulge in a pointless massacre of valuable prey, and only to hunt and kill as many as he required for daily use and for stocking an elementary larder. (Bones of Cro-Magnon men have also been found at the Solutrian site.)

Throughout the whole of the Ice Age the manufacture of weapons was determined solely by the requirements of the chase which, in the case of certain riverside settlements, naturally included fishing.

War-like clashes between individual hordes and tribes must have been rare because of the very limited possibilities of contact in the vast hunting grounds. Even the Neanderthaler would not have known that there were other men living "on the far side of the mountain".

For a long time the spear made of animal bone or wood must have predominated as a stabbing and throwing weapon. Bows and arrows first came into use during the last Interglacial, being an invention of the Mousterian-like North

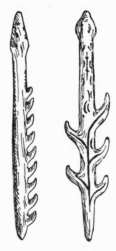

71. Harpoons from the Magdalenian

African Ater culture (named after a place in Algeria). The Neanderthal man is also thought very likely to have been familiar with "throwing-balls" similar to the South American bolas. With the use of pieces of wood and boomerangs for flinging, the Upper Palaeolithic Man attained the same level of armament as the present-day Australian aboriginal: but from this it must not be inferred that they also shared the same mental plane as the Australian natives. For it was not until the arrival of the Cro-Magnon races that there occurred the phenomenon at which the modern cultural world has not yet ceased to be astounded—the awakening of a true, deep, artistic feeling.

The discovery of the Ice-Age cave-paintings and our awareness, as a result, of a highly accomplished creative culture existing among people who, compared to us, were at a very primitive stage in the history of *Homo sapiens,* is undoubtedly one of the most exciting discoveries to be made during a century that has certainly not been lacking in surprises of that kind. Man of 20,000, 30,000, 40,000 years ago, whose very existence was hotly disputed less than a hundred years since, is suddenly revealed to us through his cultural testament as an artist of great stature, so great in fact that, from the waning of the Magdalenian to the rise of the classical era, there was nothing worthy to be set beside that wonderful efflorescence of creative art. There is nothing primitive in this art; and where it seems to lapse into the primitive, analysis of the style reveals a change in the mode of expression almost exactly corresponding to Western abstract art.

The first cave-paintings were actually brought to light in the last century; but they were relegated to obscurity again, with the usual expressions of contempt, as a result of the general scepticism of the intellectual world of the day. (There is something extraordinary about the mentality of the nine teenth century which in so many respects was a period of immense progress; for there prevailed a climate of disbelief and rigid opposition to anything new and surprising which lay outside the established frame of academic knowledge.)

However, certain events occurred here and there which should have sounded a clear warning to even the most obscurantist minds. Mention has already been made of the frequent finds of incised drawings on bones and ivory. In 1846 the French cave-explorer, Edouard Lartet, made the first discovery of this kind in La Madeleine. Once again, as usual, the very beautiful engraving of a mammoth was received with the greatest reserve. However, confirmation of its genuineness seemed assured when, in 1874, a Swiss teacher, excavating in the Kessler Hole—a cave in the Canton of Schaffhausen which was known as a former dwelling-place of Ice-Age reindeer- and mammoth-hunters—dug up a very fine engraving of a grazing reindeer. But this success was short-lived. A workman engaged in the excavations plotted a childish trick with one of the teacher's pupils. The boy scratched some animal figures on pieces of ivory, and the workman buried them on the site. Naturally, they were promptly "discovered" and handed on to the experts by the exultant teacher. It was only pure chance that exposed these examples of "Ice-Age engraving" as having originated in a schoolboy prank. A law case and confession exposed the whole painful affair, and thus further aggravation was given to the doubt already felt about other alleged Ice-Age engravings.

The same experience befell Boucher de Perthes, the discoverer of prehistoric stone implements. He wanted, as has already been mentioned, to prove the existence of Tertiary Man in the Somme valley. After endless effort he at length found a human jawbone and triumphantly claimed success. But in this case, too, the "fossil" turned out to be only a modern bone which workmen had buried in order to have a laugh at "the silly old man". It certainly needs a peculiar type of humour to appreciate this sort of behaviour.

And then, to cap everything, there came a report of "oil paintings by Stone-Age men in dark caves"!

In the matter of cave-paintings, as so often happens with epoch-making discoveries, the first find was the most dramatic. This was the now world-famous cave at Altamira in Northern Spain. Up to the year 1868 the very existence of this cave was entirely unknown even to the owner of the land, Don Marcelino de Sautuola. Its actual discoverer was an over-zealous hound who, pursuing a fox, broke through the thin undergrowth which masked a narrow crack in the side of the hill. The whines coming from inside showed the hunters, including Don Marcelino, where the dog was. The animal was rescued, and the cave's existence thus perforce became known. But that was all for the time being, and exciting only for the dog. Then, years later, Don Marcelino was again reminded of the cave on his estate, as a consequence of a visit to the Paris Exhibition of 1878, where he had become deeply engrossed in the results of recent investigations into the Stone Age. It occurred to him that his cave, too, might contain hand-axes and mammoth-bones; so he took a spade and began carefully to dig over the floor, as the experts in Paris had advised him. At first he had no success, but one day he came upon stone implements resembling those he had seen at the Exhibition. This naturally spurred him on, and henceforward he continued to find further prehistoric relics almost daily. But it was left to his five-year-old daughter to discover, by the flickering light of a pine-torch, the paintings of animals which adorned the walls and roofs of one cave gallery. Those must have been dramatic moments when Don Marcelino, torch in hand, lit up the walls and saw before him pictures from a vanished world, pictures that had remained hidden for 20,000 years or more. The animals of the Ice-Age world rose before his eyes. Bison and horses, stags, wild boar and reindeer, in glowing red and yellow colours, stared from the walls at the excited descendant of the long mouldered and forgotten artists who had created their likenesses. The colours were fresh and brilliant, probably made from ochre and red haematite bound with saliva or animal blood. The representations of wild animals resting, running or grazing were executed with a complete mastery of the subject, on an artistic level quite the equal of nineteenth-century Impressionism. It was, at the same time, both fortunate and unfortunate that Don Marcelino should have stumbled upon one of the most beautiful and richly ornamented of all caves that have so far been discovered. Unfortunate, because the completely modern "feeling" of these works of art was, in the eyes of the experts, the best possible reason for denying their alleged "barbaric" origin.

At first all went well and just as would be expected in view of the importance of such a discovery. The Madrid prehistorian, Vilanova, pronounced his expert judgment in Don Marcelino's favour and confirmed the Ice-Age dating of the paintings. Altamira became temporarily famous. Thousands made pilgrimages there to view the marvellous cave. Even the King of Spain visited the grotto which had suddenly focused the light of science on his realm.

Then came the catastrophe. In Lisbon, in 1880, there met the four-yearly International Congress for Anthropology and Prehistoric Archaeology, which was attended by the leading authorities from all the different countries. Among the delegates were the French scientist, Cartailhac, and Germany's Virchow. Vilanova's carefully prepared copies of the paintings were now laid for judgment before the assembly. The verdict was annihilating. It was pure impertinence on the part of Don Marcelino, they said, to expect that informed and experienced men of science would be taken in by such gross forgeries. These artistically mature paintings, in the modern idiom, could not possibly have originated in the primitive brains of Ice-Age men who, moreover, were technically quite unequipped to produce such work. Probably the pictures had been executed within the last ten years by a highly gifted, but morally extremely reprehensible individual acting in collusion with Don Marcelino. It was most regrettable that a man of Vilanova's reputation should have fallen for this.

That was the general judgment for which Cartailhac was spokesman. The planned visit to the Altamira cave was naturally cancelled. And Don Marcelino was now branded with the dreadful and widely publicised reputation of being a forger and a cheat who had not scrupled even to make a fool of his own sovereign. He died an embittered man, never having been able to vindicate himself, and all his personal efforts to have the discussion of the wonders of Altamira re-opened ending in failure.

The Altamira scandal had other stupid and far-reaching effects. For during the next twenty years further cave-paintings were discovered in the French caves of Pair-non-Pair, La Mouthe, Marsoulas and Chabot, but apart from local reports which attracted no attention, they never received any publicity. Indeed, no one even dared to speak up for the great antiquity of the paintings. In the case of the Pair-non-Pair find, the discoverer, Daleau, was so afraid of ridicule that he never said anything about it.

But as it happened Fate chose as the trail-blazer of this new knowledge the very man who had most viciously attacked it in Lisbon—Cartailhac. Among this professor's younger pupils and collaborators in Toulouse was one who subsequently became famed as the Abbé Breuil, one of the greatest of all palaeontologists, who dug with such success in that Mecca of Ice-Age explorers, the Vézère valley in the Dordogne.

Quite close to the village of Les Eyzies lies a cave, Les Combarelles, at that time extremely difficult of access, in one passage of which there had once been unearthed a modest find from the Magdalenian. Another passage, leading deep into the mountainside, was said to contain no traces of primitive culture. Here, Breuil and two companions found more than they had ever dreamed of: over 300 rock-engravings representing wild horses, bears, bison, stags, reindeer, mammoths, lions, foxes, and even human figures. These engravings only began far back in the interior of the cave, at least 120 yards from the entrance. Since the roof of Les Combarelles is exceedingly low, only three to six feet above the floor, the engravings are all correspondingly small, being four to twelve inches in height.

The excitement aroused by this discovery was tremendous. One of Breuil's companions, a teacher named Peyrony from Les Eyzies, immediately carried on with his explorations in the same rock massif. His intimate knowledge of the neighbourhood led him to the Font-de-Gaume cave where—knowing now what he was searching for—he very quickly discovered further engravings. Only eight days after the find at Les Combarelles—it was in September 1901—the three explorers penetrated right inside the Font-de-Gaume and were even more startled than by their first discovery, for here, in contrast to the rock-engravings at Les Combarelles, they found themselves suddenly faced by a whole gallery of polychrome animal drawings. There were over 200, mainly representing animals that had been hunted during the Upper Palaeolithic. Among them were animals depicted almost life-size.

It is difficult to imagine what must have passed through Cartailhac's mind when Breuil led him a little later through these caves. Every one of those works of art must have mocked and reproached him. But now he did what he had failed to do twenty-one years before: he went with Breuil to Altamira. It was a pilgrimage to Canossa, to Maria de Sautuola, the daughter of Don Marcelino, who was the real discoverer of the cave-paintings of Altamira. The almost incomparable beauty of the pictures, even more impressive than those of Font-de-Gaume, moved both men profoundly. Breuil spoke openly of the "Sistine Chapel" of prehistory, omitting to state whom he considered the most honoured by the comparison, the Italian master of the Renaissance or the inspired Cro-Magnon artists of the Magdalenian. The German authority on prehistory, Professor Herbert Klein, one of the foremost connoisseurs of Ice-Age art, wrote about Altamira: "The weirdness of the cave, the immense impact of the pictures and the thought of eternity, combine to produce one of the greatest experiences that can possibly befall man on this Earth."

Cartailhac, however, was a man of character. His penitent admission of "mea culpa" resounded loudly throughout the world, but unfortunately it was too late to redeem the honour of Don Marcelino de Sautuola.

Thus it will be seen that the discovery of Ice-Age art was not merely a matter of searching and finding, but primarily of overcoming human prejudices and conservative ways of thought. The fact that resistance to this new knowledge collapsed at the very beginning of the present century is certainly a coincidence. But strangely enough it was just during those few years around the turn of the century that epochal discoveries were made in various spheres of science, which necessitated the jettisoning of many long-accepted ideas and a complete re-viewing of the world, in many respects, in a very different light from that in which it had appeared in the past. The overthrow of all hitherto accepted physical concepts by Einstein and Planck in the years 1900-5 is well known. Equally revolutionary was the discovery of radio-activity (1896 onwards) by Becquerel and the Curies, which destroyed all notions about the indivisibility of the atom and led to entirely fresh conceptions. For biology, the revolutionary turning-point was the re-discovery of the Mendelian Laws of heredity and, above all, the immensely important discovery of mutation by de Vries (all in 1900), which provided solid support for Darwinism and the theory of evolution. It was as if mankind, at the turn of the twentieth century, suddenly made a great jump forward in scientific knowledge.

Now free of futile hindrances after the days of Font-de-Gaume and the vindication of Altamira, the study of pre-history progressed rapidly. Among the most successful scholars in this field were the Abbé Breuil and the German, Ober-maier. Advances now were made at a tremendous rate. Scarcely a year passed without the discovery of one or more caves containing cultural relics of our Cro-Magnon forefathers.

Carefully planned exploration of likely territories frequently produced results. Children played no small part— mostly by having the advantage of knowing the prehistoric treasure-stores in their own home territories—scouring the neighbourhood in their free time and even, with youth's adventurousness, climbing dangerously down cracks into the subterranean world.

Of all the painted caves known today, the richest and most

beautiful is that of Lascaux, near Montignac in the Dordogne, which again, like Altamira, was discovered by a dog. The animal was playing with two boys and suddenly disappeared down a crack in the earth—an extraordinary repetition of circumstances. One cannot do better than to quote here the words of Abbé Breuil:

"The art of Lascaux," he wrote, "in spite of traces of primitive ideas in design, discloses a remarkable mastery in the execution of the figures, some of which are very large; their technique is both skilful and varied. At times it achieves a combination of elegance and power which produces in its full development such masterpieces as some of the great bulls, although these are drawn with the greatest simplicity. The Lascaux figures represent the peak in the final development of the first phase of Upper Palaeolithic art and their primitive character and liveliness of movement, sometimes a little rough and naïve, reminds us of the work of early Renaissance artists. The variety of techniques, which were developed in a relatively short time, points to a sort of artistic fever, rich in inspiration and experience. No one would have expected in this far distant period, of which we know only a few sure fragments, such an outburst of an art so great and, of its own kind, so perfect."

Up to date, well over one hundred caves with paintings and many thousands with a single drawing are known. The Dordogne has proved a veritable El Dorado; its river valleys and rocky cliffs head the long roster with 31 sites so far discovered. In Spain the lead is taken by the province of Santander, with 14 caves including Altamira.

Those who live in the lowlands or on the sea-coast usually have far too limited ideas of what is meant by a "cave". Most people will say that a cave is a large or small space lying behind an aperture in a rock face; but this simple description only applies in a tiny minority of cases. Ice-Age caves mostly consist of a whole system of passages and chambers, often of labyrinthine complexity, leading deep into the earth and super-imposed one on another in storey form. Frequently stalactites bar the way and ornament the caverns with their bizarre shapes. Narrow streams dash through and drop into mysterious chasms in the rock. Black lakes lie deep and stagnant. Crevices vanish out of sight; chimneys lead to unknown regions. The discovery and exploration of almost every cave was a regular adventure story. The total darkness, the complete, unreal silence of this underworld was always eerie in the extreme. Often there were unexpected, frequently dangerous slides down wet clayey slopes; many passages were so low that they could only be penetrated by crawling on the stomach. In the subterranean darkness, which is very hard to illuminate, distances seem greater than they really are. Very rarely do drawings appear near the entrances, and most of the masterpieces are found in the remotest parts of the caves. In the famous Niaux Cave on the northern slopes of the Pyrenees the chamber with the finest pictures lies almost half a mile from the entrance. The labyrinth itself extends for a further 320 yards and ends at a lake. Even today it is a dangerous adventure to explore these silent worlds, and it does not require much imagination to realise how profound must be the impression when suddenly, in the beam of the explorers' torches, charging bison or gigantic mammoths stare out from the walls.

All the greater and more astonishing, therefore, were the achievements of those half-naked "savages" working with the primitive means and tools of that time by the wretched light of flickering brands. How much courage and nerve must have been required to penetrate into the unknown bowels of the earth to take possession of a world fitfully lit by smoky torches, where at every step there might appear ghosts and daemons of nameless powers. We know nothing of the way in which they set about their task and how they overcame the terror of the unknown. All that is sure is that these caves must very soon have become centres of magical cults, providing a fit setting for the dark evocations by magicians, medicine-men and priests of a supernatural world beyond the real one. Undoubtedly, the caves were a place of privilege, and access to them for ordinary men was barred by an invisible but nonetheless effective taboo. The "laity" would only have been admitted for ritual ceremonies, and then they had to obey the rules laid down by their priests or magicians. For it must once again be stressed that the painted caves, lying deep underground, were not for habitation. Apart from the priests, few would have penetrated beyond the entrance caves.

The nature of the mysteries devised by the minds of these most astonishingly intelligent Cro-Magnons will probably remain a secret for ever, for there can be no written testimony to tell us of what took place. We can only guess and deduce, by analogy with the way of life of contemporary and historical aboriginals, what this or that may have meant, what purpose it may have served, and what part it played in the ceremonies of those primitive pagans. Certainly, we would be misjudging the Ice-Age artists if we assumed that they practised their art for the sake of art, from an aesthetic sense of beauty, or out of joy in their work.

Some of these motives may, indeed, have played a part; but the reasons for producing the paintings, at the behest of the magicians, were purely deliberate and purposeful. Not for nothing are all the pictures found only in the remotest, most awe-inspiring parts of the caves. Art done for purely decorative purposes would have been expressed in the form of open-air pictures, or rather engravings, something that only became common very much later. Emphasis has already been laid on the paramount importance of hunting in the life of these prehistoric men. It is because of this that, again and again, the only subjects appearing in these pictures are prehistoric wild beasts, hunting scenes, weapons of the chase and pit-traps. Representations of human beings are comparatively rare, and when they do appear they are, in most cases, extremely sketchy, mostly in the form of childish "matchstick" men, very different from the realism which distinguishes most of the animals. It is regrettable that men are not portrayed with the same brilliant verisimilitude; then we would know everything about their appearance and not be dependent entirely on the evidence of fossilised bones. The first portrait of a human face, engraved on stone, dates from the late Magdalenian, and was discovered in 1948 in the *abri* of Louis-Taillebourg. It is in the form of a semi-relief which, as surviving traces of pigment show, must originally have been painted. As a whole the effect is clumsy and not particularly artistic, little more than a first feeble attempt to use man as a model. In the case of three female figures carved on the rock walls of the same *abri* and discovered in 1951, the highly emphasised sexual characteristics are the chief feature, which immediately suggests that once again they were intended primarily for ritual, magical purposes.

Otherwise the subjects everywhere are animals, nothing but animals, in all aspects of their existence: attacking, grazing, sleeping, copulating; young animals, herds, solitary animals. As well as simple outlines, there are coloured paintings, miniatures and colossal pictures, frequently given a plastic, three-dimensional effect by skilful use of the contours of the rock surface. Curiously enough, from the Aurignacian to the Magdalenian the technique develops along very much the same lines as Western art—from Naturalism, via Impressionism and Expressionism, to something resembling the Abstract. So that we are confronted with an almost unbroken chain of all the art styles with which we are today familiar, maturing according to some inner law of artistic evolution.

The commonest and certainly the most intrinsically likely explanation of these cave-paintings is that they served the purpose of sympathetic hunting-magic; the vitally important hunting expeditions must be blessed and the animals invoked. The hunters gathered by torchlight in the magician's cave, and there, under the pictures, wild hunting-dances were enacted, during the course of which the performers, swinging their weapons, worked themselves into a state of frenzy. Spears were flung against the paintings, arrows shot at them, to the accompaniment of magical incantations from the priests who, wearing fantastic and hideous disguises, directed the proceedings. It is quite safe to say that such scenes did take place, for in the famous Pyrenean Trois Frères cave (named after the three young brothers who discovered it in 1914), which is rich in paintings and engravings, there is a terrifying picture of just such a magician in all his primitive daemonic frenzy. His head is eerily disguised by a mask with reindeer ears and antlers, a goat's beard and owlish openings for the eyes. Bearpaws are drawn over the hands; the base of the spine has a horse's tail attached to it. The human eyes are glaring and hypnotic; the whole attitude of the body suggests a dance-pose; and the body itself is painted to resemble a skeleton. In recent times the only comparable manifestations we know are the products of the lurid imagination of the devil-ridden Tibetans who, by other means, created similar phantasmal figures in both pictures and masks.

The very disguise of the Trois Frères magician, derived as it is entirely from the animal kingdom, proves the dominant

72. The magician of the Trois Frères cave

role of hunting-magic. It is possible therefore that this was the sole purpose of those savage and primitive ceremonies in the subterranean spirit world, where animals of the chase were captured for ever on the rocky walls and roofs. This must, anyhow, undoubtedly have been their prime purpose. Yet it must not be forgotten that these cult-ceremonies flourished persistently throughout several tens of thousands of years—a very, very long time in terms of our own historical era which can show nothing even remotely comparable. For example, the cult-practices and beliefs of the Sumerians are very little known to us and completely alien, although a mere 5,000 years separate us from them. Admittedly, in the Cro-Magnon days too the primitive urge to power and domination must have caused many changes in the traditional ceremonies practised by the lords and masters of the underground world. Secret societies among men, initiation of youths, fertility rites later concerned also with humans, even ritual sacrifice, may gradually have been added. And it is possible that—at any rate at certain periods—these painted caves were nothing more than hunting-schools, teaching the rising generation all the skills of the chase. Learning by practice in the field was never without its dangers. Often a wounded bison, wild boar or even cave-bear would suddenly turn into a savage attacker bent on destroying its adversaries, and it was, consequently, important to teach the young men the most vulnerable portions and organs of the different animals, to demonstrate to them how to aim their spears and arrows. Once they had learned to thrust or shoot accurately, their individual courage and chances of safety in the actual hunt would be greatly increased.

Despite all attempts to interpret the course of development of the Upper Palaeolithic cultures and to understand the process of spiritual awakening of the men of those times, there still remain problems enough which to this day have not been solved, and probably never will be. To a certain extent this is clearly inevitable, since mute pictures and stone implements are the only documentary evidence we have; for of course the art of writing would have been entirely unknown. Thus we are confronted with an almost inexplicable contradiction between the primitive, utilitarian standard of living of those Stone-Age savages (or semi-savages)—who throughout the long period from the Aurignacian to the Magdalenian were unable to progress beyond the hunting stage—and their consummate artistic powers which, from modest beginnings, followed a course rising to its Impressionistic climax and then, the fount exhausted, sinking to its original, primitive linear forms of expression. The one simply does not match up with the other. In this discrepancy there either lies hidden another unsolved riddle, or else we have a completely false idea about the real level of achievement of the Franco-Spanish Cro-Magnon cultures.

Their standard of living and general cultural level can be easily compared with those of their contemporaries in the other ice-free regions of Europe and Southern Russia. The cultures of the latter, at the height of the development of Stone-Age techniques, correspond in all important characteristics with those of Spain and France. As numerous finds have proved, their cultures cannot, by and large, have been very dissimilar from those of the painters. Among them, too, the artistic sense was very highly developed. Very many highly accomplished engravings, carvings, and animal sculptures indicate a pronounced tendency towards the miniature in art. Tiny earthenware or stone figurines also seem to have been characteristic, and of these the most famous example is the Willendorf Venus, a female figure little more than 4 inches tall, carved out of limestone, with enormously exaggerated breasts and an equally pronounced primary sexual organ, every other feature, even to the hair-style, being almost completely ignored—obviously intentionally. The arms are scarcely suggested; the legs end below the knees; the face is a mere flat surface without contours and plainly anticipates the widespread aversion of primitive people, even today, to having their facial features reproduced either in drawings or photographs. There evidently existed, in addition to hunting-magic, a corresponding fertility magic, exemplified in this "Venus" and several other symbolic representations of a like kind. The basic urge to propagate and the importance of ensuring progeny must certainly have made fertility-magic a power of equal importance in their lives. But very little is so far known about this. The one important thing that was lacking among the eastern neighbours of the West Europeans was any form of cave-painting. With the exception of one cave in Italy, two in Sicily and one in Germany, this form of art seems not to have spread at all, although there was no lack of caves in other inhabited regions.

Cave-painting remains, therefore, a particular manifestation of the Franco-Spanish cultures, whose representatives— rather like the ancient Greeks—must have possessed an especial artistic talent. And why not? Such a gift can be a racial characteristic. The fact that their general level of culture was no higher than that of their neighbours is no argument against this. In the case of the Greeks, too, it was perfectly possible to walk through a market-place without straightway encountering a philosophical or artistic genius. The greater part of mankind in the Stone Age were just as far behind the times as they are today and always have been. A good example of this is the Maya people of Central America. In spite of the really fantastic monumental buildings which a few geniuses created for the small ruling class, the almost propertyless masses lived in a state of abject, primitive squalor. When

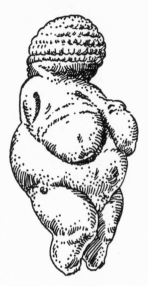

73. The Willendorf Venus

the Spaniards arrived, the Mayans had no knowledge of the wheel nor, consequently, of the construction of any form of wheeled vehicle; they were unaware of the use of animals for carrying burdens and had not discovered the plough. Metals had been coming slowly into use only a short while before Cortez' invasion. Stone was their chief material, just as in the Aurignacian days. And this was in the fifteenth century A.D.!

The comparatively sudden disappearance of cave-art at the end of the Magdalenian may have been due to various causes. The reverting of later artists to simpler linear outlines, after the supreme achievement of spatial perspectives and extremely delicate colouring effects, indicates, on the one hand, the final exhaustion of the intrinsic possibilities of the art, and, on the other, the gradual disappearance of its magical content after all those tens of thousands of years. The original, undoubted reverential awe for the skill of the artistic élite, who were able to capture the precious beasts of the chase by scratching and colouring on the rock walls, gradually yielded to disillusion when the artists no longer made a secret of their art and even degraded it to the level of something to be trafficked in. For a long time we have known of crude sketches scratched on stone which have also been found in a far more elaborate form in caves elsewhere—even in caves hundreds of miles distant from the original "rough" design. The only conclusion we can draw from this is that these Cro-Magnon "Greeks" must have led very peripatetic lives. The Pyrenees, which at that time were far more ice-clad than they are today, apparently proved no obstacle to them. Very probably there was uninterrupted contact between the neighbouring peoples; yet the journey on foot from, say, the Vézère valley in the Dordogne to Altamira in Northern Spain would have been a strenuous undertaking in the circumstances then prevailing, demanding strength, endurance and a knowledge of the lie of the land; and furthermore these nomads must have carried their stone sketches with them, for the original designs must have been transported by some means or other.

These early artists probably travelled around with their sketches and displayed them as a "sample" collection. This trend towards the profanation of art must certainly have destroyed all its inherent magic and mystery. The artists were seen in the light of day and it was realised that the works in the caves were the works of human hands—and with that a part of the original fascination had already departed. Then the practical, unimaginative people of that time realised that their hunting was equally successful without benefit of the magic they had previously believed in. Such a disillusionment would possibly have been strengthened by the abundance of wild game towards the end of the Magdalenian. The improvement of climate brought about by the retreat of the ice once again caused vast animal migrations, and as a result the dark interiors of caves with their works of art fell "out of fashion", became disused and were finally completely forgotten. Life in the warmth-giving sun of the open country, the growing art of hut-building—everything tended away from the subterranean gloom and the necessity of bowing down to the powers of darkness in order to ensure one's daily supply of food. The world around had changed, and so had every form of life that was now flourishing abundantly on every side. The greyness of the Ice Age and the cave-magic now gave way to the all-conquering Sun and life in forest and plain. Perhaps, also, the now numerous hordes and tribes broke up, left their age-old tribal territories and followed the animals—towards Central Germany, England, Sweden, into territories hitherto blocked by the ice. And the tribes that followed them from other territories knew nothing of the caves and were wary of entering, even if they discovered them.

So it was quite natural that from now on art took to the open country. After the Magdalenian, we find engravings on stones and outdoor cliff faces. The territorial area covered now became very great, which indicates migrations. In Sweden, Spain, North and South Africa, Ethiopia and East Africa, men were masters of this art, which, strangely enough in view of its style, rapidly developed into the abstract. It may be taken for certain that these men also painted in colours, but, even in the driest regions, the pictures proved unable to withstand the effects of weathering over the course of thousands of years.

The Mesolithic and Neolithic Ages were no more than transitional periods leading to the Bronze- and Iron-Age cultures which already fall within the province of history. Everywhere Man was now reaching the stage of evolution he is still at today. The modern era had dawned in every respect, for geologically too we now arrive at the Holocene, the millennia leading up to our present day.

The hitherto static life led by people engaged in the struggle for existence was superseded by a period of unparalleled nomadism. Immense migrations, mostly along the banks of the great rivers, now dominated the life of *Homo sapiens* for thousands of years. Where there were land-bridges between the continents, men crossed them, always on the move, with no definite objective in sight, but driven by some strange, inexplicable urge towards distant unknown parts. Even though the population of the world must have increased very considerably, there could not possibly have been any recognisable necessity for wandering far afield because of lack of living space. The last uninhabited quarters of the globe were now settled.

Australia must have been reached some time during the

last glaciation. The period when this move took place can be guessed at tentatively, for a land-bridge between the East Indies and Australia would have been a necessity, since it is impossible to conceive that the primeval Australian natives, at their very low level of development, could have discovered the art of regular ocean journeying and so crossed the wide seas between the archipelagos. The shelf-sea areas, which today separate the various groups of islands, could only have become dry land as a result of a lowering of the water-level due to ice-formation in the northern hemisphere. An earlier date for the settlement of Australia—for instance as far back as the Riss advance of the ice—is out of the question, since at that time *Homo sapiens*—which the aborigines most emphatically are—did not even exist.

Man's "discovery" of America was made across a land-bridge in the region of the present-day Bering Sea which also was completely dry for long and frequent periods. It is possible that the migration of the various Mongol tribes took place in a series of waves, widely separated in time. Former uncertain estimates as to the earliest date of these movements are now being more precisely established by use of the radio-carbon and potassium-argon methods.

Traces of prehistoric Indians and of their cultural remains were widely discovered during the last century. Particularly famous are the bison-hunters of the Folsom culture (named after the town of Folsom in New Mexico). Nothing resembling their very beautiful flint spear-heads, chamfered and polished on both sides, has been found in any other Stone-Age culture anywhere in the world. The men of the Folsom culture were genuine *Homo sapiens*. The successful dating of a hunting-camp in Texas gives it an age of 9,883 years (with an uncertainty factor of 350 years above or below this figure). The remains of an encampment in Illinois give an age of 11,200 years (uncertainty factor: 800 years), while a find of human remains in Tepexpan in Mexico has been dated at 11,300 years (uncertainty factor: 500 years). Other finds have confirmed such datings. Most of the North American discoveries so far made date from about that time, and one would therefore be tempted to assume that America was first settled during the last recession of the ice sheet.

Yet when one considers that the nomads who entered by Alaska must have already reached the Magellan Straits, virtually at the southern-most tip of South America, 9,000 years ago—as further dating of finds has shown—the first wave, at least, of immigrants must have come across from Asia a very long time before that. Recent discoveries have made this assumption appear more and more probable. The charcoal residue of a camp-fire near Tule Springs in Nevada has been assigned a minimum age of 23,800 years, and an extensive encampment of Llano-culture type, near Lewisville in Texas, is even considered to be more than 37,000 years old. Remains of the Sandia culture (so-called from a cave in a canyon in New Mexico) are probably about the same age; this culture produced excellent spear-and-arrow-heads resembling those of the leaf-point Solutrian culture in Europe. Thus, without any difficulty, we can trace American Man back roughly 40,000 years, to a period contemporary, in fact, with the Solutrian.

In 1916, in Florida, there were discovered human bones as well as a mass of contemporary fauna which bore all the indications of having lived in a markedly warm climate. But the last warm period in America, as in Europe, occurred about 60,000 years ago. This dating is, of course, perfectly possible. Over countless millions of years the Bering Sea bridge was far more often exposed as dry land than covered with shallow water. This circumstance was, indeed, of great importance for the animal migrations of the Tertiary. So it is permissible to conjecture that at a far earlier stage in Man's development, possibly as far back as the Neanderthal, primeval hunters may have crossed that Asian-American land-bridge in pursuit of their migrating prey. The fewness of their numbers in the gigantic double continent may have caused them to become literally lost, which could be the reason for the disappearance of all traces of them, with the solitary exception—and that a questionable one—of the Florida discovery. At all events, the view that America was first settled by men after the Ice Age is certainly no longer tenable. The solid Bering Sea bridge was probably never under ice, any more than were, strangely enough, southern Alaska and the Pacific north-west. So easy roads of migration were always available, and these would naturally have been made use of. But a great deal still remains unknown about prehistoric Man in America, and our knowledge on this subject lags a long way behind our comparatively precise information about the past of European Man.

The Mesolithic and Neolithic Periods lead directly into early historical times. The Mesolithic is reckoned as starting about 4000 B.C., and during that period men changed from nomadic hunters to settled farmers, cattle-raisers, fishermen, and founders of settlements. The oldest agricultural village so far discovered is one in Iraq, which, according to the radio-carbon method, dates back 6,707 years (uncertainty factor: 320 years). Older still are certain northern culture levels, such as the Ahrensburg culture of Holstein, which is said to be 15,000 years old; but in this case it is still only nomadic and reindeer-hunting cultures that are involved. Another Mesolithic culture—and one perhaps even surviving from the Palaeolithic—was the North African Capsian culture (named after finds at Capsa in Southern Tunisia), which from reliable evidence can almost certainly be dated as far back as 8,400 years ago.

The Neolithic Period in the Mediterranean region covers roughly the third millennium B.C., that is the age of the flowering of the Egyptian and Sumerian civilisations. In Central and Northern Europe the period lasted longer, until about 1700 B.C.; and here it was mainly a time of change-over from nomadic life to settlement into villages, lake-dwellings, and fortified strongholds. The Megalithic cultures, too, with their stone monuments and barrows, fall within the Neolithic.

And so by now we are already verging on the realm of historical archaeology, the period of the Celtic and Germanic races, of ancient civilisations—and therefore the subject of this book is at an end. It has taken us through four thousand million years in time and space; and also through outer space, too, for we must not forget that our radio wave is still, as seen from the viewpoint of this world, on its way towards us. Now, however, at the end of the Palaeolithic, it is passing through our own Milky Way. But several thousand more years must still elapse before, more than nineteen and a half centuries after the birth of Christ, it is caught by the latest discovery of *Homo sapiens,* the radio-telescope, and then it will appear as a tiny dot on a measuring apparatus and thereby its existence of 4,000,000,000 years will be ended. That wave was an emissary from the temporal and spatial beginning of our world, a survival from distances and conditions that no longer exist, conditions such as, for example, the Earth at its glowing stage.

This survey of the world's history, with all its innumerable tectonic and biological wonders, has spanned an immense period and so it has only been possible to sketch its merest outlines. In time to come, much of what we think we know today may turn out to be quite wrong or have an entirely different interpretation. There is a vast field of science about which we as yet know nothing for certain and which may provide surprises which will make our whole picture of the world we live in even more wonderful and fascinating. After all, our knowledge is only what we think today, and that is as much subject to perpetual change as everything else in the Universe.

Index

343